Table of Content

To my parents, Liudmila and Henrikas!

For your unwavering faith in my potential, for the countless lessons taught and stories shared. Thank you for being the first chapters in my story.

To my family and friends, for the love that has been the bedrock upon which I've built my dreams.

Foreword

As a teenager, I became fascinated with the notion of "memento mori" as soon as I learned about it. Despite its literal translation from Latin, "remember that you have to die," I understood its meaning as uplifting and brilliant—a reminder to value our lives in the light of knowing that our time is limited, and thus invaluable.

Before we can truly value every lasting second of our lives, we must first understand what gives it its value. This starts with identifying our purpose in life and mapping out the road to realizing it. Despite the simplicity of the question, the answer is far from simple. I stumbled upon this question again when I was older, in my years in college, and I could not answer it. I felt an existential growing pain due to my inability to come up with an answer. I realized that the elusive nature of the question arises from the ambiguity of the language used and that my best chance at finding an answer was to approach it from a scientific perspective.

People are constantly trying to optimize their decisions, even mundane ones like crossing the road. What is the shortest path to take? What is the smartest way to go about it? Maybe that question once was, "What should I plant for next year's harvest?" Today it might be, "What store should I go to buy bread?" Some delve deeper, asking, "Should I invest in my children and their possible future or save for an imagined retirement?" But the most important question is, 'What do you want to do with the life you find yourself in?' Answer this, and you will be rewarded with a kind of inner peace - a respite from the aimlessness and anxiety of a life journey without direction. That answer will be your anchor, holding you fast during difficult times.

I have managed to discover, if not the definitive answer, then several answers that resonate with my own journey. During my time in college, I developed a series of goals that appeared to be greater than my individual existence. Simultaneously, these aspirations seemed attainable and in alignment with my personal convictions. Allow me to share them with you:

During the first decade after college, my primary focus was to dedicate my life to the pursuit of scientific knowledge. It was a period of intense learning, research, and contribution to the field of science.

In the second decade, I set my sights on building a family and nurturing meaningful relationships. This phase of my life was dedicated to fostering love, support, and growth within my personal sphere.

Moving into the third decade, my attention shifted towards establishing my own business. This endeavor allowed me to apply my expertise and passion to create something of value that would endure beyond my individual efforts.

Finally, in the fourth decade, I aimed to channel my accumulated wisdom and experiences into a book—a vessel for my ideas and insights. I believe that our lives gain meaning when we leave behind a legacy of our ideas, akin to how genes endure beyond the lifespan of individual species. While I said the answer out loud it would require several chapters to thoroughly explain how I arrived at it and elucidate my thought process.

I have several published scientific works and a doctorate from Columbia University in particle physics. I have a wonderful family with two beautiful boys. I have invented a product, created a company based on it, sold it, and created another. This book is the last goal in my path.

Yet just describing my goals without explaining the thought process or giving context is quite meaningless. The underlying theme behind these goals was to create a lasting impact, to leave behind a legacy of ideas and aspirations that would transcend my own existence. My purpose through this book is to describe the framework and process to help you discover the meaning of your own life and fulfill it based on the circumstances of your own life. Within the book, I not only delve into the process of how these ideas unfolded but also provide practical examples and personal anecdotes that illustrate how I navigated the path towards achieving them.

The book is roughly divided into two halves. The first part talks about building a framework to fulfill the meaning of your personal life. It is the story of discovering the meaning of my own life, and I use my life as an example of how to build this type of generic scaffolding for your answers and goals. As a result, it is filled with personal stories, recollections, and anecdotes.

In the process of discovering the meaning of my life, I also realized that our own meaning in isolation doesn't mean much. We are dependent on other people, most importantly on humanity. This realization culminated in my conviction that not just I, but all of us need to think about the future of mankind. This is reflected in the second half of the book.

I hope that after reading this book, you will be exposed to ideas that will help you find and set up your own goals and start on a path of achieving them.

The second half expands the scope from personal meaning to fulfilling the meaning of life for humanity as a whole. It delves into the past to explore the history of religion and science. All of these topics will stay within the confines of a scientific point of view. In the final chapters, I invite my readers to imagine and design a future religion combined with science that would ensure the fulfillment of all of our personal meanings and serve as a protector of humanity.

A couple of warnings regarding the book...

This book is intended for mentally stable, adult readers who are on a quest to find answers to life's bigger questions. I am neither a doctor nor a psychologist, so if you are dealing with mental health issues, please seek professional help.

Furthermore, this book is not focused on debunking religion or discrediting science. If you have already found a religious doctrine that you find true and acceptable, or if you are a scientist who is solely focused on your work and not interested in the meaning of life, then you may not find this book useful.

That being said, this book adopts a scientific approach to the question of life's meaning, striving to anchor it in evolutionary biology. If you are seeking religious or spiritual guidance, please be aware that this book is not focused on those topics.

The reason I take a scientific approach is because, in my view, fundamental science provides a powerful way to separate falsehoods from reality. However, it does not necessarily provide guidance on how to find meaning and direction in life. I believe it is time to address the meaning of our personal and collective lives from a scientific point of view.

People often ask me who my target audience is for this book. When I started to write this book I pictured a younger self as my audience. However, I hope that this book will be helpful for anyone who is searching for answers to life's bigger questions, who is thirsty for meaning, or who is experiencing doubts about the direction of their life. My goal is to describe the framework I used to discover my own meaning and to offer guidance to readers in finding their own inner peace, sense of direction, and anchor during difficult times.

P. S.

At the end of the book, there is a list of references and links to notes. To preserve the stability of the links, since the internet can be a fickle thing, I point almost all the links to "middleman" URLs on my custom webpage and forward them to the original references. In case any link disappears or changes, I intend to update the middleman to point to the correct one. I am doing this to prevent my e-book from filling up with stale or erroneous URLs ensuring that you can continue to enjoy reading my book. If you wish to access all the reference links directly, please email me at varturas at yahoo.com, and I'll send you the webpage address. I am grateful for your time and attention.

Origins

When Did I First Ask What Is The Meaning Of Life?

At the start of each section of this book, I will diverge momentarily from the principal topic, to share snippets of my own personal journey towards discovering the meaning of life. I will describe my own motivations, the strides I have taken along this captivating path and draw from my own life experiences. Following this detour, the remaining chapters will refocus our attention on the central theme but each chapter will begin with a page from my own history. My intent is not merely to engage in an abstract discussion about discovering life's meaning, but also to demonstrate through tangible examples from my life how I've translated this exploration into practice. In other words, I want to show that my approach is not just about talk, but also about tangible actions. Let us start.

I have always been captivated by the subject of the meaning of life, not just my own life, but all life around me. Perhaps the way my mind is set up, I need to know why I am doing something in order to take action. Living our whole lives begs these types of questions: why are we here and where do we need to take our lives? When our moral compass spins at the crossroads, what is the guiding principle for making decisions? These are perhaps the most fundamental existential questions, not just for me personally, but I believe for all of us.

Why are we here? What is our purpose? Despite the simplicity of these questions, they lead to a myriad of other complex and all-consuming questions and answers, much like the ones paraphrased in the paper above.

It is not a stretch to say that this may be one of the most important questions people ask in their lives. The question of the meaning of life has captured the minds and imaginations of countless generations. Many thinkers, past and present, consider the question of the meaning of life a vital part that enables people to organize and understand their daily lives:

"In the face of life's inherent uncertainties, the search for meaning becomes a beacon of hope. It is a source of resilience, enabling us to find solace, strength, and purpose in the midst of adversity."

"Life's meaning is not something we passively receive; it is something we actively construct. It is in the choices we make, the values we uphold, and the connections we foster that we find significance and purpose."

"The meaning of life is not to be found in the pursuit of material wealth or superficial pleasures. It lies in our capacity for self-transcendence, in the pursuit of higher ideals and the cultivation of wisdom, compassion, and inner peace."

"The search for meaning is a fundamental human quest. It provides us with a compass to navigate the complexities of existence and gives purpose to our daily endeavors."

The following quotes are from Rebecca Solnit, John Dewey, Dalai Lama, and Viktor Frankl.

Not everyone cares or has the luxury of contemplating the meaning of their lives. Our grandparents lived through times of hardship, hunger, and war and had very little time or motivation to think about the direction of their lives. I will talk about this further at the end of this part, but in the past, people, including my grandparents, had very little choice in directing their lives or taking the time to think about it. In modern times, many people find themselves caught up in the day-to-day demands of life and may struggle to find the time and space to reflect on the purpose of their existence. They may feel overwhelmed by the pressures of work, family, and other obligations, and find it difficult to set aside time for introspection. Nonetheless, these questions are for everyone, and whenever we have a little time for ourselves, we tend to gravitate towards the meaning of our lives for one reason or another. What is it that makes these questions so important for us people, and what makes us so fixated on finding meaning in our lives?

We may disagree on the exact questions or how to look for the answers, but we can generally agree that these questions are important. Perhaps finding the origins of these questions would help us understand how to answer them, how to start unraveling them. Why are we so fascinated with finding the meanings of our lives? Finding the origins of the question will take us a long way towards solving it.

At the root of it is a simple idea about the most common things that surround us: the chair on which we sit, the roof over our heads, and the keyboard that I use to type these words. All of these things have a purpose, and if they lose their purpose, for example, when a chair breaks, the roof starts leaking, or the keyboard stops typing, we throw them out or replace them. Objects without a purpose are not worth keeping around. What about our lives then?

We are often told that every life is priceless, from every page and TV monitor. Life is considered priceless because it is seen as something of incalculable value that cannot be quantified or measured by any monetary means. Each person's life is unique and has its own intrinsic worth, regardless of their individual circumstances or achievements. Furthermore, life is often seen as priceless because it is finite. Unlike material possessions or wealth, life cannot be bought or sold, and once it is gone, it is gone forever. This makes life all the more precious and valuable, as it is a limited resource that should be cherished and appreciated.

If something is priceless, it must have a great purpose and meaning. So what is the purpose and meaning of life? These questions become even more important when we realize our own mortality.

Ancient philosophers also grappled with these same questions. Plato, an ancient Greek philosopher, wrote extensively about finding justice in the soul and created platonism, the theory that proclaims the existence of universal ideas. One part of his teachings was the existence of omnipresent and indestructible objects, Forms, which do not physically exist but give rise to material objects. However, at the core of platonism is the doctrine of the immortality of the soul.

Eastern religions urge you to spend your life improving your spiritual development. Hinduism believes that this process happens across many lifetimes. Buddhist writings, such as sutras, do not talk about the purpose of this current life. Quite the opposite, they talk about the pursuit of eliminating all suffering from one's life, a process that, according to Buddhism, takes many lifetimes and reincarnations.

Many centuries later, philosophers of the Enlightenment period also defined their concepts in terms of the existence of an immortal soul. That era gave rise to modern liberalism, but the basis of it is a belief in inalienable rights and freedom of choice given to a person's soul by a higher power. We will go over this in more detail and cover more ground in the second part of this book, but the recurring theme here is the belief that humans possess an immortal part.

Notice how ancient philosophers and spiritual leaders started with the assumption that our soul is immortal. The immediate presumption of immortality has to do with humanity's realization of our mortality. All earthly things perish and turn to dust. This is a defense mechanism from a psychological point of view. Believing that we do not just perish into emptiness helps us to endure hardships of our daily lives, take care of our family and of people dependent on us, and perform other duties, without actually thinking too much into the exact reasons of why we are doing this. This is why the concept of leaving a legacy behind and beyond our death is so important. If we can reincarnate into another life and have a second chance to correct all the mistakes we made in a previous life, we have the gift of having more time, the gift of redemption.

This compulsion of philosophers and thinkers to achieve a version of immortality is not coincidental but rather an inherent part of figuring out our lives and our purpose. It looks like we are defining our purpose as an opposition to our mortality, the purpose of life as a way to cheat death. We have come to the genesis of the origin of the question here: the fear of death transformed into the appreciation of our limited life.

For me, the question of life's purpose was inextricably linked with the stark realization of my mortality. Once I came of age to understand that I, along with my parents and friends, would not live indefinitely, I found myself grappling with existential queries. I would ask my parents questions such as: What happens when we die? Are you afraid of death? Why can't we live eternally? What is the rationale behind our lives having an end? If my existence is finite, why should I invest effort in my homework when I won't be around to appreciate my accomplishments?

Children as young as three can experience the fear of death but they lack full comprehension of its finality. This fear may persist through adolescence. I was fascinated with those questions throughout my school years and revisited them again when I was in college. More than a fear of death though, I was more afraid of wasting the little precious time that we have allotted to us on this Earth.

Those are not typical questions for a young child, nor for a teenager. However, I was not a typical child, and I grew up in a strange time. I grew up in Lithuania, still under the Soviet Union. The Republic of Lithuania and other Baltic countries were always romanticized by the rest of the country, which was living under the iron curtain - a term made famous by Winston Churchill that referred to the boundary that ideologically and physically divided Europe into two separate areas since the end of World War II. The iron in that "curtain" was much worn where I grew up. In Lithuania, we had inevitably begun to feel the "corrosive" effects of westerly winds.

The Baltic countries were considered a window into the West and were the first to split apart and eventually sail away towards the West. After all, it was the Lithuanian communist delegation that declared itself an independent party and walked out of the Communist Congress in Moscow in February 1990. This was an unprecedented move within the Soviet Union and marked the first time a communist party within the USSR had broken its ties with the ruling party. This was a symbolic act, demonstrating the determination to pursue independence for Lithuania.

It was a very different time when there were no cell phones, no internet as we know it, and no social media. To call somebody, you had to use a rotary disk on a phone, and you absolutely had to memorize phone numbers. In my town, there were no taxi-cabs, and you had to take a slow public bus to get around. Now, dozens of years later, as I think back to those years, they seem like not one but two centuries ago. Nowadays, we can communicate with each other across oceans and record all of our memories for posterity. When I wanted to go to another town, I had to memorize the route and use paper maps. I am able to type the destination address into a navigation app after I start driving (obviously at the stop sign or while waiting for the traffic light) and let it guide me to the destination without knowing the route beforehand.

It was a difficult but interesting time when old cultural habits collided with new influences. Cracks began to form in the foundation of the Soviet empire, allowing new ideas, ideas of freedom and capitalism, to seep in and take root, causing the cracks to widen like growing flower seeds in asphalt. I was in a quickly developing and changing world where the cost of human life was not as high or valued as it is in modern times in the developed world. Just like in the ancient Chinese curse, where you wish your enemies to live in a time of change - "may you live in interesting times" - I was growing up at a time of abrupt changes. If anything, what I learned from this time is to be skeptical of blind faith, wary of unintelligent teachers, and the value of embracing new ideas.

It was around this time when I wanted to escape the bleak reality of high school in old Soviet times with all its bullying and brainwashing, my thoughts more often than not turned to the future - my role in a greater world, and, among other things, my own mortality. As I said, these are not normal thoughts for a 16-year-old. Young adults are supposed to chase girls or boys, think about their homework, or plan where to get booze for the next party or what to wear to the prom. But I was a strange kid, and to me, it was perfectly normal to think about the future.

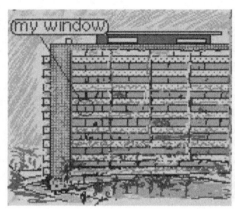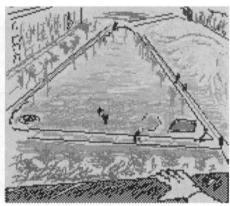

View from the six floor of my apartment building in Klaipeda, Lithuania

My mother procured many science fiction books written by Robert Sheckley, Stanislaw Lem, and the Strugatsky brothers from nearly empty shelves of local Soviet libraries in our small town by paying bribes and doing favors. Fueled by this science fiction, my imagination always strived towards the future. We can find mostly Soviet sci-fi writers on the scarce bookshelves of those times whose books were filled with mandatory praise of socialism and describing the triumph of communism in the future. When I read their "Roadside Picnic" by Arkadiy and Boris Strugatsky, it was like a gasp of fresh air. I still recall the feeling of a strange new and dangerous world, filled with alien artifacts, adventurers and strange phenomena, opened up to my imagination that looked like nothing I ever read or saw before. Many films and a computer game were made from their imagination, named after the main hero in the book. To me it was another way to escape reality.

In the grayness of my school, there was a bright exception - a physics teacher noticed my peculiarity and chose not to ignore or ridicule it, unlike other teachers. Instead, she started to teach me a curriculum that was different from the rest of the class. She took a personal interest in my development. I owe a great deal to her and my mom for nurturing my interest in science and especially physics during my formative years. I will use her example as one of the ways to leave a legacy in subsequent chapters. Science fiction provided an escape from daily minutiae, presenting gleaming and bright visions of the future where people have traveled among stars and have unraveled the mysteries of the universe. It played and experimented with various ideas, but it was in the history books that I confronted the subject of my own mortality—memento mori.

Influenced by my physics teacher and with the help of my mother, I discovered a Moscow college offering a range of physics courses, including theoretical, nuclear, particle, and biophysics. To me that seemed like a dream come true. The entrance exams were incredibly difficult, but the research being conducted there appeared truly extraordinary. I was confident enough to apply to this prestigious institution after achieving second place at the Lithuanian Physics Olympiad. A few months later, I found myself with my parents, standing in line at the application center for this college. I faced a decision: to apply to the astrophysics department and study enormous phenomena, or to apply to the particle physics department and investigate the microscopic realm. While large entities such as stars, constellations, galaxies, and galaxy clusters are indeed vast and powerful, they consist of smaller components, which in turn are composed of even tinier elements, ultimately leading to the smallest particles. I believed that understanding their properties and functions would illuminate the workings of the rest of the world.

My opinion remains unchanged. Sometimes, smaller things matter much more. There are objects far larger than humans or humanity itself, such as earthquakes, storms, and natural disasters, as well as planets and stars. Yet only humans possess the capacity to learn about and comprehend these entities, the universe around us, and the fragility of the world and our own mortality. Even planets and stars are not eternal. In approximately five billion years, the Sun will enter the red giant phase of its evolution, expanding to a size that will engulf the inner planets of our solar system, including Earth. However, humanity may yet outlive all of these massive and minuscule objects—if we find the right answers.

My quest for answers only intensified during my college years. At 18, I experienced a profound malaise, bordering on depression. This psychological breakdown resulted from an overwhelming amount of stress and pressure, culminating in a personal existential crisis and driving me to search for meaning in my life. The pressure and stress stemmed from my circumstances: studying physics in one of Moscow's most demanding universities during the 1990s. Life in the Soviet Union at that time was characterized by the total collapse of the Soviet Empire. The dissolution of the Soviet Union had a profound impact on those who lived through it, as they faced significant changes and disruptions to their daily lives. The familiar safety and certainty of ironclad socialist support networks vanished, replaced by the rise in organized crime, long food lines, and civil unrest. Established norms were dismantled as capitalist influences took root in the fractures of society, expanded them and helped to dismantle established norms. Consequently, the value of human life, already precarious, plummeted even further.

The walk from the train station, which was a local transportation hub, to the university grounds was filled with the ever present danger of being robbed or stabbed or both, and this happened to fellow students and class-mates on a weekly basis. This was a part of long hostility between the students and local gangs. They looked at the students as an entitled and over privileged invasive species and a source of sneakers, jackets and expensive watches. Nothing reminds you of your mortal coil more than being threatened with a knife or witnessing a brutal fight between university students and locals, events that actually happened and were seen with my own eyes.

At the time, my university was renowned as one of the best physics, mathematics schools, and research institutions in the country, and among the best globally. I arrived there as a blank canvas of sorts, and it rapidly instilled in me a deep respect for science and appreciation for the ever-present intellect around me. The atmosphere at this college was distinct from other schools in the Soviet Union. We were encouraged to think for ourselves and even correct teachers if we believed they were wrong.

One of my classmates boldly proclaimed that an exam question had been incorrectly solved by a panel of professors. Far from being reprimanded, the professors actually revised the answer and had to re-grade the entire class of several hundred students. We were frequently advised that it's straightforward to consider oneself as average. However, we should assert that we are geniuses and endeavor to live our lives in alignment with that assertion. This was one of the lessons that left a lasting impression on me. I may not be a genius, but I don't have a selection of alternate brains and bodies from which to choose to live my life. I only have my own brain and my body, and whatever I've been endowed with in this life, I need to appreciate, cherish, and strive to utilize it to its maximum capacity.

This college also held the unfortunate distinction of leading in student suicides and admissions to mental institutions. The pressure to outperform peers was the primary source of numerous breakdowns, including my own. I witnessed my dormitory neighbor succumb to hallucinations, conversing with voices in the walls and attempting to break through them with a large kitchen knife, until one day he attacked other neighbors with that very knife. Thankfully, no one was injured, and he was eventually admitted to a psychiatric hospital. Surprisingly, he was readmitted to the university a year later and continued his studies, but his peculiar behavior persisted. Another acquaintance crumbled under exam pressure and decided to end his life by jumping from the roof of a four-story building. Fortunately, the fall was not lethal, but high enough for him to change his mind. As a spelunking club member, he tucked his arms and legs during the fall and landed on soft soil, breaking his legs but surviving the ordeal. There were countless personal stories like these, and at the time, we had no resources available for help.

Moreover, seeking mental help or associating with mental institutions carried a stigma and signaled personal weakness.

There were bright and uplifting moments that helped me cope with the pressure and loneliness. Most of all, it was the exceptional quality of my peers who surrounded me. They were incredibly intelligent and fascinating individuals. Some came from remote parts of the country, while others were local, but each person arrived at the university through their own unique path. A few classmates were national math and physics Olympiad winners from prestigious Moscow schools. One of my neighbors, a student from the local town, applied to the school twice before finally being accepted on his third attempt. My roommate, on the other hand, was from a distant part of the country, from Armenia. Both of us, along with our mothers, met in line while applying to the university. Our friendship persisted throughout our university years, even after he dropped out to start his own company.

Despite the competition, we all supported each other with tough assignments and managed to find ways to relax in the evenings. Music was one of the primary outlets we turned to for relief from daily stress. We would often gather in the dormitory corridors, where we'd sing and play guitars, creating an atmosphere of camaraderie that allowed us to unwind. It was in this environment that I first picked up a guitar and learned how to play.

The halls of our university were surprisingly musical, considering the school's dedication to physics. This love for music culminated in an annual music festival, which served as a celebration of our shared passion. During the festival, students would perform both traditional student songs, cherished by all, and new compositions written by our fellow students. These shared musical experiences, both in the concert halls and dormitory corridors, helped us to forge lasting friendships and provided a much-needed escape from the stress and rigors of our academic pursuits.

This peer pressure was exacerbated by the mandatory military draft. The sole legal method of avoiding conscription into the Red Army was admission to a select list of exempted higher education institutions, each with a specialty aligned with a specific military function. Our school specialized in delivering vehicles for nuclear payloads, known as intercontinental ballistic missiles (ICBM). Our college granted us exemption from the military draft in exchange for becoming military officers and nuclear missile experts. To be specific we studied a particular 15A30[1] (UR-100N, n.d.) variant of ICBM. To be even more specific, we were essentially trained to push the "red button" to start a nuclear war. Upon completing our studies, we took an exam to test our knowledge of nuclear missiles, and if successful, received a rank in the Soviet army, and, as a result, we would not be drafted in the regular army.

---

[1] en.wikipedia.org/wiki/UR-100N

A photograph from military camp for ICBM training program

Even the school's location, away from central Moscow to avoid potential nuclear strikes, reflected this purpose. In the West, we were called a missile college. This location placed us in the heart of an industrial zone, alongside locals who held little appreciation for higher education. This perspective only deteriorated in the 1990s.

As I grappled with the mounting pressure to excel academically and coped with the hardships and violence accompanying the Soviet Union's collapse in the nineties, my anxiety manifested as an intense need to understand the reasons behind it all. I sought not only to comprehend why it was happening, but primarily why I existed and why I needed to endure these challenges.

To maintain my mental health and escape the mental abyss I found myself in, I had to determine the meaning of my life. Without meaning, I saw no reason or motivation to engage in hardships or pursue any endeavors. Understanding the meaning of my life would also help me confront my fear of dying, or more precisely, my fear of dying senselessly.

To answer the question of my life's meaning, I needed to construct a robust and adaptable mental framework that could guide me through my intricate journey. I required a version of the map. This is how my journey down this rabbit hole looking for the meaning started.

Map of Consciousness or Consciousness is a Map

I traced the origins of my own questions about the meaning of life to my awareness of my mortality, and more generally, to the awareness of human mortality. But where does this awareness come from? How did questions about the meaning of life first appear? What is the origin of the origin of our meaning?

To my surprise I discovered that many people around me, including my friends, seem indifferent or unconcerned with the meaning of life. Sometimes, this indifference comes from cynicism, sometimes from being too busy with other priorities in life. I see that, although my friends are curious about their meaning and purpose, they do not delve deeply into those types of questions. Instead, they concentrate on tangible aspects of life, such as their career, family, and financial stability. Nevertheless, I do believe that deep down, my friends and others trust they are on the right path; that by pursuing their life's ambitions, they will ultimately find meaning, even if they don't explicitly acknowledge it. Personally, understanding the direction I'm heading has always been crucial before taking the first step. If you are reading this book, I hope this curiosity resonates with you as well.

We spend much of our daily routine engaged in a mix of rest and activity, whether it's working at our day jobs, pursuing hobbies, or working for ourselves. Regardless of the goals or end results, the success of our endeavors depends on the amount of effort we put into them. Without the motivation—be it the fear of being fired, the thrill of being the first in your family to achieve something, or the desire to give your children what you never had in your life — it would be hard to wake up early and start your working day.

Each motivation is caused by another one in the long chain. For example, fear of being fired is caused by the desire to keep a good job, which in turn is caused by the dream of putting our kids through college or early retirement. The main root causes on top of our motivations are also complex and varied. They can be traced back to our individual experiences, our upbringing, our environment, and even our genetic makeup. Ultimately, however, it is up to each of us to decide what drives us. We may be motivated by a desire for success, a need for security, a longing for connection, or a passion for something we believe in. Whatever it is that motivates us, it is important to understand why we are driven to do what we do. By understanding our motivations, we can better understand ourselves and make more informed decisions about our lives. In the following sections, I will explore the origins behind these motivations and the root causes of what propels us, to discover why we are here.

For me, it all started with the realization of my own mortality. The intricate web of our motivations, intertwined into a complex tree of reasons, is rooted in our struggle to cope with the knowledge of our transience. We often take our awareness of memento mori for granted as humans, but it is not a universal aspect of nature, nor is it prevalent or pervasive in the life around us. We can only see evidence of death awareness in animals[2] (Pierce, 2018) capable of organizing into higher social structures. However, even less complex life forms constantly resist mortality without understanding or comprehending it. This opposition to death is inherently built into the very definition of life.

Throughout the course of evolution, humans developed a relatively large and novel brain, the neocortex, which became an essential survival instrument to help map external reality to an intricate internal web of emotions and thoughts. Older and simpler organisms had essential tasks like finding food and avoiding predators. The result of myriad trials and errors led to the creation of sophisticated mapping between sensory input and physiological reactions. For instance, an amoeba propels itself towards food sources and repels from hostile environments. The streaming of protoplasm inside the pseudopods moves the amoeba forward until it ingests food particles. It reverses direction to avoid toxic substances. This process is possible because the amoeba has an internal representation of external stimuli, allowing it to distinguish between food sources and threats.

Neuroscientists consider the human brain, more specifically neocortex, as the mapping algorithm[3] (Mountcastle, 1978, #9) that delved even deeper and further into refining this ability. Initially, our primitive ancestors relied primarily on basic instincts for survival. Their brains were mainly focused on locating food sources and evading predators. They developed spatial cognition, allowing them to mentally map their environment, helping them recognize familiar locations and remember where they encountered food or dangers in the past. This spatial awareness was crucial for their survival and helped them to navigate their surroundings effectively.

Living in groups provided safety from predators and facilitated cooperative hunting and gathering. Consequently, the brain had to adapt to handle the intricacies of social interaction, eventually developing the ability to recognize and classify individuals within the group.

One of the most significant developments in human cognitive evolution was the emergence of the theory of mind—the ability to attribute mental states, such as beliefs, desires, and intentions, to oneself and others. People could map and recognize the presence of other individuals. They could not only recognize them but also gauge their feelings, avoid conflicts, and even manipulate each other. Operating through concepts like empathy and compassion, we learned how to use these abilities to find food and fight

---

2 smithsonianmag.com/do-animals-experience-grief

3 nicorg.pbworks.com/Mountcastle

enemies in groups with much greater success. This cognitive leap enabled our ancestors to understand and predict others' behavior, allowing them to cooperate, deceive, or empathize with other individuals more effectively. This social cognition was immensely important for finding one's place in the social order. Failure to do so would put our ancestors in danger of immediate retribution from an alpha male or female. Humans even evolved the ability to decipher subtle visual cues through the development of facial recognition abilities, which allowed them to identify and distinguish between group members, and even sense others' emotional states. This skill is essential for forming alliances, establishing dominance hierarchies, and avoiding inbreeding.

Social animals, such as packs of wolves or schools of killer whales, are able to do all these things. Humans differ in that we can form much larger groups than any other mammals. While wolves and whales operate in packs of dozens, humans can unite under a single cause in the thousands or even millions. We will discuss it later in the book and will try to derive it in the appendix. The intricate conscience maps also created wonderful side effects, like music, art, and science.

As a result of the development of our brain mapping abilities, humans developed advanced communication skills, including language, which facilitated cooperation, information sharing, and the development of cultural norms and values. Eventually, we developed a map of our minds and the concepts of our own selves. People have called these concepts consciousness and sometimes soul. When humans learned how to map our own minds, we became self-aware. With the map of our own selves and our own existence, the next obvious step was the realization of mortality—our family members' mortality, our friends', and our own. With that came existential questions about our place in this world, the same kind of questions I'm attempting to resolve in this book. If we are all destined to disappear what is the point of living?

This new ability allowed mankind to coordinate and communicate better and made us more efficient builders and hunters and thus has increased our chances of survival with development of the neocortex and contributed to the vast expansion of homo sapiens in numbers and in locations. In the most recent history, the world population increased from 1 billion in 1800 to almost 7.9 billion today[4] (Roser et al., n.d.).

As the human population has increased, so too has the number of trials and errors each individual contributes to the never-ending search for solutions to humanity's survival challenges, such as overpopulation, preventing conflict, and finding a better social order. Each independent individual (with independence being a key concept) is like a roll of the dice in this game. Some individuals bring about breakthrough ideas and usher in massive change for humanity. In a way, humans form cells of what can be

---

[4] ourworldindata.org/world-population-growth stats on population growth

analogized to an emerging massive neocortex for humanity. The more cells we have, the more powerful humankind's collective brain becomes.

There is ongoing and intriguing research on the origins and properties of high brain functions by Jeff Hawkins, outlined in his book "The Thousand Brains Theory of Intelligence"[5] (Hawkins, 2019). He was a co-founder and co-creator of the Palm Pilot, one of the first commercial handheld devices, and later turned to his passion for neuroscience and founded several research centers and institutions. He proposed a theory suggesting that the neocortex consists of individual processing units, approximately 500,000 of them, called cortical columns. Each column specializes in the universal processing of mapping sensory input into sensory output, in other words, building intricate maps of consciousness. These units could apply this mechanism to a wide variety of tasks, from locating a coffee cup in relation to the fingers of our hand, to forming visualizations of the memory of a room, to localizing individual sounds and recognizing language.

Hawkins also noted how the neocortex, or as he called it, the "newer brain," works in coordination with, but also in opposition to, the "old brain" or brain stem. The brain stem is wired for survival, with instinctual reactions to fear, fight, jealousy, and other basic emotions. It also processes the sensory input from our five human senses and generates nerve output directly to our muscles and peripheral nerves. The neocortex interfaces with the old brain but does not communicate directly with senses and muscles. Parts of the neocortex, the cortical columns, constantly create and update thousands of maps, ranging from the physical locations of objects relative to our bodies to more conceptual maps of consciousness that map sounds to their meaning in language recognition and comprehension, and even more complex maps of our reality. Some of these maps are also maps of our own minds, demonstrating the recursive and mind-bending ability of the mind to create a map of itself, or in other words, self-awareness.

According to Hawkins' model, our brain constantly builds models of reality, providing its best approximation. We don't see reality through our eyes as it is, raw. For one, in the middle of the eye, there is a large area without visual receptors. This is where the visual nerve takes all the input from the receptors and carries it into the brain. If we were to see it as is, we would see a large black spot in the middle of our vision. More drastically, our vision is upside down. Our eyes register incoming rays and reverse them vertically. We've all encountered this in middle school optical experiments; lenses reverse the vision and display it upside down. Our brain reverses it back and compensates for any black or blind spots by filling them in with a model of reality.

An interesting thought experiment by the ancient Greek philosopher Plato is one of the most well-known philosophical stories in Western thought. Found in Book VII of Plato's "Republic," the allegory of the cave serves as a

---

[5] numenta.com/the-thousand-brains-theory-of-intelligence

metaphorical explanation of the difference between appearance and reality, as well as the role of education in understanding the world around us.

The allegory begins with a group of people imprisoned in a cave since childhood. Chained in such a way that they can only see the wall in front of them and the shadows cast by objects passing behind them, the prisoners believe these shadows are the only reality and are unaware of the true nature of the objects creating the shadows.

Plato argues that the prisoners represent the general public, who are ignorant of the true nature of reality. The cave, with its limited view of the world, represents the physical world we perceive through our senses. The shadows on the wall represent the illusions we perceive in the world around us, often mistaken for reality. He then describes what would happen if one of the prisoners were freed and shown the true nature of the objects casting the shadows. Initially disoriented and confused, the prisoner would eventually understand the true nature of reality. They would then feel compelled to return to the cave to free the other prisoners and show them the truth.

This part of the allegory represents the role of true knowledge in freeing people from the illusions of the physical world. Plato believed that philosophers had a duty to seek knowledge and then use that knowledge to help others free themselves from the limitations of their own perspectives. Learning about the world around us, ourselves, and even our own mortality, is like freeing ourselves and escaping from Plato's cave.

With self-awareness, we become aware of our strengths and limitations, including our most significant weakness: our mortality. If we know that we exist, we also know that we did not exist at some point in the past, and we will not exist at some point in the future. This raises a simple question: why struggle and make an effort to survive if we are all ultimately going to die? In his 1973 book "The Denial of Death," cultural anthropologist Ernest Becker wrote about humans, as intelligent animals, being able to grasp the inevitability of death.

Therefore, the question about the meaning of our lives emerges from the realization that our time here is finite. In my perspective, if we were eternal beings, the urgency or intensity of questioning our existence would not be as profound. With infinite time, we'd have more opportunities to unravel this mystery, focusing our mental efforts on more immediate concerns. This explains why questions about our place in life often become more frequent as we age, when the perception of time seems increasingly limited. With our awareness of mortality, the question of our purpose here takes on a much more immediate importance.

There are numerous potential answers to the question of our purpose in life. In ancient times, people believed in enduring glory. Take for instance Greek mythology's Achilles, the central character in "The Iliad," which recounts the final period of the Trojan War. Achilles is renowned for choosing between a long, peaceful life and a brief one that would grant him eternal glory. In Abrahamic religions, there's a belief in an afterlife and an immortal soul. Eastern religions propagate the concept of reincarnation, suggesting our capacity to be reborn, which completely transforms the perception of death from an inevitability into a continuous cycle. All of these answers deal with the question of what happens to us after we die, with the possibility that parts of us will continue to exist, whether through glory, our souls, or our inevitable rebirth.

This brings me to the conclusion that the genesis of our quest for meaning lies in our instinctual desire to evade death—a desire inherited from our genes' drive to persist in spite of all adversities, coupled with our minds comprehending our own mortality. In simpler terms, the answer to the meaning of life lies in solving the ancient riddle of how to outwit death. This leads us to the concept of "memento mori," a reminder of our inevitable mortality.

Memento Mori

I don't recall where I saw this phrase for the first time or what book it was, but I recall seeing it again and again in the books on the history of Europe. It was a salutation exchanged by the hermits of St. Paul in the 1600s, "remember death." It was in the descriptions for paintings depicting skulls or skeletons standing next to portraits in the works of Frans Hals or Arnold Bocklin. I also recall my surprise and kind of relief when I realized the true meaning behind it. Instead of dwelling on the inevitability of death, "memento mori" emphasizes focusing on being alive, valuing, and celebrating every moment, knowing that it will not last forever.

This celebration of life is only possible if you find value in it. It is not possible if there is nothing to celebrate. The alternative of not finding any value and merely going through the motions until time runs out is a haunting prospect that troubled my younger self. That is the real fear of realizing your mortality. Questions like, "Why do I need to struggle with my life when it will eventually and inevitably come to an end?" kept popping up in my head.

Filling your life with meaning is easy if you live forever; you have all the time in the world to try every single thing, taking millennia-long breaks in between, until eventually you will wonder into the meaning of it. However, if your lifespan is limited, you have only so many chances to get it right. Your time becomes the most precious resource that you should not waste thoughtlessly. Your limited life also makes the meaning of it so much more valuable.

One logical solution is to dedicate your life to a cause that will outlive you, something bigger than you, such as your family, your children, your tribe, your country, your glory, or another higher purpose.

For me, filled with the wonders of science fiction and the knowledge of how powerful science can be, I wanted to ensure that if I find a solution, it will be the best and the right one based on science. Dedicating your life to meaningless causes and wasting your priceless years is depressing and wasteful. I also wanted to find it based on science. If I wanted to spend a significant portion of my life pursuing a cause to make my life meaningful, I had to get it right from day one. And the "memento mori" phrase reminded me of that.

This phrase traces back to classical antiquity. In his dialogue "On the Soul" (or Phaedo), Plato recounts the death of his mentor Socrates and introduces the idea that the proper practice of philosophy is "about nothing else but dying." While death is certainly a common theme in philosophical discussions, it would be an oversimplification to say that philosophy is solely concerned with this topic. However, it is true that death is a fundamental aspect of human existence and that it raises many important philosophical questions about our mortality and the meaning of life in the face of death. In this sense, the practice of philosophy, according to Plato, can be seen as a form of preparation for death, helping us face the end of our lives with wisdom and courage.

In medieval Europe, two texts dated from about 1415 and 1450 offered advice to their Christian readers on the protocols and procedures of a good death. These books, called Ars moriendi or "The Art of Dying," were very popular and became the de facto prescription for Christians on how to prepare for a "good death" in order to escape the temptations of the devil and reach heaven.

One of the oldest discovered texts, older than the Christian Old Testament, "the Epic of Gilgamesh", is about a Sumerian king Gilgamesh who witnesses the death of his friend. He then becomes afraid of his own death and visits the sage Utnapishtim, the survivor of the Great Flood, hoping to defeat death. Gilgamesh repeatedly fails the trials set before him and returns home, realizing that immortality is beyond his reach. This quest to escape death and reach immortality is a common theme throughout human history.

My college years brought me face to face with the concept of mortality, as I witnessed escalating acts of violence during my studies in math and physics at a university in Moscow. This was in the early 90s, a tumultuous period following the collapse of the Soviet Union, when established societal norms had disintegrated and new ones had yet to form. I saw professors from lesser-known colleges struggle to survive on their shrinking salaries, eventually resorting to selling their possessions at flea markets. In stark contrast, their former students, who had managed to devise lucrative schemes, were buying expensive cars and hiring bodyguards to protect themselves from potential theft or homicide by rivals. The value placed on life had drastically declined, and scenes of violence had become a daily occurrence on the streets.

To me it was quite a shock coming from a smaller town in Lithuania. Even there the violence between classmates was quite a usual thing in school and in the backyards, but it would stop with the first blood drawn. After the bloody lip or nose you would quite often be back to studying and playing games with the very people who you just had a fight with, as if nothing really happened. Quick school yard fights were a version of quick conflict resolution, before conflicts would brew into something more permanent and dangerous.

At my college located in the Russian suburbs, the violence between students and local folks escalated to another level. It involved dozens of people armed with knives and chains on the side of the locals. Students would wield metal legs of disassembled beds, with large screws protruding from the ends, resembling medieval weapons rather than furniture pieces. When someone, either a local or a student, got jumped and beaten up by locals, the way to resolve the conflict wasn't through a one-on-one fight. Instead, both sides would gather a small army of foot soldiers and attempt to resolve the dispute through negotiations, using the sheer numbers they brought to the site as leverage. For me, this was utterly barbaric, unnecessary, and dangerous, yet at the same time, insanely fascinating in its adrenaline-inducing craziness. At any moment, horrific violence could break out, with the two crowds confronting, bashing, and slicing each other with steel; this happened a couple of times in the past history of our college, but not when I was in the crowd. I participated in a few of those "council of war" assemblies, and every time they were broken apart by Soviet police (called militia), with both sides dropping their weapons into the bushes and running separate ways, trying not to be captured and booked by the police. However, after a couple of times, when the novelty of the action wore off, I stopped heeding calls to arms by senior students and focused on my nightly studies instead.

Surrounded by this sea of violence and pressure to perform academically, this is when I started questioning my motives: why am I doing all of this and what is the point of sleepless nights and endless stress. To save my academic career, along with my general well being and my sanity I had to crawl out of my misery myself and get on with my life. And recall that failure in academic performance would eliminate waiver from the military draft which would send us right into the meat-grinder of the Red Army. I needed an answer and I needed it fast. Instead of fearing expulsion and finding inspiration to study I was getting more and more sad, to the point of losing any motivation to get up and go to classes.

What propelled me towards my never ending sadness was not a mere fear of dying, rather it was lack of meaning in my daily routine and the fear that my life will end without finding any meaning in it. Or worse, that I would live a wonderful life that would end without leaving a trace of all those wonders I have experienced. What comes to mind is one of the most iconic speeches in sci-fi movie history, the original Blade Runner:

> " I've seen things you people wouldn't believe.
> Attack ships on fire off the shoulder of Orion.
> I watched C-beams glitter in the dark near the Tannhäuser Gate.
> All those moments will be lost in time, like tears in rain."

I yearned to experience moments of wonder and a sense of belonging before death inevitably arrived. Since our ancient brains became self-aware, realizing that we are born and will eventually die, people have been conscious of their own mortality. At present, in the contemporary state of medical affairs, there is no escape from death. There are some notable exceptions, the organisms that exhibit remarkable longevity and resilience. One example is the "Turritopsis dohrnii", also known as the "immortal jellyfish." This species has the ability to revert to its juvenile form after reaching maturity, essentially starting its life cycle anew. Although it can still die from predation or disease, this unique ability allows it to avoid aging and live indefinitely under optimal conditions. However, the vast majority of living organisms on Earth will ultimately cease to exist.

Once I understood this inevitability, I also recognized that there is no logical sense in fearing death. Instead, my memento mori has shifted towards fears about dying pointlessly, without meaning, and squandering my most valuable resource: time. To address this, I had to discover the meaning of my life. That was my way of dealing with mortality.

As a physicist in a scientific institution, I approached this problem the only way I knew how. I decided to formulate the meaning of life as a scientific problem and solve it using scientific methods. However, even formulating the question as a scientific problem proved more difficult than I anticipated. The question itself had multiple layers, each with various meanings. The word "meaning" has several definitions, and the concept of life is complex enough to fill pages in a biology textbook. As I tried to decipher the question and break it down into manageable parts that could be translated into the familiar language of equations, I found myself going in circles. When examining one possible solution, other possibilities would interfere with the original path. For instance, when considering a personal, narrow perspective, I would doubt whether I was missing the bigger picture. On the other hand, when I shifted my attention to global issues, they appeared less relevant to my individual life. This conundrum raised an important question: If I were to sacrifice my own life for the sake of the greater world, would I truly fulfill my life's purpose?

At that time, my thoughts revolved around the idea that to uncover a formula or recipe for life's direction, I needed to identify what made my life meaningful on a global scale. I believed that anything less would compromise the true meaning. However, this mindset led me into a mental loop. There were countless factors beyond my control on a global scale, so I had to narrow the problem's scope. Yet, if I limited it too much, I feared missing the true meaning, and so I continued to circle around in my thoughts.

At that time, amid my frustration, I longed for a magical handbook containing all the answers I sought. This desire partially motivated me to write this book years later, knowing that at least my younger self would find it useful. However, back then, I couldn't find any meaningful literature on the subject.

Without such a magical book, I had to come up with answers on my own. I had to take a step back and start from scratch, to examine the problem from first principles: What does "the meaning of life" actually mean?

Deconstructing the "Meaning of Life"

The "meaning of life" is a deceptively simple phrase, easily understood and seemingly familiar. However, when examined closely, it becomes apparent that there are multiple interpretations embedded within it. These were the questions that sent my thoughts into a mental merry-go-round:

- Is the meaning singular or are there multiple meanings?
- Is there a main overarching purpose or several important ones?
- What does "life" mean in this context? Does the meaning apply to someone's personal life and their specific circumstances? Or is it more of a global concept applicable to many or all?
- Could there be one answer to both global and singular versions of this question?
- Is there an answer at all, only one answer, or a set of many answers?

To make progress, I needed to define the scope of the questions and navigate the complexity of the problem. The best way to achieve this was to start with the very basics and examine the phrase "meaning of life" itself.

Let's begin our deconstruction with the first word, "meaning." Intuitively, "to live a meaningful life" implies making choices that maximize your life's meaning.

According to the Oxford Dictionary, "meaning" is "the thing or idea that a sound, word, sign, etc. represents," and also "the real importance of a feeling or an experience." Merriam-Webster defines it as "significant quality; implication of a hidden or special significance." This suggests that there is some undiscovered purpose in the context of our lives that we need to find. It does not guarantee that meaning exists. Many concepts around us lack meaning. For instance, it is difficult to assign meaning to a comet on the other side of the galaxy or a neutrino particle that passes through you as you read this without ever interacting with any atom in your body. It's challenging to assign meaning to something you do not observe or know about. Numerous natural phenomena and events do not affect or interact with us, making them essentially meaningless. Meaning involves some effect on a conscious observer and some form of interaction; without any effect, these events are just that—meaningless.

Our actions, however, are directly observable by and affect people around us. Our actions and choices can be assigned meaning as long as they have an impact on other people. Yet, our actions can leave different types of impacts. I might help an elderly woman cross the road or save someone from drowning. Chances are the former action will eventually be forgotten, while the latter will leave a truly large, if not maximum, impact.

This distinction is captured in another interpretation of the word "meaning," which implies that it must last long enough for us to register it and for it to have an impact on our lives. If the meaning lasts only a second, it is not a very meaningful second. Meaning implies that what you've found and accomplished in your life will not disappear. Ideally, meaning should outlast your life. Having children and providing them with the best education, or contributing to one's country's advancement, and leaving a legacy in one's chosen field, such as sports, art, or science, are all good examples of a meaningful life. The key concept here is that you are leaving behind or working on something with a lasting, hopefully permanent, impact. Meaning cannot be fleeting; it requires duration.

This raises questions such as: Is the meaning self-contained within the scope of your life, does it span across humanity, or does it reside somewhere outside of it? Do you search for the "raison d'etre" within your own life, or is the scope much broader, like in Aristotle's form or the commandments of Abrahamic gods?

The second word, "life," in the phrase "meaning of life" encompasses multiple connotations. Merriam-Webster defines "life" as "the quality that distinguishes a vital and functional being from a dead body" and "a principle or force considered to underlie the distinctive quality of animate beings." We can notice that the mere linguistic definition of life means the opposition to death.

Unlike inanimate objects that may remain unchanged for a long time, a stone left undisturbed by the elements will stay a stone for centuries until a river or a mason's hand finds it, moves it and eventually destroys it. According to the Standard Model of physics, a constituent of an atom, a proton, left in a free state may exist indefinitely without destruction or decay.

On the other hand, living matter may cease to exist and will eventually succumb to death and decay. In this sense, life is defined in opposition to non-existence. Life is a state contrary to death and distinct from the stability of inanimate objects. In the context of evolutionary biology, life represents survival and expansion. Although biology does not have an unequivocal definition of life, with current definitions being descriptive rather than prescriptive, exploring these definitions can be helpful.

Life is a complex and dynamic phenomenon involving the interaction of numerous components. Generally, life is an entity or system attempting to preserve its internal environment amid changing external environments. This property is characterized by the ability to grow, reproduce, adapt to changing conditions, and respond to stimuli. Life is also associated with the capacity to absorb energy from the environment and use it for growth, development, and the preservation of its internal cellular structure. Many processes, such as metabolism, reproduction, growth, and response to stimuli, are carried out by various organelles within a cell, including the nucleus, mitochondria, endoplasmic reticulum, and Golgi apparatus. These organelles work together to perform the necessary functions of life.

Living organisms that fail to preserve their internal environment and structure become unable to live or simply die. In this sense, life is defined relative to its opposite, death. Death occurs when the internal structure merges with the external environment. This definition is almost poetic; after death, our temporary home finally merges with the external environment, and the cellular structure fights this process with everything that evolution has bestowed upon living beings.

In a previous chapter, I mentioned that the search for the meaning of life goes hand in hand with the realization of our own mortality. In both the strict lexical and philosophical senses, death is a state diametrically opposed to life, representing the permanent termination of all living processes. Whatever the meaning of life may be, it must be opposite to death and mortality.

The word "life" also refers to a specific person's life, applying to the sum of a person's experiences throughout their lifetime. Merriam-Webster defines this as "the sequence of physical and mental experiences that make up the existence of an individual"[6].

During my college years, I went over this deconstruction process. It helped me narrow the focus of the question and direct it specifically toward the realm of living, excluding inanimate objects like mountains, rivers, or protons. It captured the general meaning of all living things and the particular details of our lives.

While reading on the subject, I noticed that many philosophers and thinkers, including those mentioned at the beginning of this chapter, defined the search for the meaning of life relative to mortality and concepts of death. Some of these concepts involved the existence of entities, such as the soul or reincarnation, which were opposite to death; that is, immortal and not subject to decay.

This lexical analysis led me to a conclusion that the meaning of life is opposite to the meaning of death. This, in turn, is directly related to leaving a long-term impact on our lives and the lives around us. To summarize the conclusions from my lexical and logical analysis, the meaning of life should satisfy the following properties:

1. Has to do with life and staying alive, i.e. survival and expansion
2. Have a profound and lasting impact on your life or life in general
3. Be personal, i.e. specific to a person's life

The first point to consider is that the meaning of life should also provide an answer to our fear of mortality. This idea started me on this path, captivated the minds of many thinkers, and made me feel that the answer must be related to "memento mori." The absolute opposition to mortality,

---

[6] merriam-webster.com/dictionary/life

taken to an extreme, is not just life itself. Like in the ancient tale of Gilgamesh, we aim to extend life and defeat death. We will explore this further in the next chapter.

Another observation was that the "meaning of life" could be divided into answers to at least two separate questions: one concerning the meaning of our personal life and another, more global, about the meaning of all life in general. The former will be addressed in this part, while the latter will be examined in the context of the broader problem of meaning for all people and how to connect the meaning of your personal life to the global meaning of all.

While this approach to examining the meaning of words guided me in the right direction and helped create interesting and insightful observations of potential meanings, it also revealed the limitations of a purely lexical approach. Despite our careful analysis of each component of the phrase "meaning of life", the language's meaning still changes depending on the context.

For instance, consider the ambiguity of defining what life is. Life could describe an individual's life or the lives of many individuals. Alternatively, it could describe not just people but all of humanity or all living beings. If we want to make a profound and lasting impact on life, which life should it be— ours, our family's, or all humankind's? Does life only include people or all living organisms? Is this the meaning of my personal life, in which case it may be too narrow and specific and miss the global picture? Or is it a meaning for all life on this planet, in which case it may have nothing to do with my life personally?

Pursuing each question is like taking a winding path that curves and branches off in numerous directions. This is akin to finding the right path in a complex labyrinth without a compass.

To seek a formal solution, I had to make a few assumptions and narrow the search. I decided that finding the meaning involves focusing on aspects that are comparable to the length of our lives and, hopefully, outlive us and last longer after we are gone. It seemed logical to think that the meanings of our lives need to be at least as significant, if not more so, than our lives. It also addressed my fascination with memento mori.

I hoped to start with this assumption and, as a budding physicist, try to understand and reformulate the question as a scientific problem, taking a scientific approach but using this specific assumption. The scientific formalism and scientific method would become my proverbial compass in the labyrinth of my search for the answer.

Before we start using a scientific approach to solve our questions, let us define what is it. What makes methods scientific? What is actually science?

Scientific Approach

When we ask about "the meaning of life," we pose numerous questions: What drives our life's journey from the moment we became self-aware to now, and to this specific point in our lives? Is our life predetermined by a higher power or being, and do we need to find and discover this meaning? Are our life steps random or predetermined, and do we have control over them? If so, can we retrace the steps we took, analyze them, learn from them, and map our path forward toward an intended future? In the later chapters we will discuss the concept of karma and consequences of our choices.

The challenge with everyday language is that terms can have multiple meanings depending on the context. This ambiguity hinders our ability to articulate complex subjects and prevents us from narrowing down problems to a set of specific questions. In the last chapter, we discussed how the word "life" could have numerous meanings depending on the context of the question.

I also had doubts about the stability of my solution. If I find a purpose for my life now, will it change with my age and as my life experiences evolve? Would multiple evolving meanings of life negate the quintessential "true" meaning of life? My thoughts went in circles until I realized I needed a better system to assign exact meanings that depend on a context to avoid mixing them or using the same word with multiple meanings.

I didn't have to look far, as this was a well-known problem with a well-established solution. Science routinely addresses difficulties in representing complex and abstract structures using linguistic terms and constructs. There is even a branch of science dedicated to formalizing this approach: formal science. Numerous examples exist of developing a language tailored to a specific problem, such as the system of formal logic (proposed in 1921 by David Hilbert) used as the foundation for knowledge in mathematics. Math typically solves this issue by locking the context of the problem within a series of axioms, trading flexibility for specificity. This way, the arguments remain within the context of the problem until a logical resolution is reached or a contradiction arises.

Scientific formalism is by no means the solution to all known problems. Rather, it serves as a toolkit that must be applied to specific issues. Contrary to common beliefs, fundamental science does not attempt to answer existential questions, such as discovering our true nature or finding the meaning of life. Traditionally, these questions have been the domain of philosophy and religion. It is unfortunate, as science possesses tools to provide precise and unambiguous answers. People are often drawn to disciplines and institutions, like religious institutions and philosophy, that claim to provide answers to existential questions—even though the answers provided are often imprecise and vague. If only science had developed an interest in questions like finding the meaning of life. We will address this intriguing possibility in later parts of this book.

On the other hand, physicists and mathematicians seek to establish previously undiscovered links between known physical or mathematical phenomena. Even when a new paradigm emerges, it is based on previously established knowledge. Any new scientific breakthrough builds upon existing paradigms, like a pyramid or concentric circles. Each new paradigm does not overthrow the past one; rather, it extends and builds upon it. Science is incremental, not revolutionary. Its aim is not to uncover revelations but to connect the dots. Nonetheless, fundamental science provides essential tools that I can apply. The scientific method and scientific formalism are among the most important tools, so we should discuss them next.

Scientific formalism is a methodology that enables the scientific method. The scientific method, a process characterizing natural science since the 17th century, consists of systematic observation, measurement, experimentation, and the formulation, testing, and modification of hypotheses. As an example, we can consider an application of scientific method to watering an apple tree:

1. Make a systematic observation: I observe that the leaves on my apple tree are turning yellow.
2. Formulate a hypothesis: I hypothesize that the leaves are turning yellow due to a lack of water.
3. Test the hypothesis: I can test this hypothesis by watering the tree and observing if the leaves turn green again.
4. Analyze results and draw conclusions: If the leaves turn green again after watering, then my hypothesis was correct and the leaves were turning yellow due to a lack of water. If the leaves do not turn green, then my hypothesis was incorrect and I must look for another explanation.

This method allows us to separate accurate scientific theories from falsehoods within the complex structure of facts, observations, and measurements. Sir Francis Bacon, an English philosopher, statesman, and scientist, is generally considered the father of the scientific method. A key figure in the scientific revolution of the 17th century, Bacon is known for promoting the use of empirical observation and experimentation as a means of understanding the natural world. He emphasized the importance of systematic observation, careful measurement, and the use of logic and reasoning to draw conclusions from data. Bacon's ideas were influential in shaping the development of modern science and the scientific method. However, it is essential to note that the scientific method has evolved over time and has been influenced by many thinkers and scientists throughout history.

In simpler terms, the scientific method involves scientists predicting future outcomes with over 99% accuracy. They predict the results of an experiment before conducting it, and then test their predictions through numerous scientific experiments. If their predictions prove true in 99.97% of cases, or according to the three-sigma rule, their findings are considered significant[7] (68–95–99.7 Rule, n.d.), the hypothesis becomes a scientific theory. You may ask such a specific number of 99.7%. The simplified answer is that most physical phenomena follow a specific pattern that repeats from observing stars, looking at sand movements in a wind or looking at movement of prices in financial instruments. The chances of observing a pure coincidence drops significantly the further away your measurement is from predicted values. Scientists count the significance of discovery in how far the measurement is from the pure coincidence in the counts of standard errors. The distance of three standard errors corresponding to 99.7% is considered statistically significant in many scientific disciplines, but it is not universally used across all fields. In particle physics, for example, a much higher standard of five sigma (corresponding to a 99.99994% confidence level) is typically required to claim a discovery. An example of this is confirming the existence of the Higgs particle, which gives mass to all matter in the universe. This is why it is important to measure quantity, values and their errors, i.e. have measurable predictions.

Science is in a process of continuous self-validation and correction, with a constant stream of experiments whose outcomes are unknown until they are conducted and subjected to thorough peer review.

It's intriguing how even terms common to both scientific and everyday language can convey very different meanings. Take, for example, the word "theory." In colloquial language, a theory often implies a guess or uncertainty, while a fact is considered an absolute certainty. In the realm of science, however, the meaning is reversed. Theories are the closest thing to the ultimate truth, while facts are secondary. Science starts with facts as observational points to find patterns and links between them to form a scientific theory. Theories are represented using mathematics as equations that connect the phenomenon on the right side with the left side. Theories also depend on assumptions and axioms, which are usually confirmed in experiments and appear as constants in equations. For example, Newton's law of gravity contains a gravitational constant that needs to be measured experimentally.

Eventually the parts of the scientific method morphed into two distinct branches of science, an experimental and theoretical branches. The formulation of hypotheses has become so significant that many scientists specialize solely in this area, earning the title of theoretical scientists. On the other hand, experimental scientists focus on the validation and confirmation of theories and hypotheses. This distinction exists across multiple scientific disciplines, including chemistry, physics, and even biology. Both branches hold equal importance. Theorists consolidate existing ideas or propose new

---

[7] en.wikipedia.org/68-95-99.7_rule

ones that dictate the course of entire fields. The most intriguing and impactful results in experimental science occur when experiments contradict theoretical predictions, signaling new scientific directions and potential flaws in an old theory's foundation. For instance, I had the privilege of studying neutrino physics at Fermilab on a project called NuTeV[8] (Vaitaitis, n.d.). Neutrinos are extraordinary elementary particles that are abundantly produced in nuclear reactions yet barely interact with matter. This interaction is facilitated by a natural force known as the "weak force," aptly named to reflect the subtle nature of this interaction. Thankfully, this is the case, as approximately 65 billion neutrinos originating from the Sun's nuclear reactions pass through every square centimeter on Earth every second. If their interaction was any stronger, all life on Earth would be devastated by neutrino radiation. Fortunately it is not the case, but the neutrinos abundance and shy nature served as an inspiration to John Updike's poem[9] (Thornberry, 2022) who wrote:

" Neutrinos they are very small.
They have no charge and have no mass
And do not interact at all. The earth is just a silly ball
To them."

Up until the late 20th century, neutrinos were considered massless particles, similar to photons, that did not interact with other mass particles. However, in 1998, the Super Kamiokande experiment[10] conducted by a collaboration of about 120 physicists, discovered that neutrinos indeed have mass. The possibility had been speculated by theoretical physicists for many years prior, but Japanese and US scientists confirmed that neutrinos possess a tiny mass, shaking the foundations of the established paradigm of physics known as the "Standard Model"[11] (Standard Model, n.d.). This discovery reiterated the importance of both theoretical and experimental branches of physics.

Without the ability to prove or disprove theoretical predictions, science could become as dogmatic as religion. For example, we have the elegant string theory that unites gravity and quantum mechanics. Unfortunately, it cannot be verified by modern technologies and remains just that—a beautiful theory to be taken almost on faith. We will discuss this topic again in subsequent sections of this book.

---

[8] en.wikipedia.org/Sterile_neutrino

[9] themarginalian.org/john-updike-cosmic-gall poem about neutrinos

[10] en.wikipedia.org/wiki/Super-Kamiokande

[11] en.wikipedia.org/wiki/Standard_Model

I wanted to apply the same concepts to redefine and translate the problem of the meaning of life into measurable concepts that could be used in a formula to arrive at a provable solution.

One of the main ingredients of the scientific method is the ability to measure things. Without a measurable outcome for your hypothesis, it is difficult or nearly impossible to design an experiment or test that either proves or disproves your assumptions. Without scientific proof, it is impossible to distinguish a correct solution (a scientific truth) from a falsehood. That's why science tends to avoid philosophical and theological arguments, where it is inherently challenging to form a measurable quantity, and the answers are often binary in nature.

Hence, my initial step towards a scientific formulation is to define a quantifiable parameter for the concept of life's meaning. Once achieved, this will enable us to devise thought experiments, such as analyzing the past history of successful individuals who we intuitively perceive to have led meaningful lives. We can then measure the parameter that corresponds to the meaning of their lives. If our hypothesis holds true, we would hopefully observe a general increase in their life's meaning over time, surpassing the average of a population deemed 'average' in terms of success.

The concept of "living a meaningful life" suggests making choices that amplify life's meaning, which can be perceived in two distinct ways: comprehending its essence and actualizing it. To my understanding, this poses two challenges: first, quantifying the value of meaning, and second, arranging our actions and choices based on this quantified value. I propose addressing the first challenge through a formula that attributes a 'meaning value' to each of our actions. The second challenge appears to be a question of optimization, a concept familiar in mathematics, physics, computer science, and economics, which entails finding the best possible solution from all viable alternatives.

Both challenges can be tackled using a scientific approach that employs scientific concepts and notions. This approach simplifies the identification of logical contradictions and helps in navigating ambiguous terms found in common language. However, to make this process work and to create testable thought experiments, it is necessary to find a quantitative and numerical representation of meaning. When maximized, this value would result in a life filled with meaning. In science, this is referred to as a utility function or rule. For instance, if we aim to become wealthy, we seek a method to earn money and maximize the amount while minimizing our expenses. Consequently, the amount of money serves as the objective measure of becoming wealthy. If we want to solve equations of motion, we must formulate a functional expression and minimize it. With happiness and meaning it is much harder, because we do not have a single quantity to measure happiness or calculate the meaning. Once we have a way to do it, the problem becomes so much easier.

Social scientists and economists have addressed optimization problems by employing mathematical models of interaction among individuals, known as game theory. This approach has been so successful that eleven game theorists have been awarded the Nobel Prize in Economics, with the most recent accolade going to Jean Tirole in 2014. However, the outcomes of specific strategies can vary considerably based on the selected acceptance criteria.

Once a utility function for life is established, one can pursue the path where it increases and ultimately reaches its peak value. At this point, life achieves its fullest meaning, and ideally, this process provides an answer to the meaning of life.

The metric for the meaning of life must be represented by a singular value rather than a series of numbers. We can still have multiple meanings, or even change our mind, but the metric that compares the meanings needs to be a number. A fundamental property of optimization is that it requires sorting by a single value. When making decisions, we need one criterion to guide our choices. It is impossible to simultaneously rank first in two distinct benchmarks or be ahead in two separate queues. One can only occupy a single queue and make one choice. One can not be both the richest and most pious person, one priority would stand in the way of another. When we have two competing ranking values it would create inevitable contradictions. We could find a compromise, for example we could be both rich and charitable, but this requires both priorities to significantly align, essentially merging into one. Therefore, to organize all actions and priorities in life, I needed to devise a single quantitative representation of life's meaning.

Another challenge lies in the ambiguity of defining what constitutes life. The term could refer to an individual's life, the lives of numerous individuals, or even encompass all of humanity or living beings. On a personal level, if we are fortunate, our lives hold importance to ourselves and our immediate circle, including friends and family. However, there are times when I also desire to make a significant impact on a grander scale, not only for my benefit but for everyone's.

The scale of significance considerably alters the perspective. For instance, let's consider health as a quantifiable measure of life's meaning. While I could have selected another metric, such as happiness, health is easier to consolidate into a single value. Medical instruments can measure health, and the data can be combined into a single index or value. In this example, I can focus on my own health or the collective health of those around me, such as family and friends. Another possibility is to evaluate the health of all people worldwide as a consequence of my actions. Focusing on your own health versus the health of all people would lead to two different life choices and very different decisions.

This line of reasoning forms the foundation of the utilitarian school of thought. Although its origins can be traced back to Epicurus, Jeremy Bentham, an 18th-century English philosopher, jurist, and social reformer, is credited with its development. Bentham posited that "nature has placed mankind under the governance of two sovereign masters, pain and pleasure," and formulated the Rule of Utility: "that the good is whatever brings the greatest happiness to the greatest number of people." Whether happiness should represent the meaning of life is a separate question, which we will explore in the chapters of the next part of this book. The issue I am addressing here pertains to the scale of measurement: should it be localized to my own life or globalized to encompass everyone else, that is, the greatest number of people?

In the first scenario, where we concentrate on a localized meaning centered on our own well-being and health, the goal is to maximize our individual lives' quality, health, and longevity, which might conflict with the lives of those around us.

Conversely, during wartime, soldiers and warriors frequently sacrificed their own lives to protect their families and fellow countrymen. In this case, maximizing an individual's well-being contradicts the well-being of the tribe and nation.

This implies that the representation of the meaning of life, which I referred to as the objective function, is fragmented into at least two parts, or even multiple objectives. There was the meaning of individual life and a more global issue concerning all living beings. There was not a single objective function or representation of the meaning of life, but numerous and potentially conflicting objective functions. However, to make a clear choice, we need a single principle and a single objective function that, at a crossroads, will guide us to go left or right, fight or flee.

One observation I made later in life is that, regardless of the overarching principle, it must be enduring and stable. The impact of a fleeting action or accomplishment diminishes with time. An infinitesimal and brief interaction could go unnoticed, much like neutrinos not interacting with matter on Earth. Although billions of neutrinos may pass through us, any interaction will be imperceptible. A single large asteroid could cause irreversible and lasting damage to our civilization. The same principle applies to our actions. Holding a door open for someone will not be remembered as long as saving someone from drowning. Permanent changes leave the most significant impacts. This is why the longevity of an action or impact is a primary factor in contributing to its meaning.

Even if one discovers the answer to the global question of the meaning of all life, if that answer contradicts aspects of one's personal life, then what use is knowing the global meaning if it does not apply to you? On the other hand, focusing solely on your life risks arriving at a meaning that is insignificant. This localized meaning would hold no value for others. If the meaning is too specific, it won't be applicable beyond the confines of your own life.

While I was working on this problem and studying physics and math at one of Moscow's top universities, a year had passed since I left Lithuania. During that time, significant events unfolded: the Soviet Union disintegrated, rampant inflation wiped out the savings of ordinary people, and a few well-connected nouveau riches plundered state enterprises. Inflation skyrocketed to unimaginable levels—more than 150% per month or about 2000% per year. The state stipends that qualified students received were obliterated by inflation, forcing us to fend for ourselves. My classmate and I started a small business to earn some extra cash, manufacturing and selling phones with caller ID features, just to get by on our shrinking stipend.

About a year after the initial upheaval, another coup d'etat took place. This time, it was the president against the parliament, and the conflict was much bloodier, with hundreds of civilians in Moscow alone becoming collateral damage to sniper fire. The president urged the people to take to the streets, build barricades, and protest, while the parliament summoned rebellious armed divisions to the capital. I had missed the original rebellion a year prior when I was stranded in Lithuania, facing a complete energy and food blockade. This time, I was determined to do the right thing and defend a burgeoning democracy from a repressive parliament—or so I thought. I joined a large crowd in central Moscow, where we tore down benches, fences, road signs, and anything else we could use to construct makeshift barricades. Warplanes flew overhead, and I saw tanks firing directly at the parliament building, eventually setting it ablaze. The coup continued well past midnight, and we built a sizable barricade. Lacking a place to spend the night, I took one of the last buses back to the university—a wise decision, as the entire area soon fell under sniper fire, resulting in numerous casualties. The coup was ultimately quashed violently. It seemed to be nothing more than a power struggle between two power-hungry factions, with many people losing their lives in vain. This senseless violence only underscored the importance of finding a meaning outside of that pointless rat race: a truly meaningful, global, and all-encompassing purpose in life.

Despite my efforts, I wasn't making much progress. Confronted with multiple objective functions for the meaning of life, I opted to begin with the most convenient choice: to seek a universal utility that would apply to all cases. In other words, to find the meaning of life within the grand scheme of things.

In conclusion, what makes our approach to be scientific is two things:
   a) I had to aim to find a quantifiable measure for the meaning of life, i.e. formula for the quantity, and
   b) That this measure will lead to verifiable and testable conclusions

By going after the most encompassing meaning, I was hoping to find the measurable answer to everything. I wanted to find a quick and robust shortcut to the question that was eating at me: What is the universal meaning of life?

Looking for a Universal Meaning

My motivation to find a universal meaning was simple: if your life is important and meaningful, it must have a purpose and place in the universe. By uncovering how life enhances the entire universe, you will discover the answer to the meaning of life. Spoiler alert: if that seems too good to be true, it is.

While I was attempting to understand my life's role and place in the universe, the exams grew increasingly challenging, even bordering on brutal. This was happening during my third year at university. We students shared a running joke: "Failing English language studies becomes a duty for the motherland." It implied that failing to meet academic expectations, including in required English language studies, would result in losing exemption from the Red Army and automatically being drafted for a two-year service within a few months.

The stakes were already high for me personally, and amidst exam preparations, my roommates persuaded me to take a break for a few hours and complete an application for a trip to New York City. This was a time when the Iron Curtain had fallen, and there was immense curiosity about the West in general, and the USA in particular. The application was sponsored by the church of a Korean preacher, Sun Myung Moon, so called the "Moonist" organization, who had relocated his church to the US. They were basically a cult, but a cult with an open invitation to the US and we were ready to go for it. To qualify for the trip, applicants needed to meet minimum educational requirements and demonstrate basic English comprehension. Both requirements were easily met by us students, and those who showed up first for the in-person interview would receive approval.

I was about to join my classmates for the interview, but I decided to call my parents first. We didn't have cell phones or landlines capable of intercity communication. To make a call, one had to take a short trip from the student dormitories deep into the blocks of worker housing in the local town. That area was controlled by local youth gangs, with whom students historically had an ongoing conflict, and one had to be cautious about entering hostile territory. I was so preoccupied that I didn't notice the danger until I was ambushed by a group of four locals. I held my ground for about 10 seconds before falling, and the beating continued. An older local saved me by screaming at the group, likely fearing they would kill me. At that moment, one of them was hitting me with a large tree branch while the others kicked me. The yelling distracted the group; the guy with the stick even began chasing the older man and started hitting his car windshield. This gave me a chance to get up and run back to the dormitories. There, I gathered my roommates who, instead of going to the application interview, spent a few hours seeking local guys to exact revenge on. This was a standard operating procedure for the students. There was no going to the police, as you end up being detained yourself. The only way to exact justice and not lose respect from your fellow student was to try and find your assailants and teach them a lesson not to attack a student. In the end, we didn't find them and missed the first interview. I ended up with a concussion and severe headaches that persisted for several weeks. This was a double blow, as I also missed all subsequent interviews and lost my chance at the trip to New York City, which at the time I thought would be my only chance.

This was not even the worst event to happen to me during my student years in Moscow. One time, I was attacked by two guys on a train platform in broad daylight while returning from the local black electronics market where I was selling phones with caller IDs. It was a Saturday afternoon when I was getting back from very successful sales from the market with a backpack filled with cash, when two hoodlums started kicking my backpack, and one of them pulled a knife on me. I was more concerned about the cash than myself, and through luck and reasoning, I somehow managed to calm them down. Originally I thought they were after my cash, but my backpack looked very rugged, and the cash was covered with apples. It looked like those guys were just looking for trouble. Mostly, it was the assailant who was overly agitated, and it seemed he was high on something. His friend managed to pull him away from me after we had a bizarre conversation, where I tried to dodge the knife while talking to his friend and trying to calm them down. A few minutes later, I was sitting on a train when I saw the same couple running away from a burly, bloodied man chasing them. From the looks of it, they managed to cut someone. This was a regular day in the 90s in Moscow.

Surprisingly, instead of tipping me into deeper depression, this latest encounter with a local gang completely cured me of my semi-depressed state and brought me back to my feet. I realized that the universe was not inherently fair, not under my control and had no intention of waiting for me to find my own place in it. Up until that time, I had been waiting for a perfect solution to visit my brain as some sort of eureka moment. I then understood that time was more valuable than perfection. I had to make a place for myself, and I had to do it quickly.

I used this as motivation to brute-force the solution. There is a well-known psychological effect of being consumed by a problem to such an extent that we get locked into loops that are hard to break, making finding a solution while in the loop nearly impossible. It takes an external event or disruption to routine to reassess your priorities, realizing that some things are not as important as you thought, and others are more important. Sometimes this is called thinking outside the box. There is an interesting story behind this term, written by Norman Vincent Peale in 1969 in his Chicago Tribune article[12] (Peale, 2019).

The popular puzzle of those times involved connecting a three-by-three grid of dots with four lines, requiring the lines to go outside the grid. This

---

[12] newspaperarchive.com/chicago-tribune-archive

puzzle and its solutions represented the way many people think—they get caught up inside the box of their own lives. To approach any problem objectively, you must stand back and see it for exactly what it is. From a little distance, you can perceive it much more clearly. For some people, this disruption comes as a near-death experience or reaching a certain age. In my case, it was the shock of sudden and random violence. I realized that there is randomness in our lives, the randomness that eats away at our significance. Life itself can end randomly and suddenly: Memento mori!

That realization showed me that I was not only looking for meaning, but also for the significant meaning of my life. In my eyes, significance was a guarantee and I just had to find it. But this is the crux of my question: Is there a significant meaning or any meaning at all to our lives?

For my scientific approach, significance meant that we have some important function to play in the universe. I wanted my life to have not just any meaning, but a meaning on a scale larger than just my life.

This is the core definition of the word meaning. The meaning cannot be too small. Imagine if the meaning of our life is as small as taking a single breath or a sip of water. While this may sound like a dream for people dying from pneumonia or lost in a desert, for most of us, these are mundane activities that are part of everyday life—things we take for granted while we are alive. Meaning implies achievements that are difficult in nature and grand in scale, with scale being the keyword.

This is when I realized that the right question is not what our life's meaning is on the grand scale, but rather what the scale is for our life to have an impact and what the meaning is on the correct scale. It is very likely that my life, or the lives of the entire human race, does not have a significant or even noticeable impact on the universe as we know it. In common language terms, the universe does not "care" about me personally, where "care" signifies my life leaving a legacy or impact.

This is not because I was beaten into a concussion, missed the trip to the US, or was failing exams. Nor is it because of hurricanes, plagues, and natural disasters that have befallen mankind throughout history.

This is because there are some things that are outside of our control. It is because the meaning of our life only has significance when it comes to the choices we make and the actions that follow those choices. If something happens to us beyond our control, it has no place in impacting the meaning of our life. If we are born into great wealth and inherit a distinguished family name, we don't inherit the meaning of our life. It is what we do with our wealth and our reputation that constitutes the amount of meaning we have engendered throughout our lives. Having a great life has to do with our choices and actions, with things that we have under our control.

During that difficult time in my life, I learned a valuable lesson. I realized that not everything is in my control; some events happen without my knowledge or despite all my efforts to stop them. I need to value my time, as we never know how much we have. Instead of falling into despair and giving up on making a difference, this event showed me that I need to pick my goals carefully and dream big, but not too big. Goals that are too grand may take too much time to accomplish and may never come true. My dreams need to be at the edges of my abilities, and my goals need to be of the right scale. The question becomes what is the right scale?

It's About Scale

Scale is a pivotal concept that permeates every facet of our lives. It influences our perception, shapes our goals, and imbues our existence with a sense of purpose. Misjudging the scale of our ambitions can lead to disappointing outcomes or, conversely, trivial pursuits. If, for instance, we harbor dreams of journeying to Mars within the next year, we might be setting an ambition that's both too grand and prematurely timed. On the contrary, setting a goal as mundane as cleaning our closet cannot be considered a truly ambitious endeavor.

Same goes for the meaning of our life. Choose a scale that is too large or too small, the essence of our purpose could easily lose its impact, fade away, and our meaning dissipates.

This principle of scale is particularly evident in the realm of astronomy. The intricate movements of galaxies are hardly influenced by individual stars or even constellations. If a star were to explode in a far-off galaxy, its impact on us would be negligible—it's either too minute relative to the expanse of our galaxy, too distant, or both. In stark contrast, the colossal black holes residing at the heart of galaxies have the capability to devour stars larger than our Sun.

In this context, the challenge lies in comprehending our individual significance amidst the vast, nearly incomprehensible scale of the universe. We must strive to understand our role and impact within this cosmic theater, and this understanding hinges on our ability to calibrate our perspective to the appropriate scale. So, how do we make sense of our individual impact in the vastness of the universe?

Let's begin by trying to understand just how vast the universe is. First, we don't know what lies beyond the observable universe; there could be an infinite universe beyond what we can see. But how large is the observable universe? It is estimated to be 93 billion light years across, and it is also expanding faster than we previously thought. This means that the observable universe and what's beyond it are continually growing.

Second, when we think about how Earth compares to the universe, it makes sense at the start. Earth has a radius of 3,963 miles (6,378 km) at the equator. Our brains can process this: the flight distance from Los Angeles to New York is 2,475 miles (or 3,983 km). Then it gets a little more complicated. The moon is about 238,855 miles (385,000 km) away, which is still manageable—it's about 100 times the distance of the NYC to LA flight. This we can still imagine.

Then, there are currently almost 7.8 billion people living on planet Earth. While that is a large number to comprehend, it is also manageable. Nearly 8.5 million people live in NYC, while twice that—fourteen million—live in Tokyo. A hundred times that—almost 1.4 billion—live in India. We've been to these places, or seen photos, so we can also imagine it—sort of.

However, when we zoom out to the solar system, we realize that the Earth is incredibly small. The total mass of the solar system is approximately 333,000 times the mass of the Earth, which means that the Earth is just about 0.0003% of the total mass of our solar system. (It's not that big compared to other planets in our solar system either—just 0.2% of their total mass.)

Then we get to the Milky Way, the galactic center of which is a staggering 28,000 light years away. The Milky Way Galaxy contains around 100 thousand million stars and at least 100 billion planets, some of which are much more massive than our planet and our sun.

Consider this: since life started on Earth 3.8 billion years ago (with humanity existing for a hardly mentionable fraction of that time), we have completed only about 15 orbits around the Milky Way center, which by itself is home to about 300-400 billion stars. Other galaxies, such as IC 1101, the largest known to date, are thought to have more than 100 trillion stars.

Now it becomes more difficult for our brains to grasp: the Milky Way is one of almost 50 galaxies in our Local Group. Groups of galaxies held together by gravitational pull are called galaxy clusters. Clusters may, in turn, form superclusters; for example, the Virgo Supercluster contains about 100 galaxy clusters and 2,000 galaxies. Superclusters can form a supercluster complex, one of the largest structures in the observable universe, which is still only 1/10th of the size of the observable universe. This scale is getting too big for us to understand.

And yet, astronomers have discovered that sometimes there is a happy medium between too large and too small—or rather, too close and too far. Because Earth is the only planet known to be inhabited by life, and because liquid water is critical for life to exist, astronomers have postulated the conditions that escape the extremes and are "just right." The resulting range for the distance at which a planet orbits a star is called the habitable zone. Too close to the Sun, and it becomes too hot—the water boils; too far, and it becomes too cold—the water freezes. Just like the items Goldilocks chooses in the proverbial tale, the conditions of the habitable zone are just right for life to exist (or have existed) there. There are estimates that as many as 40 billion Earth-size planets are orbiting the habitable zones of the Milky Way's sun-like stars and red dwarfs.

Yet, when we compare the scale of a single human life to the scale of the universe, we find that the comparison is absurd. You are one of the billions of people on Earth. Even when you combine the mass of all the people on the planet—at an average of 65 kilos per person, times 7.753 billion inhabitants, which comes to 554 million tons—it is still a measly 1.2-trillionth of Earth's mass, which is approximately 5.97 x 10^24 kg. Clearly, size is not the only thing that matters.

Humanity, in its relatively minuscule scope, experiences this interaction in a predominantly one-sided way. We find ourselves subject to the immutable laws of physics that oversee this universe, some benign and others notably hostile. Our Earth, the habitat we inhabit, is incessantly subjected to asteroid bombardments, cosmic ray irradiation, and sweeping solar flares. Even the most cataclysmic ecological disaster that humanity could induce on this planet would only impact the thin layer of Earth's crust, including the bodies of water and the atmosphere that encases it. This is the layer on which we exist, varying in thickness from 5-10 kilometers in oceanic regions to up to 70 kilometers in continental zones. Even at its thickest, the crust comprises merely about 1% of Earth's volume. Therefore, humanity doesn't even possess the capability to obliterate Earth. The most probable consequence of a significant ecological disaster would be the self-destruction of mankind itself, subsequently paving the way for other life forms to thrive. Inversely, the prospect of humanity significantly influencing the universe is virtually non-existent. The gulf between human existence and cosmic realities is so immense that it renders linking concepts on such divergent scales almost impossible.

What if we were to consider the opposite, something on a smaller scale yet of utmost importance? Let's take an atom, but first let's really try to understand how small it is. Compared to the size of the universe—and even to our planet—atoms are incredibly small. The height of an average human is approximately 1.65 meters. Let's go smaller on the decimal scale: a centimeter is 10^-2 and a millimeter is 10^-3. So far so good. A bit smaller than a millimeter, and we get to the width of a human hair—still something we can easily comprehend—at about 70-180 micrometers, where a micrometer is 10^-6. Smaller yet, and not visible to the naked eye, are viruses and DNA (we are getting into the nanometers here), and only then do we get to atoms.

The diameter of a hydrogen atom, for example, is approximately 1 × 10^-11 m (which seems small, until you think of the proton at its center that is 100,000 times smaller). By comparison, the diameter of Earth is 1.3 × 10^7 m. And yet the Earth, and all things on it, consist of atoms. Planets consist of atoms; all matter in the universe is made of these fundamental building blocks. A single atom is too small to have a significant effect on life in the universe, right?

Wrong. The properties of an atom affect the entire universe. Take, for instance, the electrical charge of an atom. Electrical charge is a fundamental property of matter and plays a crucial role in a wide range of natural phenomena. If the value of electrical charge were to change, it would alter the behavior of charged particles and the interactions between them. This would, in turn, affect the stability of atoms and molecules, which form the basis of all matter in the universe. For instance, if the value of electrical charge were to become smaller, the attractive force between oppositely charged particles would decrease, potentially causing atoms to become unstable and fall apart. Planets, stars, galaxies, and other celestial bodies would not form. There would be no universe as we know it—nor us.

Alternatively, if the electrical charge was larger, atoms would repel each other, resulting in different types of molecules. A change in the value of electrical charge could alter these processes, potentially leading to a vastly different universe from the one we observe today.

This is because most of the observable universe consists of atoms and is affected by their properties, with the exception of dark matter (the material thought to exist in the universe and responsible for the way galaxies form, move, and stay together) and dark energy (an unknown form of energy observed during star explosions, providing proof that the expansion of the universe is accelerating). Dark matter is thought to cover about 90% of the Milky Way.

What's more, the force of the electromagnetic interaction of atoms is dictated by a force constant called an electric charge, which is the charge of one electron. The more particles in an object, the larger its force. The gravitational force works similarly: it is determined by the mass of the object. To put it simply, an object substantially smaller in size can hardly make an impact on the object that is substantially larger in size.

What matters in nature is not just the size of objects but their ubiquity. Atoms and gravity can be found everywhere, in every observable natural phenomenon.

Life, however, is a different story. Comparing the meaning of human life to the scale of something as small as the atom doesn't work either: unlike atoms, life is not ubiquitous across the universe. According to Fermi's paradox, given the vastness of the universe (93 billion light-years wide and expanding) and its age (13.8 billion years), there should be a high probability of the existence of life outside planet Earth. Yet there is no evidence for such extraterrestrial activity. Even on Earth, humans make up a very small share of life on the planet—only 0.1% of the total and just 2.5% of the animal biomass.

Unlike atoms, life is rare, and, as far as we know, it only exists on Earth. Out of the hundreds of billions of planets in the universe, Earth is the only one known to host life—or at least we haven't found any evidence to the contrary. Until we become as ubiquitous as atoms—that is, until humanity grows tremendously, potentially spreading to other planets, there's no way for us to form goals that are important enough on the scale of the universe. And that is why I've realized that there is no way for me to formulate the question of the meaning of life in the universe correctly, because the universe is just too big, and humanity is just too scarce.

This begs the question: what is the right scale for humans to find meaning? Let us approach this question quantitatively by finding the average measure between the smallest known scientific object and the largest known object.

The smallest known scientific phenomenon is not a particle or the objects that make up the smallest particles; rather, it is the smallest scale at which the effects of fundamental forces become comparable to the effects of quantum gravity, at which point all known approaches and formulas begin to break down. The Planck length or scale is about 10^-35 meters, and those are also the scales that are not reachable by any known human technologies. The way fundamental scientists probe the smallest scales is by accelerating particles and smashing them together in experimental technological machines called particle colliders. The higher the energy of the colliding particle, the smaller the distance the particles could reach. Scientists have managed to probe the smallest distances of 10^-19 meters, which corresponds to about 6.5 TeV (six and a half trillion electron volts). To achieve that, the largest man-made Hadron Collider, or LHC, draws about 200 MWatts from the European electrical grid. To achieve Planck scales, humankind would need to increase its power output by 15 orders of magnitude by conservative estimates, but in reality, probably a lot more. Modern science and technology don't have access to such energies yet.

On the other side of the scale, the largest known object is the edge of the observable universe. At present, astronomers and astrophysicists can observe remote constellations of galaxies through space-based telescopes and exploratory probes at a distance of about 93 billion light-years or about 10^27 meters. If we take a geometric average of the smallest and largest distances, (-35 + 27)/2 calculation yields about 10^-4, which is the size of human cells.

In a poetic universal gesture, the average scale of the universe is about the size of the building blocks of living organisms. Most likely, this is because we start reaching out to the largest and smallest objects from the scale of our own senses. This is also most likely the most appropriate scale we should consider for the impact of our actions. Anything bigger or much smaller would go against our abilities and place us in a territory outside of our control.

The same argument applies to the scale of our abilities. For millennia, alchemists on at least three continents spent their lives in pursuit of immortality and a substance that would turn base metals into gold. Their search for the philosopher's stone, which could produce a transmutation of metals and be a source of eternal life or eternal youth, or a cure for illnesses, was futile. Similarly, engineers have tried—and failed—to create perpetual motion machines that would continue working infinitely, producing an endless amount of energy without the need for an outside energy source. I would argue that both the alchemists and the engineers failed to achieve their goals simply because their goals were too large—unachievable, in fact.

On the other hand, getting the scale of your life too small is also likely to leave you unsatisfied. Focusing on minutiae or immediate gratification—or on goals that are too small—may mean that you are selling your talents short. Achieving a small goal will not make a difference in your life or in the lives of others—if you aim too low. Getting the scale of your life too small or too big will invalidate its meaning. It has to be just right.

Then perhaps the meaning of our lives depends on what's around us, just as interactions between physical bodies are dictated by scale in nature. Newton's third law of motion dictates that every action creates an opposite reaction; however, if one of the bodies is infinitesimally smaller than the other, then the reaction of the smaller body can be discounted[13] (*On Causality, n.d.*).

An individual human being can have a significant impact on another person or even a large group of people. However, our impact remains measurable only on our scale—that of humanity—and comparable to things on the same order of magnitude as us, not on the scale of the universe.

The interaction between entities of different scales adheres to the principle of locality. This principle posits that for an action at one point to exert influence at another, the influence must traverse the spatial distance between these two points. Essentially, any impact is bound by the limitations of space and time.

When we consider humanity's scale, it becomes evident that a global impact is practically unachievable—humanity, at this point in history, has yet to coalesce around a common, unified objective on a global scale. The principle of locality suggests that what is indeed possible is the impact we can have on each other. However, even this interaction is not at a global scale.

The simplest answer to the question of what significance our lives have on the universe is this: there is none, at least as far as the universe is concerned. The universe does not care about the meaning or legacy of each individual life. In other words, there is no effect or consequence of our individual lives on something that is vastly larger than us.

Is there an upper level of the scale when our individual lives start to matter? What ultimately cares about the existence of humans? If we focus solely on the size of the universe, we could conclude that there is no higher purpose. This would lead us into the abyss of nihilism, to the rejection of all moral principles and the belief that life is meaningless. We will touch upon this in the upcoming chapters of the next part of this book, but this point could be a valid choice. If we choose for our life not to have any meaning, then we will get what we wished for—a meaningless life.

Nevertheless, when we contemplate the question of our significance in the universe from a less all-encompassing viewpoint, and focus on the immediate world surrounding us, the answer becomes clear. The objects around us hold no concern for humans, yet we care deeply for our fellow human beings. Rather, our influence tends to be localized, affecting those around us and rippling outward gradually. Our actions can carry a profound impact within our immediate surroundings—our local communities, societies, and ecosystems. I sought the most comprehensive, universal meaning, but

---

[13] kenbenoit.net/on-causality

the reality is that the largest scale at which humans still matter to each other is the scale of humanity itself.

The fact that the universe is not affected by the existence of humanity does not mean that we don't have any effect on each other. People are another story. Even at the scale of all of humanity combined, individuals still matter. Every decision and choice that people make can contribute to making our lives more meaningful.

We almost certainly have an impact on other people's lives. We care about others, and many people in our lives care about us. There are individual leaders, thinkers, and artists who leave a permanent influence on humanity and engrave their names in human history. Names like Newton, Michelangelo, Gandhi, Buddha, Jesus Christ, and unfortunately, the likes of Caligula and Adolf Hitler. Even on the scale of individual lives, it is in our nature to assign, evaluate, and judge how meaningful or meaningless someone's life is, whether they are our friends or neighbors. Our well-being depends on how accurately we estimate the impact of our lives on others and where we stand in the social hierarchy. The structure of society is determined based on our perceived usefulness to others. For instance, parents may assign meaning to their lives based on the achievements of their children, especially if the children manage to achieve the long-sought but never fulfilled dreams of their parents. In other cases, people find meaning based on their careers, the material value they create for themselves or others, or how many people they lead or inspire. There are multiple examples of the meaning of life in human societies, wherever people are encountered. The problem here is not finding any meaning; the problem is choosing the correct one.

I kept asking, though, if meaning is abundant around us, why is it not at the largest scale, and why is it not universal? The problem was that I was looking for a single, universal meaning of all life that would be the root cause of all other meanings, including the meaning of my personal life. It would have been a solution for all meaning, greater than life, and all of humanity.

The contradiction here is that the greater the scale, the less impact or even a chance of impact we have. Imagine concentric circles with you in the middle; the immediate circle around you signifies the immediate impact. Those are the small things, like remembering to call your mother or feeding your cat. The larger circle indicates a larger impact, like sending your children to college or saving someone's life. The larger the circle, the larger the hypothetical impact. It also gets harder to achieve as you appear smaller and smaller in relation to its size. With multiple circles, there are also multiple meanings at different scales. Only the largest one encircles all of them and signifies the one true meaning, but it will also dwarf you in scale.

Asymptotically, when we approach the limit of the entire universe, our meaning disappears entirely. On the other hand, if the scale is not at the maximum, then there are many scales corresponding to many meanings. In other words, the absence of a universal, all-encompassing meaning means there are numerous meanings.

I was steadily arriving at the conclusion that I was simply looking for the wrong thing—an all-encompassing answer. There is nothing unusual about not having a single, all-encompassing answer. This is actually similar to poorly formulated mathematical equations that have either no or multiple solutions.

Consider this simple example: 4x-2x+5=2x+7-3. When we simplify it, we get 2x+5=2x+4. Simplifying further: 2x-2x=4-5, and finally 0=-1. We know that statement to be inherently false, and therefore, our equation has no solution. This is a badly written equation with no solution.

At the same time, an equation can have multiple solutions. Consider 2x+5=2x+5. Simplifying this equation, 5=5. The x in this equation can equal any value, and it will still remain true that 5=5. This is an example of a badly written equation with multiple solutions.

Extrapolating to the meaning of life, if there is no single answer to the problem, then there is no universal meaning of life. This is not to say that there is no meaning, not by far: you and I know that there certainly is, but it is more of a local question. There can be multiple, perhaps infinite, meanings. However, these meanings are of the same scale as we are and are specific to the circumstances of our personal lives and the lives of those around us. Finding meaning and the right scale becomes a matter of choice. Instead of a universal, global answer, there are a myriad of possible answers that we may or may not choose.

What does this mean? Like a mathematical equation with infinite answers, there is a multiple – possibly infinite – number of meanings to life, and each meaning can have multiple goals. The conclusion to draw here is that the meaning of life has no global meaning; rather, it is a set of goals.

Perhaps we need to reevaluate our understanding of the "meaning of life." Traditionally, "meaning" implies an intrinsic property waiting to be discovered. However, if this becomes a matter of personal choice, the term "meaning" might be better replaced by the "direction" in life. This shift reflects a proactive approach towards life, suggesting that we have the ability to shape our own destiny rather than passively uncovering a predetermined purpose.

In conclusion to this chapter:

A. First, our lives cannot play an immediate role in the universal scheme of things because of the massive scale difference between our own lives (or even humanity) and the known universe. The difference in scale is too big.
B. Second, I've realized that there is no way for me to formulate the question of the meaning of life in the universe in a way that can be solved both uniquely and universally. The universe is too big, and life is just too scarce.
C. The meaning of life becomes a direction in life.

The Meaning Is Our Choice

The meaning of life is our choice, albeit not the arbitrary one!

When I understood this in college, it was a huge relief to me. Since I could not formulate a universal objective for my life (or any life, for that matter), there was no global meaning. Before that realization, my mind kept racing, and in my head, I was running in circles trying to solve the impossible.

The academic competition among my peers was brutal, and the pressure only intensified around the 3rd year of studies. This is when mid-college exams were starting, and whoever would pass them would most likely stay till the end of the program. It was a make or break point. Many of my fellow students cracked under pressure to perform. We had our own version of a suicide forest in the form of a birch tree grove located right outside the student dormitories across railroad tracks, where students found the last refuge from all the stress and academic pressures. At the same time, the third year was when students began to spend more time in research labs, working directly with scientific advisors on modern problems. I believe the Moscow Institute of Physics and Technology had its academic curriculum and teaching philosophy modeled after MIT. We spent the first few years focused on fundamental math and physics, and the later years focused on actual scientific research in designated base research institutions. During the third year, students spent one day of the week inside the labs and research groups as equal contributors. In the fourth year, we spent two days of the week in the base institutions, and in the fifth and sixth years, we spent almost all of our time working on actual research papers that would become our master's thesis by graduation. In other words, around the third year, we finally got a taste of real science, the very thing we came to dedicate our lives to. Spending more time and energy on my mental issues and finding a fleeting solution to the meaning of life was wasteful and inexcusable.

With all of this going on in my life, as a young man, I kept asking, am I making the right choices? I was desperate for an answer and attempted to answer the most global question. I was coming to an inevitable conclusion that there is not a single answer. Just like in badly formed equations that may have multiple, even an infinite number of answers, there are many answers to the meaning of our lives, and one has to make a choice and pick one.

That realization came as a relief. Now I could finally calm my overworked brain and focus on a concrete problem that became much easier to solve. I shifted my focus onto a set of goals under a common theme for my own life. This seemed much more manageable. Finally, I could concentrate on exams and homework that piled up while I was at a dead end, and on my life, lifting a burden off my shoulders and a headache that would finally go away. I also made a choice to see the problem of my life's meaning in a different light. This new perspective turned my thoughts towards the importance of choice.

Firstly, the capacity to make choices is a fundamental prerequisite for pondering the meaning of life. Without the freedom to choose how to live, any contemplation about life's purpose or significance is essentially futile. This was probably the reason why our ancestors did not think about the meaning of life, as they had little to no choices and no free time to think about it. Life was about survival, and there was only one path to follow – the one laid out by necessity and circumstance.

Choice features prominently in multiple aspects of human life, from history, social constructs, political structures, to religion. In the realm of religion, the concept of choice is pivotal, largely because most faiths revolve around the principle of love – divine love for mankind and human love for the divine. Love, as traditionally understood, can't be compelled or imposed; it must stem from the exercise of free will. This is why choice and free will form the bedrock of Abrahamic religions. Moreover, the notion of choice offers a plausible explanation for the existence of evil, a topic we'll delve into more deeply in the second part of this book. In essence, the presence of evil in a world purportedly under divine control can be rationalized through the variability introduced by free will and choices. This underlines why the theme of choice is so integral to religious doctrines.

Politics, too, is heavily influenced by the principle of choice. Historically, democratic political systems have outpaced dictatorships, primarily because they create an environment that's more conducive to economic growth, innovation, and overall prosperity. This achievement can be attributed, in large part, to the element of choice. Democracies institute a government that's accountable to its citizens, promotes competition and innovation, and safeguards individual liberties and human rights. In democratic societies, citizens exercise their voice through free and regular elections, holding elected officials accountable via peaceful means such as protests, petitions, and media scrutiny. This system of checks and balances ensures policies align with public interest, making it difficult for any governing body, even at the local level, to evade accountability.

In contrast, dictatorships are characterized by a concentration of power in the hands of one person or a small group of people, who make decisions without the input or consent of the citizens. Dictatorships often lack political and civil liberties, including freedom of speech, assembly, and the press. This can stifle innovation and competition and limit the ability of citizens to advocate for their own interests and hold their leaders accountable. Over time, this can lead to economic stagnation, social unrest, and a decline in living standards.

When a clear roadmap exists and it's merely a question of implementation, central authorities tend to excel. However, in situations where the path forward is uncertain—much like the unpredictability of free-market mechanisms—financial markets outperform by decentralizing decision-making structures and fostering competition for accurate choices and successful ideas.

In truth, it's unfeasible to definitively determine whether democratic or totalitarian systems are more effective at organizing, sustaining human societies, and fostering human happiness. One of the recurring themes of this book is that only time serves as the ultimate judge and executioner. It alone will reveal which system, or systems, can endure the test of time and ultimately prevail. But as a general principle, systems with robust feedback mechanisms are typically more stable. Dictatorships and authoritarian regimes often suffer from weak or entirely broken feedback mechanisms, leading to stagnant social structures, innovation deficits, and escalating levels of corruption

Ability to make independent choices is crucial in evolutionary biology. The prerogative of selecting the optimal survival strategy is borne by individual species, whose approaches differ due to genetic mutations. As entities striving for survival, our actions are largely guided by choice, a critical factor in determining the most effective survival tactics. The multitude of independent trials and errors within the evolutionary lineage can be viewed as an analogue to the process of making free choices.

Nature is blind and does not know which path or decision will maximize the survival of a species. The best solution is to have as many different paths as possible and reward the most successful ones. This is essentially what happens in evolution. Random mutations represent making a choice, and a beneficial mutation is rewarded with a higher rate of survival and a higher number of offspring who can pass on this mutation to their descendants. Without randomness, there would be no survival. Even if all of our choices are predetermined by past conditions, each path that has led us to where we made our predetermined choices is random and represents our uniqueness. I may have chosen science when I was a child because some of my personal traits were amplified by a random choice in my genes when I was conceived, or because of the upbringing I received from my parents who also got their parental traits from their own genetic history. Whether this difference occurs at the exact time of my decision on which college to apply to (in the case of true freedom of choice), or was determined in advance by my genetic makeup and circumstances of my upbringing (in the case of a random path choice that happened long before I was born), is irrelevant. What is important is that I am making choices different from the person next to me.

Greater diversity in evolutionary pathways enhances the probability of stumbling upon a beneficial mutation, which could lead to advantageous adaptations. Conversely, biological systems with fewer degrees of freedom face a heightened risk of failing to discover such beneficial adaptations, increasing their chances of extinction. Low biodiversity often leads to ecosystems that are less resilient, and more vulnerable to environmental changes and threats such as diseases, invasive species, and climate change. Examples of low biodiversity, which can be thought as a lack of choices within species, include the Irish potato famine, where Ireland's population relied heavily on a single variety of potato, the Lumper. When a potato disease struck, it quickly spread and wiped out the majority of the crop because there was no genetic diversity to limit its spread. This led to mass starvation and emigration.

There is another argument frequently made suggesting that our choices, including our choice to vote for politicians, are merely illusions. The idea that choice is just an illusion implies that people do not genuinely have the freedom to make decisions and determine the course of their lives. When we vote for a political party, we are merely choosing a flavor of a political force that will disappoint us either way. This perspective posits that things are already predetermined and the odds are stacked against us from the beginning. Our choices are determined by factors beyond our control, such as biology, environment, and circumstance.

This viewpoint is based on the idea that human behavior is not entirely free and autonomous, but is instead influenced by unconscious factors such as genetics, past experiences, and societal norms and expectations. Our decision-making processes are also influenced by the way information is presented to us and the options that are available.

There are philosophical views that all the events in our lives are entirely determined by previously existing and preordained causes, thereby denying us agency. It is called determinism[14] (Determinism, n.d.). This type of viewpoint denies people the agency for making decisions and the responsibility of individuals, which can lead to fatalism and a lack of motivation to make changes in our lives.

There are multiple forms of determinism, including fatalism, which is more of a theological argument stating that everything is fated to happen, leaving people with no control over their future. These views were mostly popular at the beginning of the 20th century when it was commonly believed that physics had discovered almost everything there was to know. Ironically, just a few short years later, in 1905, Albert Einstein published a paper that marked the beginning of a new type of science, which by the mid-1920s evolved into what is known today as quantum mechanics. According to quantum mechanics, the outcomes of any physical interactions and events are uncertain. We can only calculate probabilities with some degree of certainty, but not the outcomes of events on both micro and macroscopic scales.

With quantum mechanics disrupting the old understanding of the universe, the freedom of choice was back on the table. Even if a choice is not absolute, it does not mean that it is entirely illusory. Even if our personal rights and belief in personal freedom are illusions, so are any societal and sociological norms. If enough people believe in democracy, they manifest it into reality. If millions of people believe in banking systems, they will deposit their real money into banks. Even the concept of money exists because

---

[14] en.wikipedia.org/wiki/Determinism

enough people believe in it, be it green pieces of paper, plastic cards, or cryptocurrency. People turn illusions into reality, including believing in our personal choices.

While choice plays an important role in defining and shaping the future of our lives, it cannot and should not be entirely random. I have failed to derive any universal objective meaning in life and discovered that meaning is highly subjective. However, this does not render it completely arbitrary.

There are several problems with the randomness of choices regarding life direction. First, completely arbitrary choices would not offer any guidance or direction and would lead to a nihilistic approach to life, where anything goes. This defeats the purpose of choosing or knowing the meaning of your life, as any arbitrary choice would meet the criteria for your life's purpose. The meaning of life implies guidance or direction for all of our important actions and choices. Randomness annihilates meaning. There must be a core principle or focal point to direct our lives in a deterministic fashion.

Second, in a subjective world of diverse human cultures and opinions, it is difficult to find such a core principle unless a majority of people believe in it. However, if enough people believe in a certain principle, be it the value of money, the power of a king, or a constitution, this principle becomes a reality within society. People can manifest their beliefs and make them real. The same can happen to the meaning of life. There is no universal objective meaning of life, but people's beliefs can create a "subjective" reality for humankind. This, however, requires that the underlying principles behind the choices for the meaning of life be relatable and acceptable to most people. Arbitrary choices of life's meaning will not convince or unite people, will dilute focus on a single direction, and will not create any subjective reality that becomes a guiding principle for us all.

This means the meaning of life should be relatable to our interactions with people and their interactions with us. This removes complete randomness or arbitrary choices but leaves enough degrees of freedom to choose our own path in fulfilling life's meaning. The meaning of life has to do with our interactions with other lives, similar to circumstances in our lives, where they are not entirely under our control nor absolutely predetermined.

Some people choose not to think about the meaning of their life and simply live life as best they can. My grandparents spent most of their time working in fields to earn a living. They led busy lives, with many responsibilities that left little time for introspection and reflection. Caring for their children and grandchildren, maintaining relationships with friends and family, and working or pursuing other activities left little room for quiet contemplation or existential questioning. They did not have the luxury to think about choices in their lives, nor did they have free time to do anything but work on land, attend to farmland and farm animals, and use any free minutes to rest and regain their strength for the next day.

Then, the Second World War happened, and they had to fight for survival during wartime. During that time, they focused on survival, and their attention was directed towards finding food, shelter, and safety for themselves and their families. My maternal grandfather fought against invading Nazi forces, while my grandmother worked in a Siberian tank factory with two small children left unattended in their apartment all day. When my grandmother realized that her daughters would end up starving, she made a dangerous but lifesaving decision to take her children and move across the entire country back to her village. She traveled over 1000 miles from the middle of Siberia towards the front line on a train track with her small children during wartime—a perilous journey on its own. With my grandmother's act of leaving the military factory considered an act of desertion without any tolerance or leniency towards her small children, the journey became doubly dangerous. She managed to make it to her village in a few weeks and due to this act of both courage and desertion, my mom and her sister survived.

During the same time period, my grandfather was part of a fresh reinforcement unit sent to the frontlines to fight off the German offensive. Unfortunately, they arrived before the delivery of arms and ammunition, and were ordered to attack with fewer rifles than soldiers. Like the scene from the movie "Enemy At The Gates"[15] (Annaud, 2001), my grandfather had to run behind his comrades in arms, waiting for the man in front of him to be killed before picking up his weapon to continue. However, unlike the movie, his entire platoon was taken prisoner and sent to a concentration camp where they faced certain death. My grandfather survived because he and a few of the prisoners made a hole in the bottom of the train cart and jumped from the still-moving train to escape. He made it back to the Soviet frontline, but his ordeal was not over as he had to spend time in a Soviet concentration camp to repent for his capture and clear his name. During those times, if you did not die defending your motherland, you were considered a traitor. Meanwhile, my grandparents on my father's side suffered first at the hands of invading German troops and then from the hands of Russian troops liberating Europe a few years later. Each wave of soldiers would take all the food and supplies, leaving them practically to starve. It is impossible for those of us living in peaceful times to even imagine the wartime hardships, but wars continue to occur all around the world. Neither of my grandparents had time to think about the meaning of life, but they did focus on survival, and I owe them, especially my grandmothers, for the fact that I am here on this Earth.

Undeniably, not everyone has the privilege to choose when and under what circumstances they are born, and not all have the luxury of leisure time to contemplate the meaning of their lives. This is the stark reality of our existence; not everyone has the opportunity to select their life's purpose. In the absence of choice, there is a lack of direction, and without direction, meaning can be elusive. However, it's worth acknowledging that even when we opt not to ascribe any meaning to our lives, our existence inevitably impacts others, and in so doing, provides value.

---

[15] imdb.com/title/tt0215750

When I refer to the "meaning of life," it signifies an intentional choice of life's trajectory. This does not imply that a life lived without clear direction fails to make a positive impact on others. A compelling example is portrayed in the film "Forrest Gump," where the eponymous character, despite living life seemingly adrift, finds himself at the epicenter of numerous historical events and profoundly influences those around him. If one drifts through life as aimlessly as a leaf in the wind, the value and impact generated, while significant, are fundamentally unintentional, and could be purely accidental. Under different circumstances, the outcomes of a life lived without the capacity to make choices and take decisive action could indeed be deeply detrimental.

In this context, a more fitting phrase for "the meaning of life" might be "the direction in life." Henceforth, I will use these two terms interchangeably, recognizing their deeply interconnected essence.

This realization brings me to the understanding that the presence of meaning in our life is not a given. We have to work hard to even have a chance to have a meaningful life. Let's delve deeper into this notion. We often hold the belief that every human life is invaluable, including our own. If life is indeed priceless, it should inherently possess meaning, right? This notion indeed holds some truth: every life carries intrinsic value. In our lifetime, we contribute to others through our work, emotional and material support, and even in death, our bodies serve as a valuable resource, providing nutrients for myriad living organisms. However, these values are not exclusive to us, they are shared among all humans. All decent individuals are expected to help one another, and upon death, our decaying bodies are equally repurposed by bacteria and fungi. As a matter of fact all living organisms are useful to each other in one form or another. This usefulness forms the baseline of our shared value. I do not consider this common value to be the meaning of our life.

What I refer to as the 'meaning of life' is the unique combination of our actions that set our lives apart. It's a relative value that transcends (or sometimes drops below) the standard baseline common to all. This meaning is unique to us and continues to live beyond our time. Achieving this requires dedication, time, and the fortune to choose the correct paths for our lives.

Personally, I consider myself fortunate to have been granted the time, the will and ability to choose my own path. For me, it was important to have a choice in the meaning of my life. Rather than choosing random themes and goals and mindlessly toiling at daily chores, I wanted to do something that would be representative of my life, but would also be my choice and unique and different. I was hoping this choice of the right meaning would make my life distinctive.

It felt as if the meaning I was looking for in my life was similar to the concept of a "soul." If it sounds familiar, that's because the notion of the soul in Christian religion is a similar concept. By making the right choices, you determine the destiny of your soul. We will touch upon this subject in more detail in the fourth part of this book.

Another important point about the right scale is that it is best to choose your goals at the edge of your abilities. Choosing goals that are too small and easy to achieve makes them insignificant. On the other hand, choosing goals that are too large can undermine your resolve or crush your determination.

The idea that the meaning of life is not determined by fate but a choice that we make ourselves is sprinkled through literature and there are many articles in the field of psychology and philosophy that touch upon this subject. We can find a few examples in the modern scientific publications: (Frankl 1979; Steger 2012; Wong 1998)[16].

Frankl emphasizes that you are unique, with your own purpose, and suggests that implementing that purpose with a focus on your greater community propels you forward. Steger argues that the pursuit of meaning involves determining whether there is meaning in your life, and if not, striving to acquire some. To achieve this, you must acquire knowledge, organize it, and use it to self-direct your life. Wong posits that meaning is something you construct yourself, based on what is personally important to you. From this foundation, you create a map to navigate your forward movement, setting you off on your path.

What these perspectives often lack is a unifying principle, one that can assimilate these diverse viewpoints. Even though the specific meaning of life can be a matter of individual choice, the principle guiding that choice isn't arbitrary. Instead, it gravitates in the same direction as the cumulative inclinations of all people. I believed that uncovering this principle would pave the way for me to articulate my unique understanding of life's meaning.

While contemplating how to quantify the meaning of life, I noticed that the evaluation of our actions is heavily skewed towards things that last longer and extend further in time. This not only plays upon our fears of death, such as memento mori, but also highlights that a brief or minute action or achievement is not considered significant. Sand castles and fleeting jokes cannot compare to ancient pyramids and classical literature. Even if a moment in time is deemed significant, it is only due to the lasting effects it creates after it has passed. In religion, people often think of the afterlife rather than this life because they believe that the next life will last forever. If we base our actions and choices on a foundation, it should endure for a long time. If our actions outlive us, they become our legacy and provide meaning. I understood that time plays a crucial role in how we should choose our meaning.

Another important issue when choosing the appropriate action to best represent the meaning of our life relates to survival bias. Typically, this phrase refers to the logical error of focusing attention on entities that have passed a selection process while overlooking those that have not. In our case, this

---

[16] nih.gov/the-role-of-the-meaning-in-life

means that if we choose actions that will produce a short-lived outcome, then in the long run, no matter how large or significant those actions were, they will disappear. Only the longer-lived or surviving actions will remain, no matter how insignificant they are.

This is essentially true if we care for the meaning of life that lasts beyond our lives. Given that assumption, I equate the meaning of life to leaving a legacy, specifically among people. Our choice for meaning will preserve its significance only if its impact survives and multiplies. To put it differently, it must be compatible with life's principles of survival and expansion. The choice of meaning is especially important for the people around us. The universe is too vast to notice us, but we have people around us - parents, children, friends, or neighbors - who are directly affected by our choices. People know and care about other people. If humanity were to eventually perish without a trace, no matter how significant an impact we leave, whether it's Einstein or Gandhi, it will disappear with humanity. More specifically, our choices for the meaning of life should be compatible with the survival and expansion of humankind.

There are various ways to leave an impact. One can have many children and leave a genetic footprint. However, with every generation, your genetic footprint is randomly diluted by half until almost nothing remains. Imagine a teacup with a strong flavor you like. After 4-5 top-ups, there will be almost nothing left to taste; this is similar to what happens to our genes in our offspring. Moreover, our genetic footprint is not even uniquely ours—it also belongs to our parents and grandparents. On the other hand, memories can persist much longer through generations, especially if they are unique and make an impact on storytellers.

If there is no universal meaning imposed on us by the laws of nature, then the meaning of our life is not guaranteed—it becomes our own choice. This choice is not entirely arbitrary and follows some important rules. Our choices need to create lasting value. We could opt to live without any meaning and goals, and in that case, our lives will lack purpose by our own volition.

If we choose to live with meaning, it should be specific and unique to the course of our lives. Additionally, we ought to attach our names to our deeds to ensure that both our actions and our names are remembered. Otherwise, they will be diluted by time, just like tears by rain droplets.

To weigh and prioritize various meanings, decisions, and actions, I needed a single quantifiable measure that conformed to the scale of human life. Having a singular criterion simplifies the decision-making process and allows for a more focused approach to evaluating available options. This is particularly useful when faced with complex dilemmas involving numerous factors and potential consequences. That is why science utilizes the scientific method, which enables the experimental verification of complex hypotheses as either true or false.

By adopting a single criterion, we can eliminate confusion and indecisiveness that often arise when attempting to weigh multiple factors simultaneously. This clarity enables us to objectively assess each option based on how well it meets the chosen criterion and ultimately select the best course of action with greater confidence. We can only sort priorities using one property.

For instance, if the single criterion is maximizing personal well-being or happiness, then when faced with a difficult decision, one can evaluate each option based on its potential to contribute to one's overall happiness or well-being. By using this criterion, the decision-making process becomes more streamlined, and the individual can choose the option that best aligns with their personal well-being. It does not mean it is the correct benchmark—we could have used a measure of wealth or happiness as a benchmark. What I am trying to demonstrate in these examples is that by applying several criteria, we will arrive at multiple and often contradictory results. We need to choose one benchmark, one fundamental principle.

Selection of a single principle requires careful consideration, as the chosen criteria will serve as the guiding principle for decision-making in various life situations. To ensure that the criterion is both relevant and effective, one should take the time to reflect on their values, goals, and priorities, and carefully aggregate all of these factors into a criterion. It has to be based on life and living, and it has to be personal.

Upon discovering that there is no single universal meaning and that multiple meanings exist at different scales, I realized the need for a unifying principle that could bring together all these diverse perspectives. Every time I thought I was closer to finding that one principle, it seemed to elude me even more. This quest will eventually lead me deep into philosophy, religion, science, and art, searching for common themes and patterns that could help me understand the human experience. However, the initial step in this profound process entails translating these ideas into a more definitive language, such as mathematical formulae, to concretize these abstract concepts.

In other words, to make my solution scientific I needed a formula.

The Meaning Of Me

Throughout my college years, I was honing in on a definitive formula, drawing from several vital ingredients I'd gathered over time. First, it was the awareness of our mortality and inherent resistance against it that had set me on this path. Second, I recognized the significance of viewing our lives in relation to the broader scales of the universe and humanity, which in turn highlighted the third ingredient—choice. Yet, this was still insufficient, as I was lacking a critical element that would bind these components together.

My thinking took place during the breakup of the Soviet Union, when I suddenly found myself a citizen of another country, Lithuania, in the midst of a foreign land. To continue my studies and obtain a master's degree, I had to receive attestation from the military department, which required getting a Russian passport. Although this was a challenging project, it was achievable. I eventually got a valid passport and my reward was that I would be able to participate in military exercises. There we completed our education in "missile" technology and earned a rank in the Soviet Army, a prerequisite for obtaining a master's degree from our university. I have gotten to keep it for a while, and at some point in the distant future I managed to have three passports until I let my Russian passport expire. Instead I got to keep memories about my adventures during military exercises.

In those two short but intense weeks I spent with fellow students in the military camp, I made many new friends and experienced a strong sense of camaraderie. My late arrival due to passport issues meant that I was grouped with students a year my junior, but this did not hinder the connection we developed. Rather, it was our shared experiences that brought us together.

These instances of camaraderie were not birthed from conflict but from the absurdity and ineptitude of our commanding officers in the army. Our unit was lucky to be under the charge of commanding colonels who were former students of our university. This relationship gave us some leeway, a much-appreciated respite from the usual rigors of military training. Accustomed to berating conscripted soldiers without constraint, the field officers were caught off guard by our defiance. It reached such a point that one of the military doctors refused to attend to our regiment unless we ceased responding with expletives. Needless to say, we did not.

Nonetheless, we were not exempt from punishment. We faced consequences for various transgressions such as tardiness, incorrect marching or singing the wrong songs. We used to march singing songs of Queen or Metallica, and this would infuriate our commanding officers. These incidents, rather than driving us apart, served to strengthen our bond. As a collective, we took responsibility for our actions and accepted our punishments together. The punishments usually included peeling potatoes for the whole regiment of soldiers at the local canteen, or spending extra time marching around the camp. At night we used to make holes in the fence to sneak into the adjacent forest to play guitars and sing songs around the campfires while drinking vodka with the daughters of colonels and generals. Every night our commanding officers would force us to patch all the holes, just to cut through the fence again. The drinking was strictly prohibited under the threat of being expelled, which would automatically warrant a draft notice. Yet the very people who were supposed to enforce prohibition were the ones selling us homemade alcohol in huge 2 liter bottles of soda.

However, outside of our little fellowship, the actual military service was far from romantic and more akin to being trapped in a gulag, where officers had minimal control over the troops. Serving in the Soviet army during the 90s was like serving time in a third-world country jail, with daily beatings, rapes, and suicides. I still remember how shocked and disgusted I was upon hearing a military colonel's reaction to one of his soldiers committing suicide on the territory of his military regiment. Instead of offering consolation or trying to find out the reasons behind the incident, the colonel complained and half-joked that the soldier should have chosen a spot a few meters beyond the fence to make everyone's life easier. Life held little value for military officers at that time, and I doubt much has changed since.

Senior soldiers were given the responsibility of maintaining order in squads and platoons, and they did so through the process of intimidation and hazing of junior soldiers, which often resulted in injury and death. The ugly irony of this was that junior soldiers who suffered through the hazing process would eventually become senior soldiers and turn against the juniors. This meat grinder, even when one could survive it, transformed people into worse versions of themselves.

While I was at a military camp, I encountered the most mundane problem. In the midst of marching, following orders, and learning about ballistic missile operations, I developed an intense toothache. I immediately sought the help of a military field dentist. After a brief wait, she informed me that my wisdom tooth had become infected, and the only solution was extraction. However, they were short on anesthetic and regular enlisted soldiers received preferential treatment over cadets. I could either wait my turn or endure the pain without anesthesia. Unwilling to have my tooth removed without anesthesia or risk an abscess, I opted for an alternative.

The location of our military camp was not far from where I was conducting research for my master's degree, near a particle accelerator lab in a large town. I was confident I would find a more qualified dentist there, along with a sufficient supply of anesthetic. After pleading my case to the colonel overseeing our company, he reluctantly granted me a 24-hour leave.

Upon reaching the town near the laboratory, I was still donned in full military attire when I found a dentist who managed to salvage my tooth. Regrettably, the process of locating a dentist, scheduling an appointment, and receiving a filling extended beyond the expected timeframe. Consequently, I exceeded my permissible leave period, technically making me Absent Without Leave (AWOL)—a serious infraction in the military. Thankfully, our colonel was lenient and my punishment only involved peeling and cleaning hundreds of potatoes in the kitchen. Despite the incident, I felt I got off lightly. Ironically, years later in the United States, a dentist advised me to extract all my wisdom teeth, suggesting that my previous dental escapade may have been in vain.

After the military camp, I spent more time completing my master's degree in the town near the accelerator lab, Protvino. It was an odd place, half academic with coffee shops and bookstores frequented by scientists, and half industrial, with factory workers frequenting pubs. One day, several months after the military camp experience, I was discussing Grand Unification Theories in physics with a classmate in my room when I heard a knock on the door. Upon opening it, I encountered a small, unsteady man who requested my pants. At first, I thought I had misheard him, but when he repeated his request, I realized he was extremely drunk and utterly disoriented. In the dormitory, my next-door neighbor, a postdoc, lived with his family. With the door open, I could hear his children playing. On impulse, I decided to lead the intoxicated man away from the children. On a few occasions, my words rather than my fists helped me out of difficult situations. I thought that this would be that occasion where I would try to talk this clearly agitated drunkard from making any more trouble. It was not, and a few minutes later we were fighting. Despite his small stature and his drunkenness, he was really strong and almost manic in his aggression. Usually fights last around 5 minutes on average. That time we were rolling on the floor, all bloodied punching each other, for about 40 minutes until some other postdoc came through and split us apart. Together we carried that drunk guy outside and I went back to my room with a badly sprained ankle. This was just a regular Tuesday in the 90s in Russia. It took a few weeks to start walking normally again, but this encounter had a silver lining.

About an hour after the fight, a police officer came to my room. He wanted me to press charges against the guy. I, following some strange version of the men's code, refused to file a report against the guy just because of a simple fight. This cop happened to be a detective and a really cool guy. He was the epitome of a gentle giant, sporting a bubbly personality, infectious laugh, an undying love for rock and roll and, most of all, Led Zeppelin. He could strum Robert Plant's hits flawlessly on his guitar, and he exuded an indubitable wholesomeness. I ended up forgiving my assailant and did not condemn him to a horrible fate in a Russian jail, but I struck up a conversation with a detective and, in the end, became friends. Through him I saw the underbelly of this small town with its sad, violent and beautiful moments, but this is a story for another book.

I'm writing this to demonstrate the state of my mind at the time. I experienced firsthand the fragility of our existence, the sudden, brutal nature of life, where one minute you are having a conversation with a friend and another you are fighting for your own wellbeing.

Paradoxically, it was also sprinkled with moments of sheer joy, when all adversities were momentarily forgotten. Despite the hardships, those years were also filled with joyful moments. My detective friend and I spent many evenings with our respective friends, playing the guitar and indulging in vodka. He was a talented musician, able to perform impressive renditions of Led Zeppelin tracks. One day, a friend of mine asked me to take care of an exchange student from Norway. My friend was socially active and helped organize visits, hoping that one day he would visit their countries. However, on this particular day, he was busy going out on a date. He only mentioned that she spoke English and wanted to see a typical Russian landscape. When the iron curtain fell, most locals treated foreign tourists with curiosity and admiration, myself included. I jumped at this opportunity.

I was also going to the high-energy lab that weekend, located in a picturesque area next to the Protva River, far away from the city, in the heart of the Russian landscape. Unlike the city, the air is fresh and fragrant, carrying the earthy scent of moist soil and decomposing leaves, mingling with the sweet perfume of wildflowers in bloom. Majestic willow and birch trees, reflecting delicately in the current, provide shade and shelter for the myriad creatures that call this place home. The more gentle sections of the river banks are adorned with soft grasses and brightly colored wildflowers, which sway gently in the breeze. This picturesque forest patch and river banks along the River Protva offered a haven for nature lovers, so I naturally wanted to show the mysterious stranger from faraway lands the best of it.

We met the exchange student near the subway (Metro) station south of Moscow and ventured further south. The problem became obvious when we got there: the whole of the Protva River had flooded, covering all the beautiful nature with water. In a desperate effort to salvage the situation, I called my detective friend, asking him to think of other places and sites that we could show my foreign guest. I almost gave up hope and was ready to return the next day when suddenly, he showed up with a uniformed police officer, both drunk out of their wits. The next few hours, we drove to the next town where the lieutenant was the head of a precinct and visited two Russian monasteries. At one juncture, the exchange student from Norway expressed a desire to meet a typical Russian man. This request, she probably felt sorry about later, as the officer randomly picked up a local bum off the street and compelled him into our vehicle. The lieutenant showed the girl from Norway his entire life—his own girlfriend, his police crew—and we all ended up partying in the middle of Serpukhov city, dancing and drinking vodka with his entire police crew, practically in the middle of the street. I'm sure the girl went back with the most outrageous memories, far exceeding any nature experience.

I kept company with the crazy detective after that and we had many laughs in this unlikely friendship. He introduced me to more of his friends and to some of his foes, to the very people whom he caught and some even ended up in jail. Once he introduced me to a small-time crime boss of the town, who was also from Lithuania. Strange but he did not seem to hold a grudge against him. I attributed it to some small town dynamics where everybody knew everybody and little place is left for grudges. The conversation did not go anywhere as our interests were polar opposite but I was intrigued to meet my first ever crime boss. The strangest thing was that he was not my last crime boss.

Back in Moscow, I encountered a notorious crime boss of Moscow's northern region, known as a "vor v zakone", or a boss of a criminal syndicate. This happened through my Armenian friend and roommate, who had founded a rapidly growing company that employed almost a quarter of our college classmates. It was a classic rags-to-riches story, emblematic of Russia in the 90s.

His initial intent was to provide cable and TV services to elite universities and their students, a precursor to "The Facebook" but before social media was a concept. This idea evolved into a more profitable venture: buying computer parts abroad and assembling them on the university premises. This concept unexpectedly blossomed into a company that began making a significant amount of money. Its growth was so rapid that he had to drop out of college, leave the student dormitory, frequently change cars, and surround himself with bodyguards. In the 90s, prosperous businesses in Russia either maintained their own security teams or paid hefty protection fees to local gangs or criminal syndicates. My friend hired an ex-police colonel, who maintained his old connections and could call in a SWAT team at a moment's notice. I remained in contact with him even after he moved out. Eventually, his company outgrew the abandoned university halls and relocated to a proper office on the city outskirts.

During one visit to his opulent office, a group of loud, gangster-looking men suddenly stormed the office hall. Whether there was a dispute over protection fees or they were merely probing the defenses, I could not tell. Then I noticed a very short, burly man with numerous tattoos on his arms entering the room, and tension filled the air. He went around shaking hands, and when he got to my friend, he paused to look at me before moving on without offering his hand. My friend later informed me that this man was gunned down on the streets of Moscow a week later. He also shared other wild tales of attacks on him and his business, stories of revenge and threats, blackmail, and the unwavering loyalty of his security team.

Decades later this company grew up into a technology giant. However, my roommate fell victim to the betrayal of his close partners and was ousted from the company he founded by the board of directors. To be fair, this wasn't the most severe fate a businessman could encounter in 90s Russia. Assassinations and bombings of affluent bankers and business owners were so frequent that they were dubbed the "banker's disease." He managed to bounce back and eventually became a successful real estate developer, but the company he had built was irretrievably lost to him. Many of my classmates who started working for this company made a successful career there. I met one of them in New York. In the end he still ended up in the US working as a CTO for a subsidiary of a much larger company. Life is not a straight line and, sometimes we choose different paths but end up in the same place, at least geographically. Those experiences only emphasized the value of time.

The environment of the 90's back in the old country may have resembled a hellhole, but it was a fun one, full of stories like the ones I've shared. Life was fast, short, and full of uncertainty. Our uncertainty about the future and time left to live not only affects the quantity or quality of our remaining time but also hinders our ability to plan ahead.

This is when I realize my missing ingredient for the formula, time. It is the biggest arbiter of life successes and failures, as it is our most important resource. To apply my conclusions to real life and, more importantly, to test them, I needed a practical recipe. To get to a practical application I needed a formula. I was close but not there yet.

Question that still kept me from heading in this direction, why not just be happy with what you have? Why can't I just focus on my own feelings of wellbeing and happiness.

Why Not Just Be Happy?

In order to construct the formula for the meaning of life, I had to choose a fundamental principle. Fundamental principles are employed to provide a clear, logical framework for developing more complex conjectures. In mathematics, these fundamental principles are called axioms. They are assumptions in mathematics that serve as the foundation for building mathematical theories and systems.

We have several options to choose from: the well-being of all people, the elimination of suffering, but it is especially tempting to choose happiness as a fundamental principle for deriving the meaning of life. After all, we all implicitly seek happiness and pleasure. The Rule of Utility, "the good is whatever brings the greatest happiness to the greatest number of people," has been influential in moral philosophy and decision-making for the past few centuries. I would like to explore this avenue and see how far it will lead us.

Pursuing this choice creates contradictions within its own principles. Happiness is subjective and varies significantly between individuals, making it challenging to measure and compare across different people and situations. What makes one person happy might make another sad. With the great diversity of personality types, we may encounter sociopaths and psychopaths who are happy to manipulate and even hurt other people. Some people cannot find happiness, and others find happiness in destructive activities, addiction, and gambling.

Life involves a wide range of emotions, including scientific curiosity, a quest for glory, and self-discovery. These emotions require individuals to face their fears, confront their weaknesses, endure discomfort, and overcome challenges. Some of these emotions necessitate sacrifices and suffering, which contradict the state of happiness.

For example, consider the pursuit of glory. It involves seeking recognition, honor, and accomplishment in one's chosen field or endeavor. This drive can inspire individuals to push themselves beyond their limits, achieve greatness, and leave a lasting legacy. However, the pursuit of glory often comes with its share of hardships, setbacks, and even personal sacrifices. Athletes, artists, and leaders may experience physical and emotional pain, face criticism and rejection, and endure countless obstacles on their path to success. These trials and tribulations may seem to contradict the notion of happiness, but they are an essential part of the journey towards achieving one's dreams and aspirations.

The Rule of Utility can also lead to moral conflicts and ethical dilemmas on its own. For instance, it may justify actions that compromise fundamental moral values, such as honesty, justice, and human rights, if doing so results in greater happiness for the majority. There have been examples in history where the majority, to increase their happiness, engaged in the persecution of minorities or even genocide.

Happiness begins with a person's adulthood and ends with their life. This contradicts one of the principles we derived earlier, that the meaning has to be lasting and possibly outlast our life. Moreover, happiness is a transient emotion that comes and goes, influenced by various factors such as personal circumstances, relationships, and external events. As individuals navigate through life, they may experience moments of happiness followed by periods of sadness or even despair. This ever-changing emotional landscape illustrates that happiness is not a permanent state of being but rather a temporary emotion influenced by numerous factors. As such, happiness cannot serve as a stable basis for the meaning of life, as it is inherently fleeting and subject to change. It is possible to choose even transient happiness as a basis for the meaning of life, but this choice will occur at the expense of longevity and permanence.

In contrast to the transient nature of happiness, a truly meaningful life should possess a sense of purpose and significance that is lasting and enduring. This lasting meaning may manifest through one's contributions to society, personal growth, or the impact one leaves on future generations. A meaningful life should not be solely dependent on the temporary emotional state of happiness but should be rooted in more profound, lasting values and goals.

Happiness as a meaning of life contradicts another principle we discussed in previous chapters: that meaning has to be specific to a person's life. When we use the Rule of Utility, we disregard personal happiness at the expense of the happiness of all. One of the primary concerns with relying on the Rule of Utility to define the meaning of life is that it tends to overlook the individual's unique experiences, values, and aspirations. By focusing on the collective happiness of the majority, utilitarianism may undermine the importance of individual pursuits that give life meaning for each person. The individual's quest for self-discovery, personal growth, and the development of meaningful relationships can be essential aspects of a fulfilling life. These pursuits may not always align with the goal of maximizing overall happiness and may sometimes involve personal sacrifices that contradict the utilitarian principle.

On the other hand, concentrating on personal happiness introduces an array of potential complications, primarily due to the inherent subjectivity of the concept. As individual preferences and values vary, so do interpretations of what constitutes happiness. Consequently, the sheer number of possible definitions of happiness becomes vast, potentially equal to the number of people on the planet.

This multiplicity of viewpoints inevitably leads to conflicts and clashes between the various definitions. For instance, one person may derive happiness from a successful career, while another may prioritize a strong family life. In some cases, these differing values may directly oppose one another, causing friction and disagreement.

Despite the temptation to base the meaning of life on happiness, we observe that it contradicts the principles we derived in previous chapters:

1. survival and expansion
2. profound and lasting impact
3. specific to a person's life

What does not contradict these principles is the concept of survival itself. Whatever the principle we choose, if it does not survive for any given length, it becomes obsolete. No matter how happy you are in the moment, if that moment will not last, that happiness no longer matters. It could leave a good memory, but that memory will only matter if it lasts. If you seek glory and achieve it, its value will disappear the moment you lose it. You can be a great athlete, but if no one knows about your achievements, you will be indistinguishable from any other ordinary person. Whatever quality or principle you choose, it only matters if it lasts. That is, in essence, the powerful property of durability, or as I call it, survival. It is also its beauty; we have a choice of secondary principles that suit our personal preferences as long as our choices survive and make lasting impacts.

The experience can be as personal or universal as we choose, provided it endures. Survival offers a convenient framework for assessing our decisions and actions. By waiting long enough to witness the ultimate consequences of any action, we can determine whether it contributed to survival or not. This is akin to a complex chess match, where the value of each move remains uncertain. However, by observing the game's conclusion, we can discern the cumulative impact of every move, leading to either victory (survival) or defeat (extinction). Certain moves or combinations are so influential that they become ingrained in history and acquire distinctive names, such as the "Queen's Gambit" or the "Sicilian Defense."

The answer for my question is that happiness does not necessarily fill our lives with meaning, and it certainly does not last, at least does not last past our life boundary and it does not belong to the fundamental principles. Let us discover what should be the first principles.

The First Principles

In physics, certain fundamental principles or laws cannot be deduced from other concepts; instead, they are accepted based on experimental evidence and observations. These principles are embodied in specific equation generators, which are employed to derive equations of motion, such as the first kind of Lagrange's equations[17] (Lagrangian Mechanics, n.d.).

From the previous chapter and moving forward, I will utilize survival as a fundamental principle and a foundation for deriving the meaning of life. Evolutionary biology will serve as a source of inspiration to inform and shape my conclusions in subsequent chapters. Survival will be considered in terms of ideas, memories, genes, and essentially everything that makes our lives unique. In this chapter, I wish to elaborate further on the concept of survivability.

Darwinian evolution accounts for the origin of species as part of the evolutionary process. Numerous books provide a comprehensive understanding of the subject and explain it more effectively than I ever could (I recommend Richard Dawkins' "The Selfish Gene"[18] (Dawkins et al., 1989). In itself the explanation is simple in its elegance to the point that it can be rephrased as a circular statement or tautology. Evolution is the process for the fittest species to survive environment changes through mutation, sexual reproduction and survival. In more simple terms, it's the process of survival of the fittest, or to put it even simpler: "what survives is what survives". In that representation, it is hard to argue against it, yet this is a simple and profound meaning. Under the destructive passage of time, when environments change, the biological systems capable of adopting will eventually find the best configuration suited to survive the change. This principle can potentially be applied not only to biological systems but to social constructs, as was first noticed by Darwin's protégé and contemporary scientist H. Huxley, and later was expanded by Dawkins who coined the term meme.

For living organisms, evolution is a means of overcoming death. In the harsh environment of the universe, sudden changes impact every scale and corner. However, living organisms manage to maintain the internal environment of their cells, seemingly impervious to external fluctuations. The key lies in the process of evolution, which ultimately relies on organisms' ability to mutate and have the environment select the most favorable mutations. The best mutations survive, becoming immortalized in the ancestral records of DNA for future generations. While organisms eventually perish, these fragments of information persist far longer, with some genes remaining since the dawn of life, as far as we can discern.

---

[17] en.wikipedia.org/wiki/Lagrangian_mechanics

[18] en.wikipedia.org/wiki/The_Selfish_Gene

Determining the exact age of the oldest genes on Earth is challenging, as genetic material does not fossilize and degrades over time, leaving no traces for scientists to examine. However, by studying the building blocks of gene molecules, researchers hypothesize that the first genes on Earth may have been hybrids between DNA and RNA (specifically ribosomal RNA, or rRNA) genes, which play a critical role in protein synthesis[19] (Extance, 2020).

Studies suggest that RNA genes may have existed as early as 3.8 billion years ago, shortly after life first appeared on Earth. Other genes believed to be ancient include those involved in basic metabolic processes such as glycolysis, the process by which cells break down glucose to generate energy, and the tricarboxylic acid cycle, which is involved in cellular respiration. You can think of genes as the original proto-life forms that appeared first on the planet and found a safe haven in our bodies and bodies of all living organisms.

The price for such a long lifespan is high. Genes must bind with other genes to be produced and expressed, and they ultimately exist only in the context of other living organisms. Our genes, when removed from our bodies, will not survive. Nevertheless, this is an extraordinary accomplishment everyone should consider. Inside our bodies, we carry self-replicating organisms that may have existed billions of years ago. We possess a solution to immortality within the structure of our bodies. The answer is not to preserve a body, organism, tribe, or collection of species, but rather in the smallest pieces of information that travel through time within our bodies.

The implications of Darwin's theory extend to outlining the primordial motivations of mammals with higher brain functions, particularly species with a neocortex. All humans have complex brains with nonlinear and interdependent processes, which can sometimes result in exceptional behavior patterns not compatible with individual survival. Yet, these behaviors do not contradict Darwinian evolution, as the unit of survival is not a person or individual—it is a gene. As long as genes survive, evolution continues, and the fate of individuals becomes less important. This is essentially an abridged explanation of the contradiction of altruism described in the book "The Selfish Gene." When bees and ants die to protect the hive, or soldiers perish defending their homeland, it is the work of genes that will be preserved and potentially multiply in surviving siblings of the species after an existential threat has been eliminated through self-sacrifice.

This call of genes translates, on the most basic level, into our survival instinct. This overriding instinct permeates our brain processes and inevitably makes its way into social and behavioral patterns through the emotion of fear. One can experience this when standing on the edge of a cliff and feeling overwhelmed by dread and fear. The same happens when driving and

---

[19] www.scientificamerican.com/the-first-gene-on-earth-may-have-been-a-hybrid

imagining turning the wheel into the side of the road or into a moving car. Our subconscious takes over and autocorrects our erratic behavior.

I believe this forms the basis of our more nuanced fears of mortality, or memento mori, which we discussed extensively in the first part of the book. These processes are not dictated or necessarily predictable by our instincts. After all, some people make a carefully considered decision to end their lives when faced with a crippling and painful ailment, which goes against the instinct of self-preservation. However, the overriding principle remains: if we make a choice that leads to our demise before we leave offspring—be it our genes or our ideas—our lineage will end. This simple concept outweighs all other considerations. No matter how nuanced, artistic, or profound our ideas and creations may be, if they perish in time, if they do not survive, they ultimately do not matter in the long run. The overarching principle is survival —not of individuals or even species, but of the pieces of information that comprise our essence: genes.

To understand the consequences of the survival principle on the question of the meaning of life, let's consider an example. Imagine we came up with an answer for the meaning of life that is incompatible with surviving in the future. Picture creating something so profound but fleeting at the same time, like the most spectacular sandcastle to be immediately destroyed. This concept is reminiscent of an art form in Buddhism called Sand Mandala. However, such art forms live on in our memory and are sometimes captured on film or in photos. Now, envision these fleeting creations of beauty being immediately destroyed without anyone even having the chance to see them. If we create something that doesn't get to exist or last, we typically don't assign it existential value or consider it especially meaningful. This is why whatever inspires us must be compatible with its longevity and survival value. Some of the most valued possessions by humanity last for many generations or longer.

The significance we derive from our lives is deeply intertwined with our actions, hence it is crucial that these actions endure and become consequential. If, in the long term, our actions are incompatible with survival, their meaning vanishes. This is why the longevity of our actions becomes a principal component in life's meaning. This underlines the importance of survival within the formula I proposed in previous chapters—the expectation operator—it is indeed fundamental.

This enduring preoccupation with the concept of memento mori, which serves as a reminder of mortality, is shared by myself and countless philosophers and thinkers. We trace this fascination back to the earliest narrative of Gilgamesh. This principle is universally applicable, relevant to individuals and collectives alike, and particularly to humanity as a whole. We can make an impact on others that lasts for generations and perhaps much longer, but if humanity perishes, so will our impact and our meaning. Whatever we choose, we must do so with the survival of humanity in mind. Whatever cannot withstand time's eroding nature will be swept away. Time is both humanity's curse and blessing. However complicated or confusing the choices we make, they will be clarified by the passage of time. Confusion and lies are washed away and cleansed by time. If there's one thing I am certain of, it's that our time is one of our most critical resources.

In order to escape the inevitable destructive power of time, people's souls must join an eternal and incorruptible entity impervious to time: humanity as a whole. Only then can we cheat death and achieve the dream of Gilgamesh!

A potential objection to this principle resides in the fact that time's trial inherently lacks a concept of morality—it doesn't distinguish between good or evil. Any principle that survives the onslaught of time's destructive nature will inevitably endure. However, how can we be certain that good triumphs over evil? This query sits at the heart of our discussion, emphasizing that notions of good and evil are profoundly subjective. Even acts deemed universally malevolent, such as taking another person's life, can be seen as justified under certain circumstances—for instance, protecting your family or defending your country during warfare as a soldier.

Historically, there are numerous examples where societal norms deemed acceptable or even virtuous subsequently transitioned to being perceived as malevolent and damaging. Slavery, for instance, was widely accepted in many societies throughout history but is now universally regarded as a horrific violation of human rights. Another instance is the treatment of women and minority groups—conduct that was once deemed acceptable is now viewed as discriminatory and unjust.

Similarly, the witch hunts of the late medieval and early modern periods were widely accepted at the time as a necessary measure to combat evil. However, today we view these events as violent and irrational manifestations of mass hysteria and persecution. In the 19th and early 20th centuries, European powers often justified colonialism as a "civilizing mission," seen as a morally righteous task to bring "enlightenment" to the "undeveloped" parts of the world. Today, however, this view is widely criticized. The devastating impacts of colonialism on indigenous cultures, societies, and individuals are well-recognized, and the practice is seen as a significant violation of human rights.

This fluidity in societal norms and ethics underscores the complexity of discerning between good and evil, given the context-dependent and ever-evolving nature of these concepts. However, time does provide us with the benefit of perspective.

There also exists a reciprocal relationship at play. In the grand scheme of things, principles historically and presently deemed as "good" often promote the continuation of life. Take love, for instance, a universally acknowledged virtue. Love fosters procreation and proliferation of species that reproduce sexually. Conversely, actions like killing pose a threat to life and could, if enacted on a large scale, precipitate extinction.

In subsequent chapters, we'll delve into further examples highlighting how detrimental behaviors—often classified as "deadly sins"—relate to the principles of biological survival. At first glance, it appears that survivability and notions of goodness share a tangible connection. This analysis suggests that what is conducive to survival—acts of care, collaboration, and preservation—is often deemed morally good, reinforcing the symbiosis between ethical goodness and life's enduring nature.

At the heart of survival, or positive outcomes, and extinction, or negative outcomes, are the choices and decisions leading to these results. The actions and choices that withstand the test of time and leave a legacy essentially serve as the building blocks of our life's meaning. These actions and choices can be distilled into and represented as ideas.

Ideas are Genes of Our Consciousness

When Darwin introduced his theory of evolution, his ideas were so persuasive to many of his fellow scientists that they not only became converts and friends but also dedicated a significant portion of their careers to promoting and educating others about it. Most notable among them was T.H. Huxley, an English anthropologist and anatomist. Upon learning about Darwin's explanation of species variety through the process of natural selection, Huxley famously responded, "How extremely stupid not to have thought of that." Far from being stupid, he was one of the first scientists to realize that evolutionary mechanisms could be applicable to things other than living organisms. If evolution occurred through natural selection, other entities, including ideas, could be subject to the same pressures and mechanisms. Ideas are reproduced, mutated through the process of imperfect copying, and selected by humans.

Huxley once said, "The struggle for existence holds as much in the intellectual as in the physical world. A theory is a species of thinking, and its right to exist is coextensive with its power of resisting extinction by its rivals." This idea was later expanded upon and promoted by Richard Dawkins almost a hundred years later, who generalized the concept of genes and created the concept of "memes".

These very memes have swarmed the internet and our minds. While Dawkins conceived memes as a metaphorical concept in his book "The Selfish Gene," another English neuropsychologist, N.K. Humphrey proposed considering memes as living structures residing in our minds. Most of these memes will perish after one cycle on social media, but some, like the "E=mc^2" formula, which encompasses the complex consequences of Einstein's special theory of relativity, will likely exist as long as humanity itself.

The progression of our ideas, our creations and consequences of our actions through time is analogous to the evolution of genes through multiple generations. There are enough parallels between those two concepts, for us to dive into this subject a bit deeper.

Living organisms maintain their life cycle through growth, metabolism, and reproduction. Reproduction involves leaving behind genetic seeds, or genes, which contain sufficient information to reproduce entire living organisms. This natural phenomenon of perpetuating the life cycle by leaving "seeds" behind has been proven in multiple scientific discoveries and has become a part of our everyday lives, with easy access to genetic tests like "23andMe" and the admission of genetic evidence in courts.

Memes, or viral ideas, are conceptually similar to genes. Both are minimal units of replication. Genes replicate within the biological context, during cell division, while memes replicate one mind to another. Both represent pieces of information required for their own reproduction that evolve through natural selection. Genes encode traits like eye color and height, while viral ideas embody key concepts that are deemed useful or interesting enough to be shared across millions of minds.

This explanation is an abridged version of the theory of memes and natural selection. I highly recommend reading books on evolution and genetics to better understand the theory (which is the closest thing to truth in science) and the similarities between these two concepts. Here, I use this understanding more as an inspiration for my approach, asserting that our value is defined by the impact of our actions on humanity's future. This value represents our purpose and our meaning.

Many, if not most, of our choices and actions can be represented as mental constructs in our minds, as ideas. For instance, we may begin with the idea of having a family or children. These ideas can evolve and drive us to take action, such as securing a good job to provide for our family or picking up arms to protect them. Most books and movies revolve around storytelling and often originate from a single author's idea. Similarly, classical and modern art depict ideas; even commissioned portrait works represent the idea of leaving a legacy behind. As an example, we can look at Malevich's Black Square as an idea signifying that the modern art we knew in the last century has died, and the Sistine Chapel, which was commissioned to represent the glory of God and Rome. Michelangelo took artistic liberties with his assignment, and to this day, we continue to admire the manifestation of his work.

When we act upon our choices, we transform our ideas into reality and manifest them through our actions. Some of these choices and actions will not survive our lifetime, while others will outlive us by generations.

There are numerous examples of actions and ideas persisting for extended periods. Cold viruses shed their external cell membranes and hijack the reproductive mechanisms of cells. Internet memes go viral, captivating many minds. Cuckoo birds lay their eggs in other birds' nests.

The ideas that spread the fastest are viral ideas that easily infiltrate a multitude of people's minds. Just as Darwin's idea of natural selection propagated into Huxley's mind, who then educated even more people with the concept, this is how "viral" or impactful ideas are created. If they survive the propagation process, they have a lasting impact.

To illustrate a more relatable example, when I was taking exams to enter my dream college, for which my school teacher prepared me, I received top grades in all subjects except math, where I earned a grade "B". That year, the average grade for the department I was applying to spiked due to a large number of well-prepared candidates. My final exam was an oral physics test, where I had to score an "A" grade to gain admission. Two teachers halted the examination and inquired about my aspirations, which was highly unusual. This conversation helped convince them to award me an "A". They could have been less compassionate and simply rejected me, but they chose to make a goodwill gesture. This decision had a snowball effect, leading me to college and eventually into the field of science. On the other hand, there were instances where teachers, striving to maintain high school standards, would intentionally lower the grades of all students across the board. I learned to recognize such acts of kindness and made an effort to mentor and be kind to younger individuals seeking or asking for help. These actions create a lasting impact on the people who receive help, empowering them to help others when it is their turn. These are examples of how our choices can significantly impact the lives of others.

The idea of sorting out information on the internet using a novel algorithm eventually led to the creation of an enormous billion-dollar company that changed the way we live our lives. In a more down-to-earth example, when I had my firstborn son, I had the idea of monitoring his breathing due to the anxiety of being a first-time parent. This idea eventually became a startup company.

The most successful examples of how an idea can grow, spread, and eventually become a reality are religious ideas. Siddhartha Gautama's lifelong quest to alleviate suffering ultimately became the worldwide religion of Buddhism.

The impactful actions, tokens of mankind's attention — I'd like to call them "perma-impacts" — that affect other people begin with ideas and the choices we make to act on those ideas. The ideas do not have to be your own, but it is much easier to act upon ideas you are passionate about. Turning an idea into action and reality takes a considerable amount of work, and it helps if the ideas are close to your heart and represent your personal beliefs. They should also be of the right scale and have a lasting impact on others.

Not all ideas evolve into actions. Children often aspire to become astronauts, firefighters, or teachers, but few get to live out their childhood dreams. Much occurs between childhood and adulthood, and our minds change as we grow. Some ideas may sound appealing but in reality they are dead ends, or worse, are manipulations by people to fit to their agendas. I remember a time when I had a fight in a school yard because one of the boys insulted Lenin, the beloved father of Soviet revolution. I was 10 at the time.

Now I look at the ideas of dictatorship and revolution from a different perspective.

Sometimes, people choose the wrong ideas to act upon or outright manipulate someone else's ideas to twist them into their own version that serves their agenda. In university, I came across a quote attributed to scientist and political dissident Andrey Sakharov. He was a renowned Russian physicist and human rights activist who played a critical role in the development of nuclear weapons for the Soviet Union. Despite his involvement in the arms race, he became increasingly concerned about the potential catastrophic consequences of nuclear war and began advocating for arms control and disarmament. He was awarded the Nobel Peace Prize in 1975 for his efforts in promoting human rights and advocating for disarmament. Sakharov was also a vocal critic of the Soviet government's repression of dissent and was subsequently exiled to the city of Gorky, where he spent several years under surveillance before being allowed to return to Moscow. His legacy continues to inspire many people worldwide, both through his scientific achievements and his unwavering commitment to promoting peace and human rights.

In an interview with a British newspaper, his contemporaries claimed that when asked about the meaning of life, Sakharov responded without hesitation, "The meaning of life is in expansion"[20] (Lipman, 2013). There were several counterclaims stating that it was uncharacteristic for a humble and deeply conscientious academic like Sakharov to make expansion the main focus of his or anyone's life. I recall how I was inspired by this idea when I was a young man, only to learn later that his contemporary, a businessman, twisted his answer to better fit his choices and lifestyle of monetary expansion and power-grabbing, which was typical of ruthless 90s Russia.

After careful consideration, I believe life's focus is not expansion but rather survival, with expansion being one of the many strategies to survive. Incidentally, I believe what the academic meant was an expansion in the mental dimension, the realm of ideas and concepts. Considering these examples, ideas are powerful entities that can transform our lives for better or worse. Ideas, especially powerful ideas, can be both incredibly useful and strikingly dangerous, and one has to be careful on adopting and basing your beliefs on them.

Our ideas, goals, choices, and actions are the true building blocks that give our lives meaning. Ideas are also what make us unique. There are thousands of people worldwide with the same distinct traits and attributes. However, a combination of our ideas and convictions is too unique and specific to reproduce or find by chance. It is akin to a fingerprint of our minds, or the soul, if you will.

Deciding which ideas to pursue is another matter. Implementing them into reality will be challenging in itself. To pursue something that is not close to

---

[20] https://www.newyorker.com/boris-berezovsky-an-oligarch-dies

your heart will be particularly difficult. If the ideas contradict the core of your life or are even destructive to your life, they also contradict your life's meaning. Pursuing ideas that you don't believe in will likely result in failure. To truly pursue an idea, you must have faith in it.

The cost of choosing the wrong idea and pursuing the wrong dream is wasted time. We don't have unlimited time to try out countless things. Our lives are not sketchbooks that we can redraw over and over again. Often, we only have one chance to get it right, and once we choose a dream, it takes a long time to realize it. For example, it took the Beatles about 10,000 hours of practice to become the most influential rock band of the 20th century. The 10,000 hours rule had many critiques and objections, but the essence of it still rings true. The truly important things in life take time to achieve. In my case, it took 10 years to earn a master's degree in physics and another 10 years to become a high-energy scientist. It would have been much harder or even outright impossible if I hadn't dreamed of becoming a scientist as a teenager. When I read science fiction books, I envisioned myself as a heroic scientist inventing powerful lasers, saving the atmosphere, or soaring among the stars. The books and my dreams became my choices and actions.

I came to realize that I could generalize the concept of evolutionary genetics and apply it to the question of life's meaning. The fitness of genes could be replaced with the fitness of our ideas. Genes and memes are not so different from each other. Both genes and ideas (as memes) are semi-contained pieces of information and knowledge capable of reproduction in biological organisms. Genes are passed from parent to offspring through meiosis and sexual reproduction, while memes are passed from person to person through imitation and repetition. Memes can be spread through verbal communication, written communication, or even nonverbal communication such as facial expressions or body language. Both are means of leaving parts of ourselves behind after we are gone.

It still takes time and effort to see an idea through. The best way to know if a dream can come true is to pursue it. There is no magic calculator that will provide an exact estimate of the success of your actions. Without practical applications or an actual formula, it was still very hypothetical. However, I was getting closer to a method with which I could evaluate and weigh my choices and organize my life.

I sensed significant progress in my quest, inching towards the realization that, perhaps, the meaning of life lies in leaving behind as many ideas as possible, with the hope that at least a few, or perhaps even just one, will endure, and evolve into our lasting legacy.

Throughout history, humans have sought to leave behind something that transcends our own existence. The ideas that outlive us become our legacy tokens, the units of the meaning of our life. While some aim for physical legacies like monuments or art, others hope to be remembered for their ideas, values, or contributions to society. These "legacy tokens" can assume multiple forms:

- Literary Works: From Shakespeare to Tolstoy, authors leave behind works that continue to inspire, entertain, and educate.
- Scientific Discoveries: Think of Newton's laws or Einstein's theory of relativity. These ideas continue to shape our understanding of the world.
- Philosophies and Ideologies: Philosophers like Plato or Confucius formulated thoughts and ideas that still influence how we view life, morality, and existence.
- Artistic Expressions: Whether it's Da Vinci's "Mona Lisa" or Beethoven's symphonies, artistic creations can carry an individual's essence through time.
- Technological Innovations: Innovators like Steve Jobs or Nikola Tesla have left behind technology and principles that continue to shape our lives.
- Cultural Movements: Leaders like Martin Luther King Jr. or Mahatma Gandhi led movements that created ripple effects in how society operates.

Given that our ideas become surviving tokens of our life, I now had a few ingredients for the formula:
- Time as an arbiter
- Ideas as tokens of our meaning
- Impact on other people as a way of relevance
- Opposition to mortality through leaving your legacy

In the next chapter we finally will reconcile these elements into a formula.

The Formula for the Meaning of Life

By the middle of my college years, I tried to formulate the question of the universal meaning of life but struggled to find a proper mathematical language. At that point, I was fairly convinced that there was no universal equation for the meaning of life, and that the question breaks down into many sub-questions depending on the context. It could pertain to the meaning of my life, the lives of people around me, or all of humanity. However, going beyond the scale of humanity quickly loses all meaning. I was also convinced that if an answer to that question existed, it would be based on scientific principles.

When we think of mathematical formulas, we imagine equalities where the left-hand side of the equation equates to the right-hand side. One side represents a set of measurable parameters that belong to one phenomenon, and the other side represents another set of parameters. These equations usually represent an equilibrium state, and we seek a quantity to maximize in order to get the most out of our lives. Typically, such an equation describes a static system or a set of laws that don't change with time. However, since our proposed definition deals with actions changing with time, either disappearing or surviving the passage of time, our formula cannot be an equation. Instead, I propose a formula for representing our actions that needs to be maximized over time. We can use this formula to measure the value of one action versus another, of one effect versus another, and prioritize our choices based on value.

The second principle is rooted in the word "life." Life refers to a system that preserves its internal environment and structure, striving to avoid death by adapting to continuously changing external environments. The tenet that principles promoting survival tend to be considered good, while those undermining it tend to be seen as evil, also provides an interesting perspective on morality.

Indeed, the principle of survival is foundational to life itself. Organisms strive to maintain homeostasis, adapting and evolving in response to their ever-changing environments to ensure their continued existence. These survival strategies are inherent to the process of life, dictating the behaviors and traits that are most likely to be passed down through generations.

This principle extends beyond biology to replicating systems such as ideas or religions, which can be viewed as cultural or conceptual analogues to biological life. Ideas and beliefs also "survive" by adapting to changing cultural and intellectual landscapes, spreading and evolving through social and psychological environments much like organisms through physical ones.

The observation that principles promoting survival tend to be viewed as good, while those undermining it are seen as evil, provides a compelling lens through which to view morality. This perspective aligns with a consequentialist or utilitarian view of ethics, where the morality of an action is determined by its outcomes, with actions promoting survival and well-being viewed as good, and those undermining them as evil. However, it's important to recognize that this is not the only framework for understanding morality, and many other factors beyond survival contribute to our ethical judgments.

The best outcome is if the actions resulting from your chosen goals continue to exist even when you are no longer on this earth. In the long term, your goals must promote life. Destroying life is the same as destroying its meaning. This is the definition of legacy: leaving something good behind. The longer your actions last, the stronger your legacy.

The third criterion is based on the uniqueness of your actions and your legacy. This means that the legacy you leave is your own and doesn't belong to anyone else. It means that the choices and actions a person makes are their own. Many of us are raised by our parents, and their influence is deeply entrenched in our upbringing. Nevertheless, at some point, we all become adults and live our own lives. This means we have the privilege and responsibility to make our own choices.

If the impact you make is not unique and everyone else has already done it, the value of the impact is lessened by its commonality. For example, learning to speak French may be a great personal achievement, but the entire nation of France has already accomplished it. Your goals need to be like the DNA of your life: unique and irreplaceable.

My time in college, witnessing the violence of the nineties, gave me an appreciation for the fragility of our time on earth, and I realized that time is a crucial concept in evaluating our choices and separating right from wrong. I believed I made the right choice by attending a challenging college, but I could have made a mistake and not been admitted, or been expelled along the way. The only way for me to know was to wait and see the outcome of my choices. Similarly, in our lives, the only way to judge the outcomes of all our choices is to wait and live through the consequences of our actions and see their results in the end.

Around this time, I also came across the problems of scale that we discussed in earlier chapters. Our meaning cannot be on the same scale as the universe; rather, it should be on the same scale as humanity. Once I localized the question to just the realm of humanity, it became much easier to reorient my problem to the goal of making an impact on humanity. At the end of my college years, I reached the point where I was ready to combine all my conclusions into a single measure to sort out my goals. Recall that I derived that in the absence of one universal meaning, we can choose our own meaning. In that sense, we should use a term of "the direction in life" to properly describe that it is a matter of our choice.

Thus far, I derived that the measure that quantifies the meaning of life needs to fall under these principles:

- Needs to be on the scale of humanity or life
- Compatible with survival and expansion of life
- Specific and unique to personal life
- Has a permanent impact on life
- Becomes a direction in life rather than meaning of it

What could fit better with all the properties outlined above than the summary of our entire life projected into the future? Time is indeed the best judge for all our actions. The actions that outlive us and continue to do good (or bad) speak loudest about our life after we are gone. Rather than picking and choosing the actions that create meaning in our life, I thought it best to take all our actions and choices, good or bad, sum them up, see which ones stand the test of time, and the surviving ideas will form the meaning of our life. Those actions and choices are represented by all the ideas, books, art projects, hobbies, and all your genetic traits preserved through your children, the color of your eyes, your complexion, your gait, posture, and your physical attributes, but also your impact on other people.

Our actions do not make much sense in isolation. We measure the impact of our actions based on their effects on others. There is a saying attributed to the 18th-century philosopher George Berkeley that "if a tree falls in a forest and no one is around to hear it, does it make a sound?". When our actions don't make an impact on other people, it's like a tree falling without a forest. The actions that make an impact on the lives of other people attribute more meaning to our lives, and the longer the impact lasts, the more meaningful our life becomes.

How can we compare impactful yet transient actions with seemingly insignificant but lasting ones? The answer is simple: time takes care of this naturally. By aggregating all our actions and projecting them into the future, the less significant and short-lived actions will be weighed down and become less consequential than our more impactful and enduring actions. Small actions will contribute minimally to the overall impact, as will those that do not last. The passage of time naturally prioritizes actions that contribute to our legacy.

For instance, becoming a mentor or tutor for a struggling student may set them on a better and different path. The student will grow up, remember your name, share stories, and perhaps become a mentor themselves. This is an example of a permanent and positive action. In contrast, creating a viral video that garners numerous likes may seem influential initially, but within a few months, it will be forgotten and its effects will fade. As we have already noticed, this definition does not employ the concepts of good or bad. Those concepts are too vague: we can use the word "good" to describe a very professionally- produced viral video of dubious moral values. This definition only differentiates between actions that create lasting effects on a significant number of people.

Instead of focusing on aspects of your life that have the most meaningful impact right now, I propose estimating the effects of all of our actions we have done over the course of our lives and will do in the future. By considering the sum of our entire life's actions, we satisfy all of the constraints mentioned previously. First, the aggregated impact of an individual's life is on both the scale of humanity and personal life due to being based on human experience. Second, it is grounded in the specifics of one's life, making it highly personal. In essence, I propose that the meaning of your life is the accumulated legacy of your actions on others, as perceived by other people and humanity as a whole in the far future.

The process I suggest involves considering the meaning of your entire life, encompassing all choices and actions—useful or not, meaningful or trivial, and even harmful. Time unlocks meaning, as most of our actions will dissipate over time, leaving only the significant ones to leave a trace. Therefore, the formula must include a summation of all your actions projected far into the future.

We will refer to the unit of our actions or choices that affect people as a permanent impact, a "token" or "perma-impact" for short. The sum of all

79

perma-impacts will be projected into the future by a time propagator or operator, which we will call operation E. The perma-impact will be weighted by how many people it impacts relative to the total number of people, or the relative reach. The strength of the perma-impact is determined by its growth. If the perma-impact affects more people from one time cycle to the next, its influence is increasing. Conversely, if it influences fewer people, it is decreasing, and in extreme cases, it can disappear completely. The strength of the perma-impact is analogous to the "fitness" parameter in evolutionary biology.

As previously mentioned, our ideas can be considered the genes of our consciousness. I will make an all too natural assumption that they are governed by similar laws as biological genes. The value maximized by evolution is an organism's ability to survive and reproduce in its environment, commonly known as "fitness," referring to its capacity to pass genes to the next generation. We will use a similar concept to fitness as a value that we will need to maximize in order to fulfill the meaning of our lives. We will call it the "power" of our meaning, to differentiate it from the term "fitness" used in evolutionary genetics.

Just maximizing the power of our impacts will not be enough. Fitness is defined as the proportional change in the abundance of that genotype over one generation, or ratio of children with a specific gene to ratio of parents with that gene. To account to the full extent of gene propagation, we will need to sum all the occurrences of the genotype, called frequencies over all populations, multiplied by a fitness.

We will do the same, but call this important property "reach", to differentiate from "frequency" used in genetics. Now we have the reach and power to account for the permanent impact of our actions, but those terms are still not enough. As I have discovered, time is the ultimate judge and executioner of our actions and we will need to take the consequences of our actions into the future in order to estimate if they will make the cut and become permanent contributions. We will need a "time operator", or more accurately an operator that takes all of the possible outcomes and calculates the most probable outcome. That type of operation is called in math an expected value or "expectation operator"[21] (Expected Value, n.d.).

Putting it all together, let me first spell out the formula for the summarized impact that satisfies all the above conditions:

"*Value for the meaning of life*" is the expectation value of the sum of all our "*impacts on other people*" weighted by "*how widespread they are*", "*taken to perpetuity*".

Graphically, I could represent this formula as consisting of two parts: one part is specific to our life, represented by a yellow block, another part is a

---

[21] en.wikipedia.org/wiki/Expected_value

common part that is shared with the rest of humanity, and both parts are relying on the future of humanity, which is the ecological part.

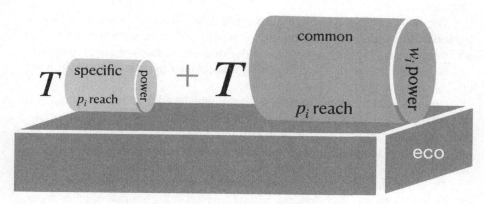

Fig. 1: Graphical representation of the formula for the meaning of life

The specific part is the impact that is made on humanity by the actions that are unique to our life and the common part is the impact by the actions that are common among people. Both actions can either increase the wellbeing of humanity in the future or decrease it and this is represented by the ecological "gray" box that both are lying on. Without an ecological part neither specific or common impact are possible.

Those who are interested in mathematical representation of the formula, I will describe in detail the formula in the appendix at the end of the book.

In this chapter, we will discuss the concept of a single value representing life's meaning and how it affects our lives. Both in mathematics and everyday life, there are instances where life is modeled by a series of numbers, sometimes arranged into complex structures like tables or matrices. However, when it comes to making choices among multiple options, we need to prioritize them according to a single benchmark, represented by a single value. This allows us to make clear choices, which is why I am motivated to distill our life's meaning into a single value. When faced with the choice of fulfilling our life's meaning, we should select a path with a higher value to maximize it.

Another important observation is that if we extend the concept of life beyond the biological life of a human body to include memories, ideas, companies, and books—essentially the works we leave behind after we die—the formula describes the probability of survival of this extended "life" after our death. Just as biological life seeks to ensure the survival of its genetic material, this broader conception of life emphasizes the propagation of ideas, knowledge, and impact. In this context, life transcends the physical boundaries of a single organism, extending its existence through its influence and contributions to society. A person's ideas, teachings, creations, or even memories held by others, can continue to impact the world long after their physical demise. This echoes the biological process where the survival of a species doesn't hinge on individual organisms but on the continuation of its collective genetic material.

The notion that our life continues through the ideas or impacts we leave behind aligns with many cultural and philosophical understandings of legacy and immortality. This conception of "extended life" challenges the traditional definitions of life and death, suggesting a continuity of existence through the effects we have on the world and others.

However, it's essential to note that while this model offers a broader understanding of survival, it does not diminish the importance of individual lives. Instead, it highlights the interconnectedness of life, suggesting that our impacts on the world and on others form a vital part of our existence and survival.

This formula measures all our permanent impacts, both good and bad, on others. I will use the term "perma-impact," which is a generalization of a gene and resembles the concept of a meme. It can be interpreted as a hybrid of a meme and a gene. I am using the term "meme"[22] (Meme, n.d.) as introduced by Richard Dawkins—a generalization of a gene, i.e. a piece of information that passes from one individual to another through the process of imitation. Nowadays it is also used to describe viral images on the internet, but in essence those are still cultural objects passed around by non-genetic means. I'm using a former rather than latter definition of this concept.

A "power" of this new hybrid gene/meme is a measure of the likelihood that the perma-impact will increase in the next time cycle or will decrease. It is measured as a ratio of the number of people who know or are affected by this perma-impact to the total number of people in a population of people. It is an internal property of the perma-impact to expand or contract in the course of one time cycle. It corresponds to the role that time plays in our equation. At each step the effects of our actions either grow or diminish.

For instance, teaching a valuable subject in school has a high value of power because it will increase throughout the life of a student. Creating a short live content on a social media platform has low "power", because it will not last past next year. For the time cycle I've chosen a year as a good approximation for a perma-impact to take hold. Less than a year would be too little to judge if an effect is lasting and 10 years sound too long in relation to typical human lifespan. In a year most internet memes die off and disappear from our combined cultural awareness, but a few survive and last unabated.

There are two ways that "power" can increase the occurrence of a perma-impact (or a trait). One way is by increasing the occurrence of a trait in the existing population of individuals, affecting more minds. An example of this is the growing popularity of a medical remedy, song, or book. Another way is by actually increasing the population through enhanced evolutionary fitness and by increasing the number of individuals. A prime example of the latter is the

---

[22] en.wikipedia.org/wiki/Meme

advent of penicillin. This revolutionary drug quickly gained popularity among medical professionals due to its profound efficacy. By alleviating the suffering of sick patients and saving countless lives, penicillin has contributed significantly to an increase in the overall human population.

A relative reach is a measure of how many individuals a perma-impact will affect in one time cycle, or in one year, in our case. In our earlier example, a viral video may have low power but high reach, as it will be shared or recommended to ever-increasing social circles until it fizzles out. Both power and reach are important for a permanent impact to expand through time.

The most beneficial perma-impact is one that both increases its occurrence from year to year, growing in reach of affected people, and also benefits the entire population, resulting in increasing numbers within the population.

The expected value term[23] (*Expected Value*, n.d.) measures the likelihood of a perma-impact expanding or shrinking in the far future, or more precisely, in the infinite limit. In essence, it is a time evolution operation that takes all the effects of the action to their ultimate conclusion. The perma-impact measures an impact from one cycle to the next, while the expectation operator calculates the same measure but not just for one cycle—it takes it to the furthest point into the future, to perpetuity. It is another summation operation, but the sum or aggregation happens over all possible scenarios that could happen to a perma-impact. The aggregation is calculated over all cycles, all steps, while considering the effects of both power and reach at each step. This is the time propagator that serves as the ultimate judge of all actions and perma-impacts.

While we can sum up all of the impacts of our actions and the likelihood that they last for the next year, we cannot really tell how long they will last in the far future. The expected value is a future value, and, as is, this operation is not observable in the present time. We may have to wait a few decades or centuries in order to evaluate the success of our actions. We however can deduce and approximate how likely the similar actions can survive by observing past experiences.

You may notice that this formula looks much like a formula for the average genetic fitness of the population with the exception of time evolution operation, or "expectation operation" that we have discussed a couple of paragraphs before. This is not coincidental but rather incidental. I took this formula as an inspiration and generalized the concept of genetic fitness to apply to the meaning of life as the summarized impact of all your life. This equation is written without a concept of limiting capacity for growth. Our perma-impacts start from zero and their initial growth is not limited by any thresholds. The older and established ideas eventually reach an equilibrium, but we are not going to consider them in this iteration of the formula.

---

[23] en.wikipedia.org/wiki/Expected_value

There is however a crucial difference that makes this formula different from the genetic evolution equation. It is the presence of time or expectation operation. This operation introduces stochastic nature to the evolution of perma-impacts, a degree of chaos and changes the deterministic nature of a classical evolution equation – Price Equation[24] (Price Equation, n.d.).

Graphically we can represent the interplay between the reach of our actions and a power as follows:

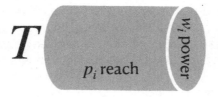

Fig. 2: Our life's impact is a product of power and reach of our actions under time operator

Power of our action is graphically represented by the size of a circle and the reach is how many people this action will reach or affect. Both the power of our actions and their reach contribute to the overall impact we leave behind.

One interesting thing I, as a particle physicist, have noticed is that this formula reminded me of the formula for the probability of two particles to interact. The probability of interaction is a product of luminosity and cross section[25] (Cross Section, Flux, Luminosity, Scattering Rates, 2013):

$$P = \mathscr{L} \times \sigma, \text{ where } \mathscr{L} \text{ luminosity}$$

or number of particles flying through the detector surface and cross section corresponds to the radius of interaction for the particle, the larger cross-section the more chances that two particles will interact, and the larger the luminosity the more particles are going to be in the vicinity of each other. A cross-section is an internal property of the particle and gives the probability of interaction when just two particles interact with each other. The luminosity is an external property of how many times the particle gets to interact with its neighbors. In our formula, luminosity corresponds to reach of a perma-impact and cross-section corresponds to power of our actions. Graphically both power and cross-section are determined by the radius of the interaction, and reach and luminosity correspond to a frequency of interactions.

To continue our analogy, the power of our action is the probability of its success when we just try it on a single person and it is an internal property of

[24] en.wikipedia.org/wiki/Price_equation

[25] phys.ufl.edu/cross_section_flux

the action or perma-impact. The reach is an external property that indicates how hard we try the same action or affect different people. I thought this little analogy is curious to notice across different disciplines and deepens our understanding of the formula.

For success of the perma-impact or for our actions to find traction we need both the power and the reach. As an example, to start a band you need to have a fitting personality and a sizable talent within a musical band. Yet that alone is not enough to get noticed, to get wide recognition of the world audience and to break free. Malcolm Gladwell in his bestseller "Outliers: The Story of Success"[26] (Gladwell, 2011) popularized the idea that the most successful experts and over-achievers in their fields put in at least 10,000 hours. The most typical garage bands would spend about 1000 hours practicing. According to Gladwell, the Beatles put in more than 10,000 hours of practice playing in Hamburg in the early 1960s. Gladwell's point is that an immense musical talent encompassed within their band came through partially through the amount of practice, or in our example, reach of application. Despite many criticisms of this book concerning oversimplification of complex social phenomena and vagueness of definition of success and validity of exactness of 10,000 hours, this idea deeply appeals to me that it links hard work with an achievement and tries to quantify it.

In the beginning of this book I have talked about how important it is to have a measurable quantity that can be associated with the meaning of life. The larger the value of this quantity the more meaningful your life is. In this part I present the formula that represents a quantity that you need to maximize in the course of your life, specifically you need to maximize the permanent impact of your life on other people, along with the scope of your impact.

The deep dive and derivation of the formula will be discussed in the appendix, but here I can discuss in broad strokes how I arrived at it and what it all means. The sum of all actions is weighted by how many people will be affected by a particular action, with each action valued by how much it will contribute to a recognition of our name. As we already discussed, expected value is a prediction for this value to survive and still be there in the far future. This is what I meant by saying a "permanent" impact. Because the outcomes are eventually determined by a combination of chance and the inherent value, the process of our actions impacting other people is probabilistic, i.e. subject to chance. The time operation also called expected value operation[27] is designed to deal with probabilities that our actions will survive the passage of time. It takes all the possible outcomes, weights them with probabilities of the outcome and calculates a final aggregate outcome. The more impact we make with our actions, and the longer they last, the larger the meaning of our lives.

---

[26] en.wikipedia.org/wiki/Outliers_(book)

[27] en.wikipedia.org/wiki/Expected_value

The formula addresses the significance and lasting effects of actions and perma-impacts, ensuring that the reach and power of minor actions and ideas are nullified through the expectation operator, or the passage of time operation. It encompasses all actions in our lives, from those that are highly specific and personal to those that are generic and common among all people. This means that the sum of all our actions consists of two parts: one unique and specific to our lives, and another that is shared with the rest of humanity. We may possess striking blue eyes or play Mozart's Piano Concerto No. 26 flawlessly, but so do thousands or millions of others. Blue eyes are not exclusive to humans, as blue-eyed black lemurs and Siberian huskies also exhibit them.

The formula posits that the meaning of our lives is the sum of all actions that have made an impact on others, projected into the future. Our actions can be viewed as manifestations of our choices and ideas. In the formula, the terms reach (p_i) and power (w_i) represent the sums of the perma-impacts passed onto or affecting others, while the expectation operator estimates the probability of those perma-impacts persisting. Although too complex to calculate and apply practically, it can be utilized in specific cases.

We can compare the most prominent actions or effects that people achieve in their lives. Most of us have a couple of moments in our lives when we were at a crossroads, not sure which way to go. We usually choose a path based on our intuition and it is usually the path to maximize the wellbeing of people we care about. This formula is trying to capture this intuition and it extends wellbeing to the maximum number of people. According to it, the choice that provides the biggest impact creates the most meaning. An action that does not create a multiplying effect that will spread across people and stay will eventually disappear and dissipate due to the effects of time.

Now armed with the formula we can try to go ahead and use it and in the meantime to prove that we are on the right track.

The Discussion Around the Proof

In my description of what makes an approach scientific, I mentioned two components: first, the creation of a formula to measure the meaning of life, and second, the ability to draw testable conclusions from it. We accomplished the first component in the previous chapter, and now we will focus on establishing the latter.

Calculating the results of an expectation operator in our equation is quite complex due to the intricate mathematics involved. I was able to compute the outcome for a specific special case, in which maximizing the meaning of life for all of humanity led to the derivation of logistic population growth. I will elaborate on the details of this derivation in the appendix; however, it is worth noting that this has never been accomplished using the genetic evolution equation, also known as the "Price equation," which makes it a promising indication.

That said, discovering a proof in this context does not automatically qualify it as scientific work. For this distinction, the proof must be subjected to peer review by authorities in the applicable academic field and, ultimately, be endorsed by them.

Instead, I plan to explore examples and thought experiments to assess the formula on a broad scale. My previous attempts involving lexical analysis and the creation of a concrete formulation using logic or mathematics regarding the meaning of life have not produced tangible results. Consequently, I arrived at the conclusion that there is no universally objective meaning of life. The meaning of life is seemingly subject to personal choice, which suggests that it fundamentally exists as a subjective construct. However, this presents a paradox: if the meaning of life is wholly arbitrary and hinged on individual choice, it negates its purpose in steering our lives, as any random choice dilutes direction, thus legitimizing any choice or action.

Indeed, the collective belief of people can manifest subjective constructs into tangible realities. Consider money as an illustration. From an objective viewpoint, it is merely colored pieces of paper being exchanged. Today, it's often not even paper, but a digital number on our phone or computer screen. Nevertheless, because nearly everyone, including the staunchest socialist countries, believes in its value, we can trade these pieces of paper or digital figures for services and tangible items, like cars and houses. The same rationale can be applied to many societal norms, such as individual rights and responsibilities. If a significant number of people adopt a definition of a meaningful life, this value will materialize as authentically as money and individual rights.

While it's accurate that there seems to be a general consensus about what constitutes a meaningful life, I propose a way to validate my formula. By scrutinizing several examples of lives widely considered meaningful or purposeful, along with lives perceived as devoid of meaning, we can verify if my formula yields meaningful values in these scenarios.

In the previous chapter, the process of proof was described as making a verifiable prediction using a hypothesis or formula and then validating the prediction through experimental measurements. An ideal experiment would involve a large-scale sociological survey to track people's decisions, followed by a poll of their friends and family years later to determine if they had lived meaningful lives. However, I do not have the means to conduct such a massive undertaking. Instead, I can engage in a series of thought experiments. My proof will consist of two steps. In the formula from the last chapter, I equated the calculated value of the meaning of life to the total permanent impact left by our lives on other people.

In the initial phase of my exploration, I will evaluate the validity of my assumption by considering the life of an ascetic in complete isolation, a phenomenon we've encountered in our civilization's history. Prominent figures like Mahavira, the founder of Jainism, Buddha, the founder of Buddhism, St. Francis of Assisi, a Catholic saint, Mother Teresa, a Catholic nun and missionary, and Swami Vivekananda, a Hindu monk, all chose lives of extreme austerity and renunciation.

However, unlike these renowned ascetics, our hypothetical hermit remains unknown and entirely disconnected from society. It is reasonable to question the meaning of such an isolated life devoid of any interaction with others. According to my formula, the lasting impact of their life, and thus its meaning, is close to zero. This hermit may have attained absolute purity and the highest state of enlightenment, but their accomplishments remain unbeknownst to others. By "others," I refer not only to people but also to higher entities or unseen forces, barring the hermit's own consciousness. The net effect of this person's life is equivalent to them never having existed. This does not mean that we cannot adopt the opposite view and assume that the meaning of life has nothing to do with other people. The issue with this approach is that it leads to a contradiction when attempting to scale it to other individuals. As previously discussed, for a completely subjective principle to become a reality within society, many people must believe in it. Without interaction, there is no way to convince others of your ideas or spirituality. The examples of ascetics mentioned earlier only emphasize my point. The reason their life was significant is not because they lived a life in seclusion, rather because they evangelized their ideas and taught other people, who, in turn, were so touched by their ideas that they taught more people and their ideas eventually became religions or movements, i.e. subjective realities in our societies.

For life to harbor meaning, it necessitates the capacity to evolve, proliferate, and, consequently, interact with and influence others. The more extensive the impact, the greater the meaning assigned to life. Any alternative interpretation lacks scalability, making it more challenging to deem as meaningful. For instance, if increased impact generates less or equal meaning, it would undermine the incentive to interact, which starkly contradicts our observations. We've noticed that individuals perceived to have achieved significance or meaning are universally well-known and remembered. In essence, I equate the enduring impact on others with the measure of life's meaning.

As the next step, let's examine if the formula correctly estimates the impact our life leaves on other people. After all, the formula tried to emulate propagation of generalized concepts of genes, memes, or perma-impacts, with one more additional operation that takes into account the factor of time. The fair question to ask is this a correct way to estimate the lasting impact on other people. In psychology and journalism article on finding relevance of the news[28] (Barchas-Lichtenstein, 2020) dependence on the impact of ideas and actions on people are defined through the following factors:

- Reach: The number of people that a person's actions or words can reach can greatly impact their impact on others. For instance, a social media influencer with millions of followers may have a greater impact than someone with only a few hundred followers.

- Relevance and effectiveness: The relevance of a person's actions or words to others can also impact their impact. If a person's actions or words are directly relevant to the needs or interests of others, they are more likely to have a significant impact. The effectiveness of a person's actions or words in achieving their intended goals can also contribute to their impact on others. For example, a leader who can effectively motivate their team to achieve a common goal can have a significant impact on the team's success.

- Time: The length of time that a person's actions or words have an impact can also be a factor. For example, a historical figure who made significant contributions to society that are still felt today may have a greater impact than someone who made a short-term impact.

Our formula combines all the three types of factors as the power (w_i), the reach (p_i) and the time operator (E). Let's examine the values that the formula assigns to various personal actions.

In order to do that I will consider a couple of actions of a historical person in the past that we can calculate an impact on other people using our formula. I can then compare the associated values with the outcome of those events, knowing the way those actions turned out and how the majority of historians view the transpired events.

For instance, let us take the fascinating life of Fritz Haber[29] (Fritz Haber, n.d.). He is a rare example of a person who combined the act of incredible goodness with the act of incredible evil. He was a German chemist who for his invention of the Haber–Bosch process received a Nobel prize in 1918. As a good deed, his invention is used to synthesize ammonia from nitrogen and hydrogen gasses on industrial scales, which can be used for large-scale production of either ammonia or explosives. It is estimated that one-third of annual global food production uses ammonia from his invention, and that this supports nearly half of the population. If we estimate power as a change in reach of this idea on the scale of small, medium and large, we would get a range of values, including negative: -1 for large negative, -0.5 or medium, -0.01 for small, 0, 0.01, 0.5 and 1. Large power means the idea propagates

---

[28] nih.gov/relevance-in-the-news

[29] https://en.wikipedia.org/wiki/Fritz_Haber

very fast. In our times this invention has already reached as far as possible and its growth equals to the rate of maintenance and replacement of worn out equipment, also its growth is generated by the natural increase in the population, so we will assign the value of 1% or 0.01. The reach is massive as it affects half of the population. In equilibrium the time propagation factor does not contribute to growth or decline, with the value of 1. The perma-impact of his good act thus has reached equilibrium of $1.0 \times 4 \times 109 \times 10\text{-}2$ or a value of 40 million.

He is also known as a father of "chemical warfare" as he spent years developing and weaponizing chlorine. His even more sinister though not direct involvement was that his invention was used in the development of Zyklon B, the poison gas used in the Holocaust to murder more than 1 million Jews. His involvement becomes even more disturbing but also sad given that he was Jewish himself and was eventually forced out from his positions in German institutions after the Nazis rose to power. Those actions had a negative power as they led to a decline in population at a rapid rate, so we will assign a negative medium factor of -0.5 for deaths and -0.01 for injuries. More than 100,000 soldiers died as a result of chemical weapons use and about 1.3 million were injured. The time propagation factor is also a non-contributing value of 1. Adding this to the deaths from Zyklon B we would get a large negative effect of:

$$(-10^{-2} \times 1.3 \times 10^6) + (-0.5 \times 1.1 \times 10^6) = -56{,}000$$

Summing up those two together we still get a large positive number valued of much more than 39000. While he is considered both as a callous villain and one of, if not the greatest industrial chemist in the history of humanity, his lasting legacy and impact is saving millions of people from starvation. This is correctly estimated and represented by our formula.

As another example let's consider the more recent phenomenon of computer games. My favorite video game is StarCraft 2. It is a real time strategy game where you play one of the three imaginary races, one terran and two aliens, with differing characteristics. The game involves fast strategic and tactical thinking, which makes it complex and hard to beat with artificial intelligence. That was one of the reasons why Google's deep mind team picked this game as a testing and battling ground for its version of a deep mind gaming AI, alpha star. It is also a popular and stable part of eSports with a dedicated fan base. We can imagine a young and talented player who is equally talented in chess. What would be a more meaningful choice for a hypothetical player to pick: an extended career of a professional player in a popular video game, or career of a chess player. Let us calculate a permanent impact that each of those choices would create.

For the StarCraft it is growing very moderately, so we can assign its power to be between 0.01 and 0.5, probably at 0.1. Chess has already reached its peak and grows at a sustainable rate of 0.01 to account for the growth of population, i.e. through inflationary pressure. The reach, or number of active players is well known for both games. For StarCraft it is 260,000[30] (SC2 Player Count, 2021) and the number of active chess players is 605 million[31] (How Popular Is Chess?, 2020).

While it is hard to predict the time effect on the StarCraft community, we would notice that the number of players is pretty stable as its growth is slowing down. We would conservatively estimate its time propagation factor as 2. For chess to have reached its stable state, the time factor is 1. This would give us 2 * 260,000 * 0.1 or 52,000. For chess our formula yield a much bigger number: $1.0 \times 6.5 \times 10^8 \times 10^{-2} = 6.5$ millions. We can compare those numbers to the earnings of the top players in both sports. Top chess players, Magnus Carlsen and Vishy Anand, make around $1 million each year, topping 7 million dollars made just from tournaments.

Top life-long earnings for StarCraft players, Serral and Maru, are around $1.2 million dollars[32] (Winnings, 2022), surprisingly not too far behind. Still our formula produced a correct quantitative estimate of two different directions.

Indeed, we could explore more examples, but it is evident that our formula, by design, estimates the summary impact of actions and consequently the meaning of life. The crucial leap in our proof was the first step, where I argued that the meaning of life equates to the permanent impact of choices, ideas, or inventions on other people.

In all fairness, it is important to acknowledge that this chapter does not qualify as scientific proof. Rather, consider it a discussion and an expression of my thoughts on the matter, as well as an invitation for you to contemplate these ideas for yourself.

When I reached this point in my exploration, a natural question arose: Is this the end? Is there nothing more to seek? Truth be told, I was not entirely satisfied with the absence of a grand unified purpose for all of us—perhaps not on the cosmic scale we discussed, but on a larger scale nonetheless. The fact that I ran out of time and energy does not necessarily mean that such a purpose does not exist.

At this moment, my intention is to delve into the practical implications of my formula. However, deep in my mind, I have this lingering suspicion that there is more to the story, waiting to be discovered.

---

[30] tl.net/sc2

[31] chess.com/news/view/how-popular-is-chess-8306

[32] liquipedia.net/starcraft2/Winnings

The Practical Framework

Several months have passed since I conceived my formula back at college in Moscow. The formula, in and of itself, doesn't create the meaning of our life. Rather, it serves as a tool to employ and apply in life, to devise a plan that determines our life's trajectory, and to construct a framework for its implementation. In this chapter, I aim to describe the practical applications of the formula for actually building this framework. To do so, I will draw on examples from my own life, which requires that I paint a picture of my surroundings and circumstances during that period.

A lot has happened in my life since. My depressed state that triggered my search for the meaning was gone and I was steadily steering my life towards my first goal—becoming a published scientist. However, life had its own agenda and abruptly disrupted my well-laid plans. The transformation of the country I had grown up in, initially promising reforms and freedom, devolved into utter chaos and decay of the 90s. The traditional culture and ideals, once familiar and comforting, morphed into something entirely new and bewildering for the citizens and for me.

As 1991 drew to a close, the country I knew disintegrated into separate republics. The scientific institutions, where I had intended to begin my research, lost 90% of their government funding. If I had been a theorist, a notebook and a pencil might have sufficed. However, experimental physics demanded substantial capital for equipment such as accelerators, magnets, large calorimeter detectors, and drift chambers. These items came with a hefty price tag, not to mention the considerable electricity costs to operate this machinery. Most of my peers in the field relocated their research abroad, either to the CERN laboratory in Switzerland or Fermilab in the USA.

I vividly remember a photo of a tall, futuristic-shaped research building on the wall of my scientific advisor's office in the particle lab located in the suburbs of Moscow. It was the main building of Fermilab, a sister laboratory with much larger energies and budgets. As I was discussing my graduation thesis with my advisor, I could not help but think about how much I wanted to end up in that building and what it would take to get there.

My memory of a photo of main Fermilab building

During this turbulent time, properties that once belonged to the people were reassigned to private enterprises. It was an opportune time to start a business and participate in the wealth redistribution process, provided you had the tenacity, ruthlessness, and a bit of good fortune. Several of my college friends managed to launch companies amidst the crumbling institutions, and I could have chosen to stay and work with them. Yet, my heart was set on physics.

Remaining in Russia and pursuing science became nearly an impossible option for me. Even theorists found themselves wrestling to provide for their families. The dream image of the towering building of Fermilab beckoned me, and it ultimately concretized my decision to study physics in the USA.

The beauty but also the scary part of life lies in its inherent uncertainty. I could not know if my decision to go to the US was a correct one or erroneous, nor can we predict with certainty if my plan will work out in the end. Our life does not have a scratchpad version, we can't try out choices in a provisional version of our lives, then erase the ones we don't like and start anew. Each decision we make is inscribed indelibly into the single life story we possess, without the option for rewrites. Ultimately, it is time and fate that reveal whether our expectations will come to fruition. Looking back now, I would say with certainty it was the right decision but at that time I was filled with uncertainty for the future.

The journey from a university in Moscow to one in New York required significant effort and a lot of luck. At that time, I was working on my graduation thesis in the area of nuclear physics at a high-energy laboratory where we used surprisingly advanced computer technology, particularly given the ex-Soviet context. This specific field of physics necessitated enormous computational power to process the trillions of particles produced by collisions of nuclear particles in the accelerator. It is not accidental that the world wide web was created by English computer scientist Tim Berners-Lee while working at CERN in 1991. Physicists shared that technology and I was pretty connected to the world in the 90s, while working on my research. We worked together with international researchers and other students from all over the world. As it turned out, luck found its way to me deep within the Russian countryside. Somehow, I managed to finish a research project in just a week —a project that another student from Japan, who unbeknownst to me, had been grappling with for over two months, with no end in sight. This project involved measuring spin interaction in colliding nuclear particles, an area of study known as spin physics. My supervisor was so impressed by my speedy results that he personally recommended me to his colleague, a fellow professor at Columbia University, who would later become my future advisor. Interestingly, this project was not related to my thesis. I had initially taken it on as a side project, drawn by its intrigue while finding my main project boring. Eventually, I switched the topic of my thesis entirely to base it on this new area of research.

The journey to the Fermilab was far from simple, involving a myriad of steps and challenges. I had to get additional recommendation letters. To this end, I found myself relentlessly, if not 'stalking,' pursuing several professors and even the head of the high-energy laboratory. I didn't shy away from approaching them during their off hours. This assertiveness and persistence yielded results— but it started with the side project that resulted in the recommendation that led to an eventual acceptance letter to Columbia University.

There is also a question of money that I needed for the plane ticket and for my initial expenses. I sold a successful side business selling caller ID phones that I had to keep me financially afloat to my former partner. I unfortunately fell victim to a street robbery that happened frequently in 90s Russia and lost 90% of the sales money. Fortunately my mom and dad answered my plea for help, and together with their help I had just enough. With their support, I managed to scrape together just enough to embark on my journey. A few years later, I found myself seated in the same towering building at Fermilab that I had once admired in a photograph, now actively involved in groundbreaking research as a particle scientist.

During my final months in my native country, I found myself reflecting on the outcomes of my hard work and the value of time. Many peers who had neglected their studies were now facing expulsion. A few of my friends who had left college to launch their own businesses had struck gold. Meanwhile, I had initiated a side venture that was yielding steady returns. The initial years of university offered no room for relaxation or negligence, as the cost of complacency or poor decisions was the squandering of our most valuable resource—time. Most crucially, I had now formulated a theory for the meaning of life. My next step was to unravel its significance and begin applying it by constructing my personal framework to realize the purpose of my life.

In my final months back in my homeland, I contemplated the fruits of my labor and the value of time. Many of my peers who hadn't dedicated sufficient time to their studies faced expulsion. A few friends who had quit college to establish their own companies had hit it big. I, too, had started a side business which, while it didn't make me a fortune, helped to pay for my trip to New York. The initial years of university didn't afford me the luxury of relaxation or complacency, as the cost of negligence or poor decisions was squandering our most precious resource—time. Most importantly, I had now articulated a formula for the meaning of life.

My next goal was to decipher its implications and integrate it into my own personal framework to actualize the meaning of my life.

Creating the Framework for Accomplishing Your Goals in Life

Having goals is not only important because it answers the question why we are here. Life is a stormy endeavor with lots of ups and downs. In the moment of crisis, goals that are bigger than your life could help us to weather the storm and recover the damages or at least give you a refuge.

> *"If you can make one heap of all your winnings*
> *And risk it on one turn of pitch-and-toss,*
> *And lose, and start again at your beginnings,*
> *And never breathe a word about your loss:*
> *If you can force your heart and nerve and sinew*
> *To serve your turn long after they are gone,*
> *And so hold on when there is nothing in you*
> *Except the Will which says to them: "Hold on!"*
> *"*

I first heard those verses long ago, before I even knew they were from Rudyard Kipling's poem "If"[33] (Kipling, 1910). They were the words that echoed in the mind of the protagonist in a movie I watched while growing up. I spent my childhood on the shore of the Baltic Sea, where we only had a few months of summer to enjoy the pristine beaches with their clean and fine sand in hues of white and silver. It was a time of change, much like the lyrics

---

[33] en.wikisource.org/wiki/Rewards_and_Fairies/If

in Scorpions' "Wind of Change" song[34] (Scorpions - Wind Of Change (Official Music Video), 2009) where old habits were being broken. Despite the limited number of Soviet television channels available (I remember we only had three or less), there were new songs and movies being made with fewer restrictions and new ideas emerging in the late 80s.

One movie in particular, "Dear Edison"[35] (Fridbergas, 1987). The film revolved around a main character faced with a choice: to live a conventional, mundane life or to follow his talents and rebel against a colossal system single-handedly.

The protagonist in the movie was a young, talented scientist - perhaps this is why his story resonated with me. He had graduated from the capital university, which was my dream school, but was assigned to work at a provincial engineering outfit. He was a brilliant mind, full of ideas that could revitalize an industry and push it forward, but he was surrounded by entrenched bureaucrats and apparatchiks who had long since lost the ability and desire to create anything new. Instead, they spent their time scheming and backstabbing one another.

The film's main setting was in a Soviet province, where corruption and apathy were prevalent. It was unthinkable to confront any aspect of the repressive system head-on at the time. The movie ended with the hero still contemplating his options, literally meditating and blocking out the noise of everyday life with noise-canceling headphones. In the background, the best translation of Rudyard Kipling's poem "If" was being read aloud. From this scene[36] (О, если ты спокоен..., 2011) it was clear that the protagonist would persevere and choose the harder path that his talent and sheer willpower had paved for him.

The ability to choose one's destiny and find refuge from everyday struggles was both fresh and fascinating to me. It provided an example that one can strive for something greater than their troubles. This was particularly useful during high school bullying and later in life when facing difficult times.

In my formative years I was inspired by the story of Michael Lomonosov, a son of a peasant and deacon's daughter of a deacon who rose to become an influential scientific figure in pre-Victorian-era Russian science. In 1730, despite his father's objections, he decided to study science and walked over 1,000 kilometers to Moscow to pursue his dreams. With utter determination, he overcame barriers of class and wealth, living off bread and water, and made rapid progress academically. He eventually made significant contributions to Russian science, including discovering the atmosphere of Venus and the law of conservation of mass in chemical reactions, in addition to being an astronomer, geographer, mosaicist, and poet.

---

[34] youtube.com/watch?v=n4RjJKxsamQ

[35] imdb.com/title/tt0090957

[36] youtube.com/watch?v=WQS2QK8-vBU

Throughout his career, he was constantly belittled and overlooked by more privileged colleagues, and even faced arrest and eight months of house arrest for allegedly insulting those associated with the Academy of Russian Science. Yet, through it all, he found sanctuary in science, holding on to something bigger than the inequities and insults he faced. Despite being undervalued by his compatriots, his legacy has prevailed, and he is widely regarded as a titan of Russian science.

Having goals that are bigger than one's life provides a sanctuary during difficult and stormy moments. It centers one's life when they lose their sense of direction and guides them back to what is important. More importantly, the direction is chosen by the individual themselves. Having goals not only makes one more confident, but also more appealing to others. People are attracted to those who they view as successful or on their way to success. While success is a vague definition, determination and following one's calling are the keys to achieving it. Those on the path to success must know their path and at least have an idea of what they want in life. This is also reflected in psychology research of attractiveness. According to the article in "Society for Personality and Social Psychology"[37] (Murphy et al., n.d.), one of the features that people find attractive in their potential partners is having confidence in themselves and having figured out what they want in life. We all strive to minimize uncertainty in our lives and are naturally drawn to those who have achieved it. By having clear goals and a plan to achieve them, we can inspire others and create a meaningful impact. Finding a partner who inspires us and is inspired by us is a significant factor in attractiveness. While factors such as luck and physical attractiveness may be beyond our control, having a life vision and setting a path to achieve it is within our power.

This desire for certainty and success has made its way into modern social media, where the phrase "living your best life" is commonly used. Psychological exercises, such as "life crafting," have been developed to help individuals find their direction in life[38] (Schippers & Ziegler, n.d.). It is clear that the desire to find one's path is a well-known and established factor in our lives. However, can pleasure have a meaning in itself?

The answer to this question is not straightforward and depends on the circumstances of our lives. Hedonism, which states that our actions aim to increase pleasure and avoid pain, is generally true. Pleasurable actions are associated with activities that are beneficial to our lives, such as eating nutritious food for energy. Pain serves as a warning sign that our body is threatened by disease or infection. Procreation is pleasurable and essential to species reproduction. Therefore, it is easy to infer that most pleasurable things are good for us, and by seeking pleasure, we will find meaning in our lives.

---

[37] journals.sagepub.com/0146167215588754

[38] ncbi.nlm.nih.gov/pmc/articles/PMC6923189/

However, there are many things in life that are not pleasurable or even beneficial to us but still fill our lives with meaning. Giving birth is a perfect example. It is a painful and often dangerous process, but necessary for the survival of humanity. In medieval times, without modern medicine, one in 16 to 20 women would die during childbirth[39] (Podd, 2020). Thus, it is an oversimplification to claim that pleasure is always accompanied by meaning. For example, raising children is not always pleasurable but is often filled with meaning and joy for parents. Pleasure is complementary to finding meaning, but it is not the same thing.

Maximizing pleasure does not lead to a meaningful life. The use of heavy drugs is a clear example of this. Although it may maximize pleasure, it can also lead to addiction and suffering for the individual and their family. Finding and fulfilling the meaning of our lives leads to a sense of achievement and eventual pleasure.

To maximize our impact, we need to choose a goal at the edge of our abilities, something we truly believe in and that brings us pleasure. However, achieving this goal may not bring pleasure in the short term, and the process of reaching it is often strenuous. The harder the goal, the more difficult the process of reaching it. For example, running a marathon is a grueling and painful process but brings a sense of achievement and pride upon completion. Our goals bring us pleasure when we accomplish them, but not necessarily during the process of reaching them. If we avoid hard work or difficult choices, we will not experience the final pleasure of achieving our goals.

The goals we choose in life are essential because they provide us with an anchor to weather difficult times, make us attractive to other goal achievers, and decrease uncertainty in our lives. These goals require and provide us with conviction that our chosen path is the right one, and faith in our abilities and determination to stay on this path to the end.

The goals we set have a significant impact and directly influence different spheres of our lives, which can be categorized into three primary areas: personal, interpersonal, and societal.

The personal sphere encompasses our individual growth, well-being, and potential. Once we are ready, we can expand our goals into the interpersonal sphere. The interpersonal sphere includes our relationships with family, friends, and colleagues. Our goals can inspire and motivate others, fostering deeper connections and a sense of belonging. Moreover, by collaborating on shared goals, we can create synergies that enhance the quality of our relationships and contribute to collective success. If our aspirations and ideas are powerful enough, they can even extend to the societal sphere and impact the broader community of the world at large.

---

[39] cambridge.org/reconsidering-maternal-mortality-in-medieval-england

This is why we should start with developing our own personal framework for discovering and fulfilling the meaning in our life.

Examples of Setting Up and Fulfilling Goals From My Life

The fundamental components of the meaning of our lives are our ideas. The formula we just discussed enables us to compare one idea to another and determine which one would have a lasting impact on other people. The more people we affect and the longer the impact endures, the more meaning we attain.

The pertinent question here is, where should our lives' focus lie? I've conceptualized life akin to a race with an unpredictable finish line, meaning that a referee could signal the end at any given moment. We cannot foresee the duration we have in this life or when the metaphorical whistle will sound.

Start by identifying the fundamental, most significant concept in your life. People often defer this step until they have secured a career or amassed sufficient wealth and time. While it may not be prudent to plunge right in, you can certainly commence preparations.

Once you choose a principal idea to act upon, it transitions into your goal. Subsequently, distinct paths will unfold for different individuals. Enforcing overly rigid guidelines for achieving life's meaning eliminates the liberty of choice. On the flip side, offering no direction at all renders any journey meaningless. The optimal strategy lies somewhere in-between, focusing on a vision rather than a precise route, while making minor adjustments along the way.

That's why this is not a rigid, rule-based recipe but rather a framework that assists you in choosing your path and, more importantly, maintaining your course. This methodology is not prescriptive, as there is no definitive, unique answer to the question. Instead, it offers a descriptive methodology of how to choose the set of goals that fits you best. This is how I transitioned from a purely theoretical formula for evaluating ideas to an actual practical path for implementing them.

The meaning of life, besides making your own choices, consists of several parts: consistency and purpose. First, I need to believe that the sequence of events in my life is not random, that there is a degree of control I can wield over my life's course, and that my life is somewhat consistent. Second, through the degree of control I have over my life, I can choose goals and make an impact by fulfilling them, thus achieving a purpose.

Given that the answer isn't prescriptive, the most effective way to elucidate my methodology is through the lens of my own life. I can only recount the choices I've made, hoping that these examples may serve others as useful guides.

Take, for example, my decision to chase my dream of becoming a physicist, which was my initial goal. This pursuit, although fraught with challenges and difficulties, always appealed to me. Since childhood, I've been captivated by the scientific world. While other kids fantasized about being astronauts or ballerinas, I yearned to become a professor. Science always felt close to my heart and bigger than myself. The legacies of numerous physicists, spanning from ancient philosophers to contemporary scientists, have inspired me through their groundbreaking discoveries and writings. As a child and teenager, I aspired to make my own contributions to the field of physics. When I came of age, this was precisely the path I embarked on.

Securing the second position in a Lithuanian national Olympiad opened several doors for me to pursue higher education. I had the opportunity to attend a university in Vilnius without any entrance examinations. However, during my Olympiad preparation, I stumbled upon a description of a far-off university in Moscow within one of my reference books, a book procured with great effort by my dear mother. This university resonated with my vision of an ideal scientific institution. My parents supported me during a visit to this university. Unlike in Lithuania, there were no personalized meetings with a dean there. Instead, a lengthy queue of fellow national Olympiad winners, resembling me in their aspirations, waited patiently. I was immediately drawn to this university and chose it without a second thought.

However, another decision was looming. I needed to select from nine faculties and as many majors. Two disciplines particularly intrigued me: astrophysics, which delves into the exploration of cosmic objects, and fundamental physics, which concentrates on the study of minute entities. This choice presented an exercise in selecting the right scale. Guided by the conviction that comprehending the smallest components would provide insights into all other elements' workings, I opted for fundamental physics. After all, even gigantic constructs like stars and galaxies consist of elementary particles and operate according to their interactions.

This choice of mine happened many years before I discovered the formula to help make choices, but we can use it here to evaluate and check if I made a correct choice. On the one hand, astrophysics offers the opportunity to study objects at massive scales, such as stars and galaxies, but these objects are extremely remote and inaccessible. On the other hand, physics studies minute objects that can be experimented with here on Earth. At the time, each major university had a department of astrophysics and particle physics, and today, the situation has not changed significantly. There are approximately similar numbers of particle physicists and astrophysicists.

A study of works by the top 25 physicists and astrophysicists[40] (Abt, 1996, 1-4), which produces about 2,000 papers per 25 years, found that they diverged in the number of citations. "Of 4,000 papers published in astronomy and in physics in the past 40 years, 40.3% and 23.4%, respectively, have not

---

[40] jstor.org/stable/26660630

been cited." However, this does not include final research papers. When included, the statistics quickly level off, and the difference disappears. But from the perspective of a fledgling scientist, the number of citations and papers determines your chances of obtaining a good position at a good university, which is the vitality and virility of a scientific career.

If we apply our formula from above given similar reach - p_i - particle physics had a larger weight, as designated by the number of citations. Regarding time operators, the longevity of physics and astrophysics papers, according to the same paper, measures approximately the same. In reality, my choice was mostly based on personal preference, but you can see how the formula could have been applied if I had it at the time of my decision.

A few years later (though a few chapters ago) I realized how important the scale is for the meaning of our life. If it is too large or too small, our life loses its meaning. It is a matter of finding a scale that is large enough for inspiration but not overwhelmingly so. This scale should propel you to seek goals that are not immediately within your reach, but would require personal growth and development. If your life hits a dark spot, you will have something to grasp onto that is larger than you and larger than the bad luck that befalls you. There is a degree of comfort in knowing that, despite anything that happens to you, there is always a lifetime of work towards your own goals that will remain untouched by bad luck. The goals should be of the right scale, not too large to become unachievable, and not too small to trivialize our life.

A few years later, I graduated from Fiztech, but just graduating from college seemed to be an insufficient goal for me. Instead, I wanted to be useful to other scientists, to create and publish scientific works that would outlive me, such as published papers with citations and references by other papers.

However, these were the turbulent 90s, when long-standing institutions, including those in the scientific field, were struggling. As a career in science became increasingly challenging, I witnessed a distressing scene—math and physics teachers selling their possessions at flea markets to scrape by. I found myself facing a pivotal decision: should I continue studying physics abroad, or should I join my friends in navigating the rough seas of the newly formed capitalist environment to establish a business? Ultimately, I chose to further my education, deciding to pursue my study of physics in New York.

During this period, I hatched a tentative plan: to devote at least a decade to physics and then, perhaps, shift my focus to personal life, family, and financial stability. When crafting long-term plans, I found it more beneficial to be flexible rather than rigid. After all, long-term plans require substantial time to materialize. A decade is a significant period, during which numerous changes can occur. Thus, it seems wise to maintain the overall direction but be prepared to make minor adjustments as needed.

Regarding the formula application, I divided the impact of my life into several parts, trying to achieve the most challenging tasks early on, when I was in my peak mental state, followed by goals that required life experience and resources. Instead of having a single goal, such as achieving excellence in science, I decided to have four consecutive goals:

1. Science
2. Family
3. Company
4. Book

I can rewrite and rearrange those goals into parts that are specific for my life and common for humanity:

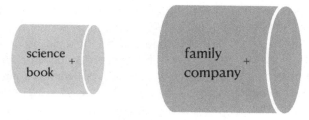

Fig. 3: Example of sets of goals

Or using simple math notation:

$$U_{specific} + U_{common} = (U_{science} + U_{book}) + (U_{family} + U_{company})$$

I've allocated the publishing of my research and this book to a specific part of the equation, as they represent thoughts and ideas unique to me. Had I not pursued my research or shared my ideas, these aspects of my life would have remained unseen. Conversely, having a family and, if not running a company then working for one, are experiences common to many people and involve the participation of others. Thus, these aspects belong to the shared portion of the equation. Still, without a family and work, life feels incomplete.

My calculation was that with each goal, I would peak and plateau in about 10 years, after which investing more years would bring diminishing returns if I only focused on one goal. By dividing my goals into four categories, I roughly doubled, if not tripled, my chances of at least one succeeding to make a truly lasting impact.

While I've shared examples from my life, it's important to acknowledge that many people may not have an interest in science but might be passionate about art, sports, or other pursuits. Some might choose to single-mindedly focus on one thing in their life, instead of juggling several goals. There are also those who are unsure of what their dream or purpose is.

If you don't have a primary idea or childhood dream, it doesn't mean you're out of options. There are always concepts and ideas central to your life. They may surface as hobbies or childhood dreams. Children yearning to become doctors or firefighters are showcasing an inherent desire to aid others, which they can channel into roles such as nursing or emergency services. Similarly, those dreaming of becoming actors may be seeking popularity, love, or a chance to embody diverse personas. Those who create beautiful artifacts are attracted to beauty and elegance and wish to share these attributes with others. Others may not want to have any goals at all, although not having any goal can paradoxically be considered a goal in itself.

However, for those seeking to give their lives meaning, the idea is to select a concept that resonates with you and nurture it. If you opt for nothing, nothing will flourish, since the meaning of your life is far from a given and we have to work hard for it.

Our plans are not set in stone but are the result of our choices. Once we choose our path, it's crucial to periodically and consistently reevaluate our direction to ensure we're still on the path we set out on. This should become a sort of a habit, as it's vital to keep us and our life centered and on track. Forming useful habits and rituals deserves its own section and we will come back to them in subsequent chapters.

This line of thinking is different from the concept of destiny and karma. Classical philosophers believed the meaning of life is global and independent of an individual's specifics, the likes of Aristotle's and Socrates' the Highest Forms of The Good. Modern philosophers like Hume and Mill believed the meaning of life was discovered through reason, faith, progress, and unalienated individual rights, known as "modernity." All these concepts are universal and discovered but not chosen.

In contrast to these philosophers, Nietzsche believed in rejecting traditional notions of morality, including the idea of assigning goals to human existence. Assigning goals to human life is a fundamental mistake that stems from a deep-seated belief in objective values and a teleological view of the universe. He argued there is no inherent purpose or meaning in human existence, and any attempt to impose one is an exercise in futility.

Instead, Nietzsche believed individuals should embrace their own desires and passions and live according to their own will to power. He argued that individuals should strive to create their own values, rather than accepting those imposed by society or tradition. He rejected the idea of assigned goals as part of his critique of traditional morality, which he saw as a tool for social control rather than genuine human flourishing. According to him, morality was based on arbitrary and oppressive standards of behavior, and true freedom could only be achieved by breaking free from these constraints and embracing one's own instincts and passions[41] (Martorano, 2019). My own point of view aligns closely with Nietzsche's, particularly for the reason that the scale of the meaning of life is too small to have any global or universal consequences.

---

[41] tapinto.net/towns/yorktown/articles/nietzsche-and-the-meaning-of-life

Once we choose our path, it becomes both steady and fluid, as we adapt to changing circumstances while remaining dedicated to our long-term goals. Our goals are the ideas that make an impact and affect others, and once we make our choice, it becomes our path.

Examples of life choices made by friends within my circle include bettering the lives of family or their community, discovering previously unknown objects, saving the environment, and leaving the planet in a better state than they found it. One friend wanted to teach people how to become leaders in conserving and preserving the environment, and spent years building a platform that now includes a podcast and several books. Another friend opened the first reusable packaging grocery store to reduce plastic waste. These friends made choices for their ideas, and these choices gave their lives purpose. Both of my friends reluctantly became preachers of their own thinking, attracting and educating others on how to embrace their ways.

My own childhood dream of being a scientist grew into a goal of publishing research papers in scientific journals, but my personality trait of not being able to focus on just one thing led me to pursue a set of several goals. I believed it was logical to increase my chances of success by choosing multiple goals. In addition to expanding and developing my scientific ideas, I also desired to start a family and continue my bloodline. The desire to have children grew as my fear of dying without leaving a legacy intensified. This motivation led me to transition from science to financial IT, where I could achieve financial stability and pursue my next goal of starting a family.

In the past, having offspring often served as the sole purpose of fulfilling one's life. This was especially important for lords and kings in ancient principalities and kingdoms, whose social stability depended on a clear line of succession. It was a widespread tradition to continue and care for your bloodline. However, from an evolutionary standpoint, with sexual reproduction, only 50% of your genes are randomly passed to your offspring through meiosis and fertilization. This means that only half of your traits are passed down to your children[42] (Gowaty, n.d.). To pass on 90% of your genes, you would need to have at least three children, and more than four children to pass on 95% of your genes. Furthermore, your grandchildren will only inherit 25% of your genes, and your great-grandchildren only 6.25%. Therefore, solely focusing on the continuation of your bloodline doesn't make sense in terms of leaving a genetic legacy. However, legacy has many dimensions beyond genetics. This was my primary logic in investing in four separate goals, including leaving a footprint in the world of business.

Raising children is a monumental task, one that deserves its own book. However, in the context of this book, I want to emphasize that while I have experienced my fair share of sleepless and stressful nights, I am forever grateful that my wife has taken on the lion's share of the responsibility. Having a family can be enough to give your life meaning, but it is certainly not an

---

[42] https://en.wikipedia.org/wiki/Sexual_reproduction

easy journey. It requires hard work, respect for your partner, and above all, love. The rewards, however, are immeasurable - love, respect, and happiness in return.

Parents of grown children often say that the most difficult moments of raising children often fade from memory, and only the most rewarding and fond memories remain. While the number of problems and worries may increase as children grow older, good memories last a lifetime. Raising children is a complex and nuanced topic that deserves its own dedicated discussion. I encourage readers to seek out additional resources that explore the joys and challenges of parenthood in greater detail. While I may consider writing a book on the subject in the future, I will switch the focus to other goals.

I would like to reiterate that these stories serve as examples of the potential goals we may set for ourselves. Another friend of mine from Columbia University chose to remain in academia, resisting the allure of Wall Street's gold rush, and is now a professor of quantum physics at a major university. This exemplifies the idea of committing to one field you excel in.

The primary goal does not necessarily have to be the only goal, and many people choose multiple equally important goals. One reason for this is that having several goals avoids putting all of one's eggs in one basket. By diversifying one's path, one can ensure that one won't extend all of one's energy on just one idea and can hedge against failing in one or a few of the goals.

My next goal was to start my own business. After spending a decade on Wall Street, amidst a zero-sum game mentality, where everybody's gain is considered my loss, I yearned to create a tangible, actually useful product that one could purchase from a brick-and-mortar store and physically hold in your hands. That product happened to be a "baby-monitor", a product to be used by parents in order to know that their babies are safe. I will talk about the experience of building a company from the ground up in the subsequent chapters but I want to say one thing here. Growing a successful business is an incredibly difficult task, but our life experiences often help in finding new ideas and knowing how to implement them.

My business idea came to me after the birth of my first son. One night, as I was tucking him into bed, I was troubled by how unsettlingly quiet he was. Babies have this uncanny ability to lie incredibly still. I panicked and tried to catch his near-inaudible breath, I inadvertently woke him up, causing everybody else to wake to my utter frustration. Right at that moment I realized the necessity of a more refined engineering solution to ensure a child's safety and wellbeing. Thus was born the idea which eventually materialized into a successful product, selling to several hundred thousand children globally. However, the road to this accomplishment was far from smooth. Yet, if it weren't for my family and the experience of cradling my first-born, I may never have conceptualized the baby monitor, nor embarked on this entrepreneurial journey.

This does not mean that you have to follow my train of thought and my goals. If a person is able to focus better on one thing, they could choose just one goal and spend all their effort on succeeding in that one thing. This is actually a preferred way to find your calling in life and focus on it. We know that we have found our calling in life if we are exceptionally good at it. For the lucky few who find their calling, such as Michael Phelps swimming faster than anyone else on the planet, Terrence Tao solving partial differential equations for finding prime numbers better than any other mathematician, Magnus Carlsen being a world champion in chess for the third time, or my friend who is one of the best experts in condense physics, it makes no sense to focus on any other goals.

However, there is also a danger in mixing being the best at something with finding your meaning in life. We can be good at something that does not impact or affect other people. For example, if a savant from the classic movie "Rain Man" was only good at counting matches on a floor, and nothing else, this skill would have been meaningless without impact on his brother Charlie. He was also good at counting cards, but being the only family for his brother was probably more important at making his life meaningful.

If there's one particular skill or passion that you excel at and can feasibly transform into a career or business, then the decision becomes straightforward—you should concentrate on that unique strength. Modern career paths often reward those who specialize, those who become experts within a specific field. The value of a niche specialist often surpasses that of a jack-of-all-trades, yet a master of none. With that in mind, it is advisable to approach the selection of your career path with meticulous care.

Once chosen, deviating from a well-established path becomes increasingly challenging with each passing year. If you find yourself in a job that you despise from the outset—even if it provides a comfortable income—it's likely that you'll be spending most of your waking hours in dissatisfaction, possibly for years. Hence, if you decide to hone in on a single area, ensure that it's something that holds personal significance for you. The endeavor should be one that resonates deeply with you, ultimately contributing to the meaningful direction of your life.

If we are good at something but not the best at it, it would make sense to explore other fields and directions, to venture into several careers and to focus on several achievements. By making several goals, we can ensure that if we fail in any of those, we can still continue to the next, with valuable lessons learned on the way.

The framework I have used for myself consists of the following steps:

- Choose a primary idea central to your life (for me, it was to publish scientific papers in reputable science journals).
- Optionally choose supplementary goals.

- Develop a strategy for executing your goal, establishing a realistic timeline. It is crucial to thoughtfully consider the duration of your plan, as it can significantly impact the outcome. If the time frame is too brief, you may inadvertently rush the process or fail to invest sufficient effort. On the other hand, an excessively lengthy time frame could lead to becoming trapped in a project destined for failure. Based on my experience, a minimum of 10 years was required to build something substantial and impactful.

At the end of the time frame, evaluate your accomplishments and move on to the next goal.

Hopefully, in the end, you will have a few accomplishments that you made by your own choice and that were deemed important to your principles. These accomplishments will affect the people around you and will solidify your impact that leaves after your life, in essence, your legacy.

To take my life as an example, I identified four goals, giving each one a decade:

1. To publish scientific works.
2. To have children.
3. To create a business.
4. To publish a book with all that I have learned in previous decades.

At the end of each goal, I would reexamine my direction and see if I needed to make modifications to the implementation details.

For example, when I wanted to write a book, I had no idea what I would be writing about as it was too far in the future. I just hoped that I would live a full and eventful life and would accumulate all sorts of ideas that would yield well to be published as a book. So I wanted to become a writer in the second half of my life. I was sure that if I focused on accomplishing my goals, I would gain enough knowledge and live a life full of experiences, and in a few decades, I would have enough topics to write about. As I got older, I got better and better ideas of what I would be writing about. This book is, in essence, a fulfillment of my fourth and last goal.

Even when you focus on several goals, it is important to focus on just one goal at a time. It is already hard to achieve difficult goals, and with the rest of personal and family obligations, it becomes nearly impossible to juggle more than one task. When the task becomes too hard, your will to carry on grows weaker.

That is another important principle: pick a goal just on the edge of your abilities. In day-to-day vocabulary, it is called challenging yourself, living your best life, or living your life to the fullest. This is again a matter of finding the right scale for your goals. If the goal is too difficult or large, it takes more time and energy to accomplish it. The bigger the scope, the longer time it takes, until the chances to accomplish it within your lifetime become impossible.

On the other hand, if a goal is too small or trivial, it may not result in a significant sense of accomplishment or contribute to a deeper meaning in life. Minor tasks tend to have limited impact and may fade quickly in their relevance or influence.

Indeed, there are no definitive "right" or "wrong" goals, at least not in the sense that we could know in advance which goals are right or wrong, which is why I employ these terms in quotation marks. Instead, individuals select their own objectives, and they instill meaning in their lives by striving towards these goals and influencing others. Only time will reveal which goals have prospered and whose impact has amplified, and which ones have fizzled out. There will be goals that we will fail to achieve and those that could tarnish our legacy, but we won't be able to foresee this in advance. Not until we traverse the journey to fulfill them.

This notion also extends to those who live without specific goals. Not everyone discovers their calling early in life. Our grandparents and people facing hardships did not always have the luxury of contemplating their purpose. A meaningful life is not guaranteed for everyone, but that does not mean that we need not aspire to try and leave the most impact we can achieve within the confines of our lives.

For those who desire a goal and meaning in their lives but remain uncertain about their direction, finding answers may be challenging. While I cannot provide a universal solution, I can share insights from my own experiences and the formula I have developed for deriving meaning from life, as if I am giving advice to my younger self.

Advice to My Younger Self

During my early college years, I grappled with questions about my life's direction and the meaning embedded in the struggles I confronted. I longed for guidance and someone to answer all of my questions. Looking back, I imagine my younger and older selves having a conversation. If I could counsel my younger self, my advice would be as follows:

Our senses and our conscience are the most intimate instruments we will ever have. We don't really have the option to pick and choose our intelligence or charm from a list of alternatives. We only have ourselves. This realization implies that we must learn to appreciate and care for ourselves. Without prioritizing our mental health and self-care, we cannot hope to attain our goals or build a satisfying life. It takes effort to create and we must focus on the perfection of our achievements.

Second, time is our most valuable resource. In the beginning of our lives, time seems infinite and we often wish it would move faster. However, time is a harsh judge and the ultimate arbiter of our choices. When embarking on a journey, whether it be education, career, or marriage, we do not know what the future holds. Only time will tell if we made the right choices.

Third, the meaning of life is not something we discover, but rather something we choose to give our lives purpose. We must choose something that will make our lives unique and meaningful. Do not despair if you have not yet found your purpose. If there a will there will always be time for it.

Next, in order to make a good choice, we must take a momentary pause in our busy lives and carefully examine our priorities. We all have something that defines us and captures our imagination. It is important to choose something that will leave a lasting impact on others while also representing our uniqueness. Although it is tempting to rush into action, taking time for reflection is crucial in charting a thoughtful path for a long-term journey.

I strongly believe that it is important to make our own choices, even if they lead to mistakes. While we may follow the advice of our parents and teachers to avoid obvious pitfalls, there will come a time when we must navigate uncharted territory. The only way to know the right path is to move forward, make our own mistakes, and learn from them. If we must make mistakes, it is better to pay for our own actions rather than someone else's.

This is similar to what Friedrich Nietzsche was stating in "the Parable of the Madman" where he dared us to be ourselves, to overcome ourselves and to make our own choices, not the choices enforced onto our lives by religious or secular institutions. Here is what the madman was saying: "Must we not ourselves become gods simply to be worthy of it? There has never been a greater deed; and whosoever shall be born after us - for the sake of this deed he shall be part of a higher history than all history hitherto"[43].

I acknowledge the irony and contradiction in advising my younger self to make their own choices while also giving them advice. However, when considering the entirety of life, this is not a contradiction. Seeking guidance and help in the beginning does not contradict the later goal of making our own choices. It is better to learn from the mistakes of others and seek advice early on, rather than making a lot of mistakes and following someone else's recipes later on.

Some argue that we lack the experience and knowledge to make the right choices and should rely on experts, mentors, and leaders. However, history has shown that even the most experienced and knowledgeable individuals make mistakes. Many world leaders and role models have made statements or taken actions that, in modern times, are deemed unacceptable or questionable. Time is the best judge of the choices we make.

For example, Thomas Jefferson, one of the founding fathers of the United States, was against interracial marriage. Winston Churchill, former Prime Minister of the United Kingdom, advocated for the use of poison gas against Kurdish rebels in Iraq. Gandhi, revered for his movement for truth and

---

[43] age-of-the-sage.org/philosophy/friedrich_nietzsche_quotes.html

nonviolent resistance, also had controversial views on race and sex. Even Charles Darwin, the father of evolution, has been criticized for his views on race.

I believe that it is better to pay for our own mistakes rather than someone else's. Prince Yuriy of Ryazan', who chose not to surrender to the invading Mongol horde and pay taxes doomed his own kingdom to an annihilation. Every citizen of this city paid with their lives and the lives of their children for his decision. It is important to make our own choices and not be afraid of making mistakes. Paying for our own mistakes is a consequence of making our own choices, and it is through our mistakes and actions that we create the meaning for our lives.

Although we may not know in advance which choices will be successful in creating permanent effects, learning from our mistakes and making minor corrections or major changes to our life path is key. It is important to seek guidance early on, learn from the mistakes of others, make our own choices, and be willing to pay for our own mistakes.

My formula provides guidance on how to choose our goals, but it is not a prescription. We should aim to choose goals that will impact the maximum number of people and have a lasting effect, but there is no guarantee of success. It is nearly impossible to predict the outcome of our efforts with perfect accuracy. We can only hope that we have chosen the right goals and that we will succeed in achieving them.

I also think that merely choosing goals is not enough on its own; we must also possess the willpower and energy to see them through to completion. It is crucial to choose goals that challenge us and push us to the edge of our abilities, maximizing their impact. This is not just about working harder and achieving as much as possible but also about fulfilling the formula for the meaning of life. By choosing goals that push us to our limits, we maximize the number of people affected by our efforts.

As a result, the goals we choose may be difficult to achieve through our own efforts alone. We will need to maintain focus and motivation to fulfill them. Therefore, it is better to choose goals that we enjoy and believe in. In the words of Carlos Castaneda[44] (Castaneda, 1968):

"Look at every path closely and deliberately. Try it as many times as you think necessary. Then ask yourself, and yourself alone, one question. This question is one that only a very old man asks. My benefactor told me about it once when I was young, and my blood was too vigorous for me to understand it. Now I do understand it. I will tell you what it is: Does this path have a heart?"

and
"For me there is only the traveling on the paths that

---

[44] en.wikipedia.org/wiki/The_Teachings_of_Don_Juan

have a heart, on any path that may have a heart.
There I travel, and the only worthwhile challenge
for me is to traverse its full length. "

This quote emphasizes that we should choose a path that aligns with our values and resonates with our heart. When we pursue our goals with passion, our determination can become infectious, stirring admiration and sparking motivation among those close to us. They may even feel inspired to rally around our cause, thus, amplifying our endeavors and marking a stride towards our definition of success.

However, achieving substantial milestones in our lives is rarely a solitary endeavor. Our journey is shaped and supported by a network of relationships, a supportive cast of characters that collectively contribute to our story. Friends and family, often the primary cheerleaders in our lives, provide emotional sustenance and encourage us to persist even in the face of adversities.

Our partners, sharing our burdens and joys alike, offer a unique perspective and complement our abilities, making our shared goals more attainable. Mentors, with their wisdom and experience, guide us in navigating complexities, offering invaluable insights that help us avoid potential pitfalls and capitalize on opportunities. Benefactors or supporters, too, play a pivotal role by believing in our ideas and trusting our potential, they provide necessary resources, be it time, finances, or connections.

It is very important to realize that success does not come in isolation. It is important to invest your time in finding partners, mentors and benefactors. This investment will make our journeys toward accomplishing our goals much easier and more likely to succeed. So, while it's crucial to pursue a path that aligns with our individual passions and values, it's equally important to ask for help and appreciate all those who contribute.

Indeed, the full impact of a goal or a pursuit is often only discernible once the ripples of its effects have settled and disseminated widely. Creating a lasting, positive legacy can indeed be a complex endeavor, as the true measure of its success often reveals itself long after the actions have been taken, and perhaps even after we are no longer present to witness it.

Consider the life of the renowned painter Vincent Van Gogh as an example of late success. Van Gogh struggled with mental health issues throughout his life, and his artwork was largely overlooked and unappreciated during his lifetime. He lived in poverty, and was virtually unknown as an artist. However, he was intensely passionate about his art, and he poured his soul into every piece he created.

Long after his death, Van Gogh's art started to receive the recognition it deserved. His distinctive style, characterized by bold colors and dramatic, impulsive brushwork, had a profound impact on 20th-century art. Today, his works are celebrated for their emotional honesty and innovative use of color and form, and he is regarded as one of the greatest painters in history. His paintings sell for millions and are displayed in the most prestigious museums around the world. In this sense, Van Gogh's true legacy wasn't apparent during his lifetime, but rather, it emerged posthumously, cementing his place as an influential figure in the history of Western art.

This underscores the importance of adhering to one's life's calling and maintaining faith in the chosen path. Persistence and tenacity are equally critical. Regularly altering our direction based on fleeting trends can deter us from establishing a unique identity and consequently, a unique legacy. Luck may favor us occasionally, but if we fail to see our endeavors through to completion, we risk wasting our time and our life.

In this respect, our choices echo nature's method of adapting to an ever-changing environment. Evolutionary biology shows us how random mutations forge divergent paths for organisms. Successful divergents endure, while the unsuccessful ones die out. If divergence is absent, the entire species becomes vulnerable to environmental shifts.

However, unlike nature, humans possess a conscious mind that empowers us to learn from our mistakes and make more informed choices. Yet, the freedom to choose comes with the risk of making erroneous decisions. That's why it's crucial to acknowledge our good fortune when it presents itself and seize the opportunities it affords.

The worst course of action, however, is to avoid making any choices at all. By default, this approach ensures a life that gradually fades into insignificance. Consequently, we must muster the courage to make choices, learn from them, and persist, as this is the path that leads to a life of substance and potential legacy.

As we increase the scale and scope of our ambitions and achievements, the sphere of our impact also grows, along with the difficulty of accomplishing it. Perhaps it is the time to talk about the circles of our influence, within humanity and beyond.

Circles of Impact

Humanity's knowledge advances in concentric circles. When describing the scope of our actions and influence I would like to start with the example of science and how science knowledge evolves over time.

Science consistently moves outward, with theorists using mathematical tools to analyze and observe nature, uncovering new patterns and relationships between phenomena, some of which were previously hidden. Experimental scientists then conduct experiments to confirm or deny the statements made by theorists. When experimentalists discover a discrepancy, it usually indicates that there is a new science beyond existing theories and that existing and accepted theories require correction. At this point, theorists work out possible corrections to formulate new hypotheses, eventually agreeing on one acceptable correction.

In this model, modern science can be seen as concentric circles, with old core theories, such as classical mechanics from past centuries, at the center. As scientists explore beyond our sensory horizon, extending into micro scales of elementary particles and macro scales of constellations and galaxies, they draw more outward circles that augment but never contradict inner circles. Science is a moving but consistent discipline of growing concentric circles of influence.

At the center of this model lies the core of classical mechanics, including Newton's laws of motion, the law of gravity, and other fundamental principles. As we move outward from this core, we encounter circles that encompass more complex theories, such as thermodynamics, quantum mechanics, and relativity. These circles are further expanded by the discoveries of modern science, including particle physics, string theory, and cosmology.

This model of circles of influence allows us to understand how the various theories of science are interconnected and how they build upon each other. As we move outward from the core, we can see how each new circle of knowledge is based on the principles of the inner circles. This enables us to understand how modern science is built upon the foundations of classical mechanics and other core theories.

Each theory is a model of reality, with inner circles accurately describing reality up to the boundary of the circle. For example, classical thermodynamics accurately describes the laws of behavior on a macro level in terms of measurable properties such as temperature, pressure, and volume. However, when we move to a microscopic level of massive sets of particles, it steps out of its boundaries, and we require a new theory, such as statistical thermodynamics. Typically, each model describes observed effects at the scales reachable with the level of technology suitable for the times when that model was developed. With time, new technologies and sensors allow us to see deeper and further beyond accustomed circles, discovering new properties of reality that no longer fit any of the old models. The old model no longer describes new data and new facts, but within its own confines, within its own circle, the old model accurately describes reality. From this perspective, new science does not invalidate old science but rather complements it with new knowledge.

When corrections happen, old core theories are not simply declared false. This is a common misconception that science is continuously changing its mind. In fact, old paradigms stay valid within the boundaries they have established. For instance, quantum mechanics does not invalidate classical mechanics, and general relativity does not invalidate Newtonian mechanics. It is not that new modern theories replace the old ones. Rather, humanity extends the boundaries of observed natural phenomena.

In a similar way, when we set a goal and work to implement it, we make an impact on the people in the immediate circle of our reach. For most people, our life achievements are like expanding circles of influence. The inner circle is our upbringing by parents and family. We have immediate effects on our dependents and close relatives with every paycheck, missed or completed homework, home renovations and family vacations.

The next circle is our education and self improvement where we meet our friends and colleagues. From there, we can draw our own circles even further. We may start with a job, move on to starting our own business, or creating a charity or organization. As we continue to grow and expand our impact, we may become involved in politics, become an advocate for a cause, or become a mentor to others. Ultimately, our life achievements are the result of the choices we make and the actions we take to make a difference in the world.

Some people may choose to start working on a new goal from scratch. While starting a new goal can be a great way to break out of a rut and gain clarity, constantly doing so would undo any progress made in achieving previous goals and lead back to square one.

Personally, I chose to build out and expand on my previous achievements. My common theme in the center of my circles was a desire to publish my stories and ideas, starting with scientific papers, and expanding to my family, business, and now this book. For you, the reader, it may be a completely different choice, such as building a bigger family or working on your career. The point is that it is simpler to work on a purpose by building on our experience and life lessons and expanding our circles of influence than starting from scratch every time. Here I would like to start with the innermost circle that is closest to my core values and progress from it.

I believe it is a mistake to begin in the opposite direction, ignoring all the inner circles and starting with the biggest circle of influence, as a shortest way to achieve your goals. History shows that incremental gains are a much more stable way to achieve progress rather than revolutions and sudden and abrupt changes. Examples include an Industrial Revolution (1760 - 1840), US Civil Rights Movement (1954 - 1968) and Evolution of the European Union (1950 - Present). The civil rights movement was a decades-long fight to end racial discrimination and secure legal rights for minorities in the United States and it was marked by gradual, steady gains. The European Union's formation offers an example of incremental political and economic integration. Most importantly, the Industrial Revolution wasn't an abrupt event, as it is frequently and mistakenly described, but a series of incremental technological and socio economic advancements spread over several decades. The gradual development and integration of innovations such as steam power, the spinning jenny, and rail transport into the economy led to massive improvements in productivity, living standards, and societal organization. While it was indeed disruptive, it's considered one of the most significant periods of human history precisely because the changes were incremental, allowing societies to adapt and stabilize over time.

It is only natural for people to move in gradual circles. As we discussed in the chapter about the scale, the largest scale we perceive is the scale of the universe, where we cannot make any impact or difference. We can only make an impact on the scale comparable to our life, within the vicinity of our circles of influence. While it is important to reflect on our lives and prepare for the next goal, this time is not a goal in itself, but a stepping stone to the next circle.

That is my conviction that we must focus on the innermost circle of our conscience. We are our most powerful resource and most important tool. Although imperfect, it is all we have. Just like any tool, we need to learn how to use and love ourselves. Our ability to achieve any goal depends on perfecting this first tool at our disposal: ourselves. If we move outward without loving and preparing ourselves, our chances of success in the next circle will be reduced.

The interpersonal circle is a crucial circle for personal growth and development. It is within this circle that we have the opportunity to test our ideas, gain inspiration, and ask for help. Our friends, colleagues, and family are the people who can provide us with constructive feedback and support as we pursue our goals. They can help us to refine our ideas and provide us with a sounding board for new ideas.

Our interactions within the interpersonal circle can either amplify or break apart our goals, ideas, and actions. When we have the support of our inner circle, it can give us the confidence and encouragement we need to pursue our dreams. However, if we do not have the support of our inner circle, it can create a sense of doubt and uncertainty, making it harder for us to move forward.

It is essential to nurture our relationships within the interpersonal circle to ensure that we have a solid foundation of support as we pursue our goals. We should be mindful of the needs of our loved ones and make time for them, even as we pursue our own ambitions. When we have a strong support system, we are better equipped to face the challenges and obstacles that come with pursuing our dreams.

Moving outwards, we reach the circle of humanity. This is where our ideas and actions take place and compete with the rest. This circle encompasses our interactions with the broader world, including our work, our community, and our society at large. It is within this circle that we hope to make a meaningful impact and contribute to the greater good.

Our success in each of the outer circles depends on the foundation we have built within the interpersonal circle. When we have a strong network of support and have honed our skills and talents within our inner circle, we are better equipped to navigate the challenges of the outer circle. We can draw on the lessons we have learned from our interactions with our loved ones and colleagues to navigate the complexities of the broader world.

However, the outer circle also presents its own unique challenges. We must contend with competition, conflict, and the sheer scale of the world around us. It is essential to approach this circle with a clear sense of purpose and a willingness to learn and adapt. We must also be mindful of the impact our actions have on others and strive to make a positive contribution to the world around us.

Ultimately, the circles of influence are interconnected, with each circle building upon the other. By nurturing our relationships within the interpersonal circle and pursuing our goals with purpose and intention in the outer circle, we can make a meaningful impact on the world and create a life of purpose and fulfillment.

Humility is key when it comes to understanding our place within increasingly large scopes of influence. It's relatively easy to become the best in a class of fewer than 20 students, or to excel in one of the numerous disciplines taught at school. The challenge intensifies when competing against an entire school, and reaching the top spot in a citywide contest can prove truly demanding.

However, such challenges should not deter us from pushing our boundaries and striving to be the best within a sphere that extends just a fraction beyond our current abilities. At the same time, it's vital to remain humble when considering the vast expanse of larger scopes. Acknowledging our small yet significant place within these broader circles can keep us grounded, encourage us to continuously learn and grow, and inspire us to make meaningful contributions, however small they may seem in the grand scheme of things.

The outer circles of our influence and reach disappear when we reach the technological capabilities of our civilization. We can see our family in the house, the house in the city, travel around the country and around the globe. A few can travel in space, but beyond that, we can only hear about space probes crossing into the far reaches of our solar system through the news. We can observe our galaxy, the Milky Way, in the night sky and trust scientists to know that there are other galaxies and galaxy constellations far away. At the other end, we can see microorganisms in school microscopes, get sick with flu from viruses, and learn about atoms from screens powered by even tinier electrons. At some point, humanity's reach reaches the horizon of our comprehension and influence. We can only look that far or that close. We can comprehend our Sun and atoms, but we cannot influence both micro and macro scales beyond certain horizons. This does not mean the circles stop at where we stop seeing them. Most likely, they continue forever outward and inward. However, we can only comprehend and influence our immediate surroundings.

Therefore, it is wise to start small and work our way up when pursuing our goals. We should focus on the things we can control and influence and build from there. This will help us create a solid foundation for fulfilling our dreams. We must also be mindful of our resources, especially our time, our most valuable resource. This will ensure that we make the most of our efforts and take the right steps towards achieving our goals.

We rely on the existence of broader circles around us. Without them, our growth remains stunted. If we lack a family, our influence diminishes. Absent scientific media, we are left without platforms like scientific journals to disseminate our research. Without theaters, we're bereft of stages on which to perform. And without humanity, we're missing the canvas upon which we illustrate our lives.

The innermost circle, composed of our individual self, serves as our most vital resource. It forms the foundation from which we sculpt our lives and chase our aspirations. Yet, it is within the vast outer circle of humanity that we find the chance to create enduring change and leave a tangible legacy.

Our distinctive ideas and actions, those that touch the lives of many, echo among people until they become part of the grander circle of humanity. In contrast, what is common to all humans has no more room to proliferate any further. Take, for instance, when Edison presented his version of a light bulb. Despite the presence of other inventors and rivals, his design prevailed due to its superior efficiency and economic feasibility, leading to its wide adoption across humanity. In today's context, however, innovating a superior light bulb is far more challenging, given this invention has already seeped into humanity's collective consciousness.

I believe that it is crucial to differentiate between common and unique ideas, or as I called them "perma-impacts". Therefore it is important to incorporate this distinction into our formula.

Splitting Formula into Personal and Common Parts

As I was maturing and moving through life, I added to my understanding of the world and kept discovering new properties and ingredients for the meaning of life. This required periodic subtle adjustments to the formula. One change that I had to incorporate was the distinction between our personal impact and the impact of entire humanity.

The best way to preserve our personal meaning and humanity's entire knowledge, as Jeff Hawkins has suggested, is to preserve humanity itself, even if it means changing its form. I had to split the formula into two parts: common and specific.

Yuval Harari in his book "A Brief History of Humankind"[45] (Harari, 2015) considers human civilization not only as a population of humans but also the accompanying animals, pets, and domesticated animals. In the future, if we create artificial intelligence that develops sentience and becomes self-aware, we will have to include those sentient beings in the fold of humanity. The entire structure of our civilization comprises not just humans, but all beings affected by human civilization, including pets, animals, and artificial beings. Our actions will, in turn, influence this entire structure.

The specific term in this context refers to the distinctive set of traits, tendencies, and behaviors that make an individual unique and distinguish them from others within the wider population. These characteristics can

---

[45] en.wikipedia.org/wiki/Sapiens:_A_Brief_History_of_Humankind

encompass aspects such as an individual's unique combination of features, such as problem-solving skills, imagination and sense of humor. While each of these traits might be found in other people, it is the specific combination of these features that sets an individual apart.

On the other hand, common terms represent the shared ideas, choices, habits, and cultural norms that are prevalent among humans across various populations and cultures. These elements may contribute to an individual's self-perception and identity, but they are not exclusive to that person. Common terms may encompass widely accepted beliefs, values, and customs that shape human behavior and experiences.

In essence, the specific term highlights the uniqueness of an individual's traits and actions, while the common terms emphasize shared aspects of human behavior and experiences that connect individuals across diverse populations and cultures.

Unique traits and characteristics often disappear with the individual unless they prove to be beneficial or appealing to others. When this occurs, people may begin adopting and sharing these traits and ideas, allowing them to become a part of the common collective. The persistence or disappearance of common traits and behaviors is largely determined by evolutionary and cultural dynamics that exist beyond an individual's control and do not depend on their personal actions. In other words the common term does not depend on our own actions or the direction of life we choose.

By its nature, a specific term will be much smaller numerically than the common term. However, it would be a mistake to disregard or minimize its importance. Within the specific traits and idiosyncrasies of individuals lie the potential for adaptations that could benefit or even save the entire population from extinction. Among these countless peculiarities, there may be the next technological breakthrough, a cure for an impending pandemic, or a recipe for an extraordinary dish. Embracing and nurturing these specific traits can lead to innovation, progress, and the betterment of society as a whole.

To gain a deeper understanding of these concepts, we can turn to evolutionary biology. Here, the notions of "specific genotype" and "common genotype" offer different methods of categorizing an organism's genetic composition within a population. A specific genotype is the unique combination of alleles (gene variants) an individual organism inherits from its parents, whereas a common genotype refers to a set of genotypes frequently observed within a population. Natural selection favors certain traits that enhance an organism's survival and reproduction prospects, thus allowing successful "specific" genotypes to proliferate within populations, eventually becoming "common."

The most natural way for our actions and ideas to transition from the personal realm to the common one is through the process of others adopting, sharing, and perpetuating them. This process can continue even after an individual's death, ensuring that their contributions have a lasting impact on the world. As other people integrate these ideas and actions into their lives, the originator's influence expands and their deeds continue to live on through others.

Redefining the personalized meaning in this context involves maximizing the impact of all the consequences that we can influence and control through our personal decisions and actions. This maximization takes into account the long-term effects our choices have on other people and projects those impacts into the distant future. By doing so, we acknowledge the potential for our actions and ideas to shape the course of human development and contribute to a collective legacy.

In this framework, the personalized meaning becomes a measure of an individual's ability to make a lasting and positive difference in the lives of others and in the world at large. This definition emphasizes the significance of our personal decisions and actions, while also recognizing the interconnectedness of human experiences and the enduring influence we can have on future generations.

This definition makes it easier to measure and analyze the personalized impact, often marked or attached to a person's name or action. For example, we know the contributions of scientific and artistic titans, like Newton or Einstein, whose names are attached to laws and formulas, like $E = mc^2$, by their names. When Einstein just derived his formula, it had a reach of just $1/N$ where 1 was only him, and N was the total population of people. In other words, it was pretty small. Nowadays almost everybody knows his formula and the reach of this idea is close to 1.

On the other hand, we recognize the enormous and permanent impact of the wheel, but the names of its original inventors were lost in time. This point is important as not just the magnitude of the impact matters. What makes a permanent effect is the attachment of the name to the action or the impact. The fire and wheel became synonymous with humanity attributes and the names of original inventors of those phenomena were lost in time.

Let's consider another, a much more personal example of the teacher who made a significant impact on my life. My physics teacher noticed and took a personal interest in my education, by giving me problems from the national olympiad and eventually giving me and another pupil a completely different curriculum.

The action of choosing a pupil or a student and trusting your instincts to give him or her extra hard questions, and pushing a bit harder, is a very specific action. It carries a risk of making a negative effect on a student, in which case student's ego and grades may suffer and in the worst case, this could also result in a negative effect on the career of the teacher, as the students' parents can complain and the school principal can punish a teacher. In this case, w_i, which is a measure of this action impact will become negative. The best outcome in this situation is that, hopefully, he will recover and forget that bad decision. If however the student would perform better and better and, as a result of this action, would get into a better school, w_i will turn positive and p_i, which is a measure of how far the actions are spread across other people, will increase.

This is exactly what happened when my teacher took a small risk to her career in order to scout for students who would perform well in the physics olympiad and in the process made a profound impact on my life. I performed well in that round and won first place in my city. It did not go without the incident and at first I was in third place. My teacher insisted on the audit by an independent agency, and after an audit done by the city commission, I was reassigned to first place. In those times one can actually buy the placement in the olympiad. My teacher continued her investment in me, sat me separately from the class and gave me a special curriculum to study over in high school. This curriculum was a preparation for the national olympiad. I got a subscription to a specialized magazine, I think it was called "Quant", with a completely new level of physics problems at a different scale of difficulty. I went on to win a silver medal in the national olympiad and it propelled me towards a career in physics.

Had she not taken a risk to request an audit and then made an extra effort to prepare me, I would not have gone to the national olympiad, would not have gone to study physics at the best universities of Moscow and New York City and would not end up doing high energy physics eventually at a Fermi national accelerator lab in the USA. The ripple effects of spirited and deliberate actions can outlive the starting point of the action, and the attachment of a name to the impact creates a lasting legacy.

Let me compare to another seemingly random action from my life. While studying with other students at Columbia University physics department, we used to constantly prank each other. One of the pranks that I recall was to take a snapshot of somebody's desktop image and copy this image into a "melting" screensaver. As a result it would look like the screen of your computer would start to melt down as if some virus or "worm" infected the computer, took over the screen and started to eat it from the inside. This prank became very popular among fellow students and was replicated dozens of times. A subject of this prank would react angrily or confused to the amusement of the other students in the known. In modern days it would have made a "reaction" YouTube video and won it a lot of "likes". This was a version of a lighthearted joke that, as many jokes of that kind, did not last long and was forgotten within a few months. The truth is I remembered it only because I was writing it as an example in this book. Despite its popularity, this prank did not create any lasting legacy.

The formula incorporates the effects of time on the impact of our actions through the time operator, represented by the expectation value. It indicates that the impacts we create with our choices can either dissipate over time or multiply through their effect on others, surviving and growing stronger. In practical terms, this means that we define the meaning of our lives by making a lasting impact on others through our decisions and actions.

But what does it mean to achieve a truly permanent impact, to attain the best possible outcome of our actions? And what should we anticipate when we fulfill the direction of our lives to their fullest extent?

To answer that question, consider that the formula has two parts, the part that is affected by our actions and a part that is common to all people. When we make our choices and create something with our actions it first appears as a part of the personal impact term, and as its impact spreads and makes it into the common to the entire mankind part, and becomes a bigger portion of it. The best outcome is to make it into the common portion of the equation and become part of humanity's cultural and scientific baggage.

Fig. 4: Merging of personal and common achievements

This is similar to some genetic changes that were so beneficial to entire living creatures that it became a part of the common genetic pool that we all share.

For instance, we, humans, all have mitochondria as a part of our cellular structure. Not just humans, all eukaryotic organisms which constitute about 50% of the entire earth's biome by collective biomass. Their function within cellular biology is complex but could be summarized as a cellular battery providing ATP molecules that serve as a source of chemical energy. Cellular organisms with mitochondria would have a great power advantage in speed and range of motions. They would get to the food source faster and escape predators and adverse elements faster than their counterparts without mitochondria. One of the theories of the origin of mitochondria is that they were results of symbiotic relationship between two separate organisms where one single cell organism was living inside the other, consuming byproducts of the cell but providing oxidized mechanisms that were not possible in the host cells. This relationship happened so often that portions of the single cell DNA got mixed with the host DNA and the host organisms could produce those structures on their own. This solution was so successful that it became a footprint of all eukaryotic organisms.

Similarly in human history there were many ideas and inventions that were so successful that they became part of human culture.

Early human societies were like live social experiments, each exploring its own version of a novel idea that set them apart from neighboring competitors. Some of these societies thrived so much that they grew into empires, ruling vast territories for centuries. Examples include the Assyrian Empire, known for its cruelty towards conquered neighbors, and the Inca

Empire, which grappled with the challenge of managing the very land that sustained them. Yet, not all ideas led to lasting success. Societies that chose poorly eventually perished, making way for others with different concepts. Each triumphant society or empire adopted the prevailing ideas of its time, which then became embedded in human culture. While we might take our current scientific and social structures for granted – be it the wheel, the rule of law, the printing press, education, or more modern discoveries like Newton's laws of physics and Einstein's theory of relativity – they stand on the foundations of bygone ideas and civilizations.

In essence the formula's right hand side represents the vitality of our lives' actions taken in perpetuity. The more people are affected by our actions and the longer the effects last, the bigger our lives' meaning. In extreme cases of affecting enough people, we can oppose mortality with our choices and actions. As Ernest Hemingway said: "Every man has two deaths, when he is buried in the ground and the last time someone says his name. In some ways men can be immortal". There is perhaps an even better quote that I particularly liked from a thought provoking 2016 TV Series, Westworld: "An old friend once told me something that gave me great comfort… He said Mozart, Beethoven and Chopin never died. They simply became music."

While we don't know who was the inventor of the wheel, both Einstein and Newton achieved a form of immortality. Their contribution moved from a personal portion of the equation to the common, carried by mankind. This also shows that it is important to attach our name to our achievements. Without the name our legacy will become the same as the inventors of the wheel, the anonymous benefactors of humanity. The name matters.

Remember the story of Gilgamesh we mentioned at the start of this book. This formula is a summary of a recipe as old as humanity, to leave behind the seeds of creations that will possibly live forever.

With the name attached to our legacy, our perma-impacts and actions get transferred from the specific part of the formula to the common part. The common side of the formula represents a footprint of our life in humanity. Essentially, the meaning of life is for us to transfer our impact from the left side of the formula to the right side for all of humanity.

Without the Future of Humanity our Lives are Meaningless

At this point in the book, we have arrived at a potential formula for answering the question of the direction of our individual lives and it may be tempting to stop here and consider this formula as the ultimate answer to the question of the direction in life. After all, we have established that creating a lasting impact on the lives of others is a key component of a meaningful life. But the truth is, our impact must be more than just temporary. It must be permanent, lasting as long as there are people to experience it.

In earlier chapters, I asserted that the meaning of our lives is a choice, though not an arbitrary one. The imperative to preserve humanity's future eliminates the randomness of this choice, directing us towards the survival of humankind.

In other words, the sum of our perma-impacts is assessed further by a time operator. Time ultimately decides what actions survive, and those actions survive in other people. Simply leaving an impact on a small circle of people is not enough. Our impact must last, ideally as long as humanity exists. Without humanity's presence in the future, without the survival of our actions and ideas, our own meaning would cease to exist and our legacy will disappear without a trace. Whatever meaning we choose—unless we decide to have no meaning at all, in which case any actions are meaningless—requires something to carry it through time. The medium for conveying our meaning is humanity itself. We may leave an imprint of our actions on humanity, but without humanity, this imprint will be erased by the passage of time. Any permanent meaning implies that humankind survives and will exist in the future.

Therefore, the primary focus of our formula for a meaningful life is leaving a permanent impact. This involves not just creating a lasting impact on a small group of individuals, but also ensuring that our impact has the potential to endure for generations to come.

The biggest threat to our meaning comes from humanity itself. If we stay fractured and keep fighting against each other, the chances that those conflicts and fights will eventually destroy us. The future of humanity requires that most, if not all, people work together in the same direction: the survival of humankind. Whatever meaning we choose, a portion of that meaning must contribute to the future of humanity.

We have established that the meaning of life has two components: a personal one and one that is common to all of humanity. While creating a lasting impact on the lives of others is an essential aspect of a meaningful life, our impact must also be permanent in order to truly leave a lasting legacy: $U = U_{personal} + U_{common}$. To leave a permanent impact, fulfill our goals and achieve a permanent footprint on humanity, we need to transfer our specific life impact from a term $U_{personal}$, to a common term U_{common}.

The first realization for me was understanding the most important resource in my life. It isn't money, self-esteem, or even self-education, although all of these are incredibly important. It's time. Without time, I wouldn't be able to spend money, earn respect, or acquire the necessary knowledge. Ricky Gervais, a contemporary comic, once shared this insightful quote: "You did not exist for about 14 billion years. You exist now & when you die you will not exist again. Forever. Enjoy your existing years"[46]. Time is our most limiting factor and most valuable resource, and how we spend our lives is the most important choice we have to make. This is the essence of the

---

[46] twitter.com/rickygervais/status/344426405897072640

concept of "memento mori" that started me on this journey: recognizing that we don't have unlimited time and that the time we do have should be spent on goals that are meaningful to us. This is why focusing on the meaning of your life can save you from wasting your most valuable resource on someone else's goals, whether they are dictated by society, esteemed leaders, or even forced by parents.

Reflecting upon the meaning of our lives, it becomes vital to acknowledge the potential enduring influence of our actions and ideas on subsequent generations. Our legacy hinges on the endurance of these ideas and actions, a testament to their longevity. Therefore, creating a lasting impression that can be perpetuated through stories, books, and the digital universe of the internet is essential.

However, history reminds us that the preservation of knowledge and ideas is not always a sure thing. Unfortunate occurrences like the catastrophic fire at the Library of Alexandria underscore this fact. Therefore, it's crucial that we take proactive measures to widely disseminate and safeguard our ideas and knowledge. With the advent of advanced technologies such as cloud computing, we are now better equipped to preserve our intellectual heritage for future generations. By embracing these tools, we can ensure that our contributions to knowledge are not lost to time, but rather, they continue to inspire and educate those who follow in our footsteps.

At the same time, we must recognize that the survival of our legacy is dependent on the survival of humanity itself. We can leave countless manuscripts and books detailing all of our knowledge and our lives, but without readers to interpret and pass on our ideas, they will remain locked in meaningless devices, and our lives will remain fleeting moments in the grand scheme of the universe. This is why caring for the future of humanity should be a crucial part of our legacy. We need to ensure that our actions and ideas not only leave a lasting impact but also contribute to the preservation and survival of humanity itself.

My next realization centered on the significance of choosing my own beliefs. I could have opted to trust in the myths of our ancestors, investing hope in an afterlife and opportunities for do-overs. Within that perspective, our present existence takes a backseat, rendering time no longer a constraining factor. Even in the hypothetical scenario where all life on Earth ceases and humanity becomes extinct, such a worldview would not regard it as a catastrophe, assuming that all our souls would ascend to an eternal haven. The notion of a worldview wherein human extinction isn't a disaster struck me as profoundly absurd. In such a scenario, we run the risk of allocating our resources based on false premises and non-existent priorities, especially when the stakes for humanity are so high. We can ill afford to squander time and resources in pursuit of illusions, especially given the numerous claims made by religion that science has readily debunked.

One of the most obvious examples is a belief that the universe and all life were created 6,000 years ago, which obviously contradicts the scientific evidence of evolution and radiocarbon dating. Many religions throughout history have proposed that the Earth is at the center of the universe, with all other celestial bodies revolving around it. However, this belief has been disproven by scientific evidence, including observations of planetary motion and the laws of physics. Some religious traditions also propose that miracles occur, such as supernatural healings or events that defy natural laws. However, these claims are often based on anecdotal evidence or subjective interpretations and are not supported by scientific evidence or rigorous testing.

I chose to believe in science, which posits that we do not have second chances in an afterlife, and that this life is our primary and only opportunity. We have a limited time to fulfill whatever goals we choose. There is time for self-discovery and finding our purpose, but this time is finite. It is better to have some goals, even if they are not ideal, rather than having no goals at all. There is time for reading books, but at some point, we must start writing our own story.

Simultaneously, science has often struggled to engage a large portion of the population, particularly in fundamental science and evolutionary biology, as they directly challenge the claims of Western traditional religions, such as claims involving the age of the universe, and the origin of species. Not to take scientific statements on blind faith, one must at least understand the basics of math and the corresponding discipline, which could take up to 20 years to master. This is too much to ask of the average person. Religion, on the other hand, was designed to appeal to the majority of the population and only made simple, easily understood statements. Religion possesses the tools to focus large groups of people on working towards a single goal that science lacks— just consider religious wars, crusades, and conquests. Merging these two disciplines and granting science that ability could help unite humanity to work on the most pressing and existential problems humankind will face.

As individuals or as an entire planet filled with people, we face the hostile and inhospitable environment of the cosmos, which is much larger than all of humankind and could rapidly change for the worse. Whether as a person or as humanity, even though we are an infinitesimally small part of the observable universe, we need to make an impact, leave a legacy, and ultimately survive. When people work together towards this goal, we, as individuals, are no longer alone on this path. To withstand the hostile universe requires the majority of humanity to work together. In the previous part of the book, we examined the history of mankind to determine which institutions can command the attention and will of the people, narrowing it down to religion and science.

Knowing that we have limited time on this Earth made me realize that I need to take even greater care of those around me, my family, and my friends. There are no second chances to fix our mistakes in a subsequent reincarnation, and there is no heaven where we will reunite with our loved ones. We only have this life, the memories we leave behind, and the impact we make on humanity itself.

This implies that our misdeeds will not be absolved or eradicated merely through a prayer, but they can be counterbalanced and outweighed by our virtuous actions. When we harm someone physically or emotionally, our primary response should not be a hasty confession, but a deliberate plan to make restitution to the affected individual or others. When we engage in harmful actions, we don't descend into an otherworldly hell; rather, we manifest a version of hell here on Earth within the memories of those we've injured. Some individuals, the likes of Hitler, Stalin and Pol Pot, can create such an horrendous negative impact that their memory persists for an extraordinary length of time, serving as a potent lesson for subsequent generations on avoiding the repetition of similar mistakes. Nevertheless, these figures are immortalized in our collective memory as embodiments of evil. Society perpetually punishes their legacy through feelings of revulsion, anger, and ultimately, rejection. Their legacy will continue to face societal reprobation, marked by sentiments of disgust, anger, and ultimate repulsion, mirroring the concept of "souls" being tormented in the purgatory of our collective memories.

Conversely, if we make a positive impact, helping or saving people with our actions and choices, we will leave behind good memories that can reverberate and potentially amplify our legacy. The fortunate few who make a tremendous impact will live in the collective memory of humanity for as long as humanity exists.

Making changes to our personal routines is a bare minimum. To truly make a difference, we must educate and lead others towards a more conservationist style of thinking. This can be done through various means, such as podcasts, social media, and other forms of outreach. By working together towards a common goal of preserving and improving humanity, we can leave a meaningful and lasting legacy that will be carried forward through the generations.

This is why it's crucial to consider and include the fate of humanity in our approach. While we may make every effort to save our planet and avoid potential disasters, such as a nuclear holocaust or a massive asteroid impact, we must acknowledge that the planet itself has a finite lifespan. Our Sun, the star of our solar system, will eventually deplete its hydrogen reserves and transition to burning helium, causing it to expand and transform into a red giant. As a result, it will no longer be a yellow star, and will expand beyond the orbit of Mars, ultimately leading to the evaporation of Earth[47] (Carter, 2019). Long before that, about 1.2 billion years from now, Earth will stop being hospitable for life. Whatever impact or legacy we leave for humanity, in the end, the future of humanity is doomed, and so is our impact, unless we

---

[47] forbes.com/in-55-billion-years

escape beyond this planet and start expanding outward, outside our regular habitat.

This perspective brings us back to the starting point, where the universe is indifferent to human existence and every environment, except for Earth, seems to pose a threat to us. Humanity can only hope that the universe won't unleash any of its destructive phenomena, such as wandering black holes, interstellar comets, gamma ray bursts, or rogue massive solar flares, which could potentially annihilate Earth. Faced with this immense scale of uncertainty, we may fall into nihilism[48] (Kaufmann, n.d.). According to Stanley Rosen, a philosopher and a professor at Boston University, Nietzsche identified the concept of nihilism with the meaninglessness, in which "everything is permitted". Nihilism denies the existence of right and wrong and destroys the personal meaning of our lives, leaving us with no purpose. Rejecting higher purposes and values can lead to a black hole of nihilism, which may threaten humanity's future.

Traditional religions of the west insist that the Earth is at the center of the universe and that humans occupy a special place with a unique status as the only beings with souls. The concept of the soul provides humans with immortality and purpose beyond the physical world. However, the notion of a geocentric universe has been disproved by science, and many other religious beliefs have been challenged by scientific advancements. The failure of Christianity to counter nihilism with its idealism and God as the source of morality led Nietzsche to declare that "God is dead," meaning that Christian doctrine dissolved due to the progress of science, leaving humanity without a purpose and morality.

When everything is impermanent and fades away, including our own ideas of everlasting concepts and immortal entities, there is no meaning that can last forever. Despite that, life has emerged with the mission to survive in a rapidly changing environment, adapt to any changes, and evolve into a new form to be ready for the next set of challenges. Although the current implementation of life may not survive the death of the Earth or Sun, the concept of living and evolving provides a mechanism for life to survive any hypothetical environmental changes, including catastrophic events and extinction-level events. Genes have successfully utilized this mechanism for billions of years surviving multiple cataclysms. Those mechanisms are a motivation for my formula for the direction in life that we discussed in the previous chapters.

Humanity can benefit from those mechanisms by applying the principles of evolution to our societies, institutions, and cultures, to ensure their resilience and adaptability in the face of unexpected and catastrophic events, such as asteroid strikes, mega-volcano eruptions, and pandemics. Isaac Asimov's book series, "Foundations," introduced the concept of psychohistory, a science that combines history, sociology, and mathematical

---

[48] https://en.wikipedia.org/wiki/Nihilism

statistics to make general predictions about the behavior of large groups of people. Using this science, a scientist made a prediction about a future calamity and worked out a solution that involved groups of people working together to salvage and save civilization.

If we had access to a similar institution or science that could convince a large group of people to work together to ensure the survival and thriving of future human civilization, our chances of survival would be much higher. Religion has been used for centuries to bring people together and motivate them to work towards a common goal. Religious institutions provide a sense of purpose and belonging, which can be a powerful motivator for people to work together. Additionally, religious institutions often have strong social networks that can help spread the message and encourage people to join the cause.

I imagine that one possible way to navigate the hidden threats and obvious dangers facing humanity could be through a hybrid approach that incorporates both science and religion. Science provides a systematic and empirical approach to understanding the world, while religion offers a sense of purpose and belonging that can motivate people to work together towards a common goal. Combining the best concepts and principles from both fields could create a framework that guides humanity towards a sustainable future.

I believe that everyone should try to contribute to the survival of mankind, and one of our lifelong goals should be about humanity. For me, science is one of the most powerful instruments for the future of humanity. It looks outward, seeking to understand how the universe around us works, and as a direct result, mankind learns about the dangers that surround us and potential ways to avoid them. Whereas religion excels in convincing large numbers of people to contribute to a singular cause.

We can use the looming danger of an asteroid strike on Earth as a prime example of the very real and critical threats faced by humanity. History has shown us that such a catastrophic event has occurred in the past and, it is a certainty, will recur in the future. Consequently, the development of advanced, long-range sensors capable of mapping and detecting orbiting asteroids and comets is not just a scientific pursuit but a necessity. This underscores the vital importance of space exploration. Our ability to peer deeper into the cosmos and identify potential collisions at the earliest opportunity increases our reaction time. Let's reiterate: time is our most precious commodity. The more of it we have, the further we can see into the cosmos and the earlier we can detect an impending collision, the more time (again stressing out that this is our most valuable resource) we will have to react, the better our chances of planning and executing effective countermeasures.

While most of the people would agree with the importance of space exploration there are still a sizable portion of the population that is against that. For example, a 2018 Pew Research Center survey found that 72% of Americans believe it is essential for the U.S. to continue being a global leader in space exploration, while 27% believe it is not essential. A 2019 survey conducted by YouGov found that 61% of Americans are in favor of increasing funding for NASA, while 17% are against it.

Opinions on specific space-related activities, such as human missions to Mars, are even more divided. This represents a significant number of people who oppose space exploration and are against allocating resources towards space travel. They believe that those resources would be better spent on combating world hunger and inequality within and between societies. Of course, there are many other activities and disciplines that demand more resources and priorities. People wage wars and engage in trade. We, as humans, can strive for world peace and the eradication of hunger, but people have existed for millennia with diseases, hunger, and wars. Nature seems to equip humans well with mechanisms to fight illness, negotiate peace, and establish food sources. However, nature does not fare well in surviving a direct collision with an asteroid. Extinction events have occurred in the past, and while some species survived, the majority of life perished. If we know for certain that Earth will be hit by a comet or asteroid, the only way to survive a total extinction event is to establish a presence on multiple planets, at least two. Going to Mars no longer seems like an extravagant project for billionaires, but an absolute necessity. Other planets may be too far away, but building orbital platforms with artificial gravity created by spinning sections of the platform seems like another possibility. There is also the option of settling deeper underwater, as the impact from an asteroid is absorbed and mitigated by vast bodies of oceanic water. All of these options and possibilities require ongoing investment in both time and resources, and more importantly, maintaining the public's attention on the importance of science for humanity. Diverting people's attention by convincing them that this life is not important and the real life is the next one, is not only deceitful and distracting, it is borderline criminal.

The people who support space travel and exploration, myself included, are familiar with that argument. Astronomers now have the means to observe the near cosmos and track the most dangerous space objects that pose an existential threat to our planet. I think what is more important is to be equipped to detect threats that we are not yet familiar with. The most dangerous things in the universe are those that we don't know about YET!

This is why geologists continue to study Earth's tectonic movements and the dangerous natural events they can create. Fundamental physics searches for not yet discovered phenomena. This highlights the importance of fundamental science, to learn about dangers that we don't know about but will discover in the future. The better technologies and sensors to probe unseen threats the more time we will have to prepare for them.

That does not mean we should neglect monitoring runaway technologies, including AI. There are even more alarming technologies in development, such as genetic engineering, which, in the worst-case scenario, could lead to an end-of-the-world scenario akin to Kurt Vonnegut's book 'Cat's Cradle,' where a new technological substance called 'ice-nine' froze all the water in the world.

Scientific principles such as the theory of evolution can be used to understand the adaptability of species and apply it to the resilience of societies, institutions, and cultures. On the other hand, religious principles such as compassion and empathy can be used to foster a sense of unity and collective responsibility towards each other and the planet. Religious institutions can serve as a platform to educate people on scientific concepts and findings, making science more accessible and understandable to the general public. This could help bridge the gap between scientific experts and the general population, which can sometimes lead to distrust and misunderstanding. A hybrid approach could utilize the strengths of both science and religion to address existential threats such as asteroid impacts and pandemics. This approach will take the best concepts and principles from science and religion and provide a framework that will guide humanity towards a sustainable future and help us navigate hidden threats and obvious dangers, much like Asimov's foundations provided help to secure the survival and thriving of future human civilization.

However, the use of religion in its current forms as a tool must be wielded with caution as it can lead to disastrous and deadly consequences when facing contradictions to its dogmatic statements. For example, certain religious sects that oppose medical treatment may experience higher mortality rates, except for Amish communities. The lack of medical data in the Amish communities makes this comparison less straightforward. Moreover, when religion is based on dogmas, it can stifle any adjustment and progress in changing religious tenets. In contrast, science has a way of adjusting and eventually correcting contradictions. For instance, the importance of handwashing in delivering babies and reducing maternal mortality was not known until introduced by a Hungarian doctor, Ignaz Semmelweis, in June 1847. Science has its share of contradictions, but it has a way of adjusting and correcting them, whereas dogma in religion does not. Dogma stiffles any adjustment and any progress in changing religious tenets.

I believe that understanding how religious ideas can contribute to society and when they become detached from reality is crucial in directing religion towards good. In my opinion, this can only be achieved with the help of science, by making religion more flexible and by removing the influence of dogma.

My fascination with both religion and science stems from personal reasons. I knew that we create our legacy through our impact on those around us, by making our actions accepted and our ideas going viral. People are open and ready to be influenced by our actions and to believe in our ideas, unlike inanimate objects. The best way to spread ideas is through writing books that people will read. And what has the biggest influence on people if not religion and philosophy? While writing this book, I naturally decided to rely primarily on those two disciplines as the best way to spread my ideas across.

My main reason for exploring the intersection of religion and science is that whatever personal goals we choose to provide meaning to our lives, they will only survive as long as humanity does.

This revelation fundamentally alters our understanding of the "meaning of life" or, as I've previously reinterpreted it, the "direction in life." Earlier, the direction of our lives was considered a matter of personal choice, thus making it a predominantly individual concern. However, if the personal meaning of life is deemed significant only in the context of humanity's future existence, then not all choices carry the same weight and not all life paths are equally valid.

While individuals may have as many choices as there are humans on the planet, humanity as a collective entity can only progress in one direction for it to maintain a unified front. Should the overarching aim of humanity veer towards self-preservation, then the millions of individual journeys comprising mankind should ideally align with this goal, all channeled towards ensuring the continued existence of humanity in the future. We cannot focus solely on our personal meaning of life without also dedicating our lives to the entire human race.

The most influential social systems that affect humanity on a broad scale are art, science, and religion, with religion being the most persuasive among them. Regardless of our personal leanings, if our goal is to probe the meaning of life, we must engage with religion, science, and possibly art. The most insightful place to seek answers is within the historical trajectory of their past, so we shall visit the history of science and religion.

History Of Science and Religion

At this juncture in the book, I found myself questioning the connection to the meaning of life (and so may the reader). Initially, when conceiving the idea for my future book, my focus was solely on recounting the journey of finding my own life's purpose. However, over the years, this narrative has taken me in unexpected and surprising directions, even surprising myself. It has become clear to me that without sharing the entirety of this story, it will feel incomplete. I will start with a chapter with a few pages from my personal history: a page on my own experience as a scientist, and another on my search for meaning within religion. I believe this approach will paint a better picture, starting with science.

It has been a year since I emigrated from the Soviet Union to start a doctoral program at Columbia University in New York City. In the ensuing years, my thesis research at the Fermi National Laboratory for particle physics consumed most of my time and energy. In this period, I found little time to ponder the meaning of life; I was too involved in the process of fulfilling it through my research, despite lacking absolute clarity on what the meaning was. I just knew deep inside that my research was important and my intellectual energy was primarily channeled into making it happen.

My first days in the USA were filled with a state of shock but mostly awe! They say that after changing your life through immigration, one should experience culture shock. However, as I strolled the streets of New York City for the first few days after my arrival in America, I experienced a cultural euphoria. Being in a unique position to observe the differences between life in America and behind the iron curtain, I noticed a newfound sense of freedom from the constant peer pressure and self-censorship that I had grown accustomed to in my home country. The watchful eyes of the crowd, scrutinizing my every move and behavior, had vanished. In their stead, I encountered the complete indifference of New Yorkers, and I felt that my personal space had tripled in size. It seemed as if I could disrobe and walk naked through the city without eliciting a second glance from anyone. While the exhilarating sense of liberation eventually subsided after a couple of years, I still cherish the memory of its surreal and dreamlike embrace for the first few weeks.

I arrived from the chaotic "wild east" reality of Russian 90s into the 90s reality of New York City. My expectations for a break from crime and grit were quickly dispelled, when I found the Big Apple to be on a par with, if not being a more dangerous city than Moscow. Columbia University was located in Harlem near two parks, Morningside and North Central Park. In my friends' apartments close to those parks you can hear the sounds of gunshots at night, sometimes merging into the chatter of semi-automatic weapons.

Due to visa delays, I arrived late and was quickly ushered into a one-room dormitory near the university campus with a "spectacular" view of a garbage alley. To lift my spirits, I drew a winding road leading into the mountains on the window blinds, accompanied by a picture of Fermilab.

My drawing on the window blinds of my room at "Harmony Hall" dorm of Columbia University

Some of my classmates and senior students at Columbia welcomed me with open arms. I had to quickly learn where to shop for food and essentials, pay taxes, deal with authorities and how to navigate the subway and buses in this entirely new country.

My friends had nicer apartments, but they were farther from campus, closer to parks, and within a high-crime area. One of my friends, who had an almost luxurious apartment, was mugged three times. Consequently, we adopted a rule to never carry more than $20 in cash. My Canadian friend was once accosted by two young guys when he had only $1 in his wallet. The amateur criminals had to settle for just $1 and even returned his wallet. As my friend walked away, relieved, he saw another man running towards him with a gun, yelling loudly. He thought, "Oh no, not again," but the man ran past him, shouting, "Don't move, police!" He was a plainclothes officer trying to apprehend the two assailants. He caught and arrested one of them, and my friend became a witness. Ironically, the NYPD took his wallet, along with his IDs and credit cards, as material evidence.

Over the years, I saw the neighborhood receive increasing attention from the police, with upscale restaurants and coffee shops moving in. Times Square, once a cesspool of crime and peep shows, transformed into a tourist attraction. I fell in love with New York City before and after its transformation, with all its grime, everchanging pungent streets, and crime, but most of all, its melting pot of fascinating people who came from all corners of the world, leaving everything behind to make a statement to the world.

A few quick and action packed months after I started at Columbia, I got to travel to a Fermi National Laboratories in Aurora Illinois and got to see a Fermilab main building with my own eyes. The same summer I started to work on my research.

In front of the main Fermilab building, circa 1995

As I neared the end of my dissertation, I found myself spending less and less time in New York City and working more days in a physics lab affiliated with Columbia University. My thesis was on the fascinating physics of neutrino particles that permeate every fiber of our existence without us noticing anything about them. At the labs, I was studying those elusive particles that were located along the path of the particle beam, where the bulk of neutrinos were produced. Despite my dream of working in the tall and beautiful science building which happened in the first few months of my arrival to Fermilab, I ended up in the porto camp trailers, which were located about a mile away.

Inside NuTeV E815 experiment porto camp trailer.
It must have been after the "owl" shift that I could not open my eyes.

It was here that I had to learn how to be a particle physics scientist from scratch. This included everything from laying cables to the correct particle detectors, scintillators, drift chambers, and calorimeters[49] (Bugel, 2000), how to store the massive amounts of data in the computer storage, how to write processing programs and how to analyze data correctly. It was a challenging and humbling experience, but it taught me the importance of learning from the ground up and gaining a deep understanding of the technical aspects of my field, basically how to be an experimental scientist.

Overall, this was a busy and exciting time filled with consequences and lessons. Next to our portacamp, there were two huge collaborations looking for one of the most anticipated discoveries in the 90s, the top quark. During the first couple of years, I spent my summers as a research assistant at Fermilab, conducting research in neutrino physics while also helping with data collection.

The laboratory life was filled with work and learning new things but the lab itself was situated in the middle of nowhere, and we did not have much of a social life. The buffalos and canadian geese were a great departure from New York City crowds. Occasionally I would get into a university van and drive into Chicago city to just walk around the crowds to fight off loneliness. The first year at Fermilab I did not speak a word of Lithuanian or Russian, but as a result I quickly became fluent in English. The second year more students

---

[49] pas.rochester.edu/~ksmcf/NuTeV/bugel/tour.html

came and among them some russians. We also had a good share of people from Texas, a couple of them were professors, including my scientific advisor.

I remember one instance when my Russian roommate was stood up by his friends on his birthday. He returned with untouched bottles of vodka, and together with our American friend, we gave him a proper birthday celebration. At some point, we decided that our colleagues deserved our company, so we made our way to a portacabin where the night shift was monitoring data collection. One of them was a professor from Texas, and we approached him, insisting that he drink with us. We were too intoxicated to realize that we were being disruptive and drinking on federal property. Any less wholesome person might have been difficult about the whole situation. The Texan professor picked up the full glass of vodka, calmly drank it, and then told us to leave using rather impolite terms. That's when I learned that Texans can be just as cool, if not cooler, than New Yorkers.

With my room mates about to drink 2 bottles of vodka

As a grad student, I often found myself assigned to the night shifts, since postdocs and professors typically had families and, well, a life. These night shifts involved long, solitary hours monitoring our experiment sensors and ensuring that the proton beam used to generate neutrinos was aimed accurately at the center of the tungsten target to prevent irradiating the entire portacabin. While the shifts were often monotonous, the work was critical. To pass the time, I kept an extra window open on an Internet Relay Chat (IRC) program to converse with people awake in different time zones around the world. IRC was a precursor to Facebook, Whatsapp and other messaging social apps.

Eventually, my scientific endeavors had a profound impact on my personal life. One late night, I started a conversation with a girl who claimed to live near Chicago. We flirted, we both pretended to speak German, discussed topics like fencing and physics, and she was adventurous enough to share her real phone number. Years later, we took a spontaneous trip to Las Vegas where she would become my wife.

To continue with my personal exploration of the meaning of life through the lens of religion, we must revisit my childhood, although briefly.

My Search for the Meaning in Religion

During my formative years, I explored various paths towards finding the meaning of life, particularly through religion. As someone drawn towards experimental thinking, I believed that the best way to find a path is to conduct a series of experiments on myself, as close to scientific method as possible. Experimental scientists take any hypothesis with a grain of salt and try to create verifiable and testable confirmations of them, i.e., conducting experiments, delivering foolproof, reproducible data that backs up one's hypothesis and objectives.

My exploration entailed visiting every accessible temple and church to garner a firsthand experience of religion. This curiosity was sparked during my childhood when I spent considerable time with the religious side of my family, my aunts and uncles and my other Baptist relatives. They often infused religious traditions into their family gatherings, creating a jovial and lively atmosphere. Although as a child I didn't fully grasp the significance and meaning of much of what transpired, I found great joy in participating in the singing and dancing at these communal events.

As I matured and ventured off to college to study physics, my understanding of these experiences evolved. My academic pursuits led me to engage in numerous profound discussions about God and science with my family, further enriching my exploration of the intersection between faith and reason.

I particularly recall a couple of conversations: one with my school friend who converted to Jehovah's Witness and another with my college roommate who converted to Krishnaism. All of these conversations had a similar theme: individuals who converted or found God anew all talked about a moment of blissful joy when it became part of their lives. My uncle, a Baptist preacher who built his own church with help from the community, also talked about this moment as a way to test the presence of a Creator. This moment of elation became my testable hypothesis to prove to myself that a personal God exists.

I endeavored to design an experiment as close to "detecting" the divine as possible, which could provide tangible proof of its existence. My hypothesis was simple: if I could open my heart to the divine and experience a unique moment of elation, it would serve as a positive result indicative of the divine's presence. The test was to capture and consciously acknowledge this moment of exaltation in each temple I visited.

To discern this proposed moment of elation, I embarked on a series of experimental visits to several places of worship: a Baptist church, a Catholic church, a Buddhist temple, and a Krishna community. Through these varied experiences, I aimed to immerse myself in diverse religious practices, with the ultimate goal of encountering a tangible sense of the divine.

During a visit to my uncle's Baptist church, I strived to cast aside any skepticism and pray fervently for a divine sign. Despite my earnest endeavors, I failed to encounter the anticipated moment of elation and bliss. Yet, I did experience a profound sense of community, intimacy, and camaraderie alleviated feelings of solitude.

In contrast, at the Krishna community, amid chants and praises for Krishna, I found an absence of introspective or existential inquiries. Though the atmosphere brimmed with joy, it did not facilitate personal encounters with Krishna or foster in-depth dialogues among the enthusiastic, yet somewhat closed-minded, congregation. This experience illuminated that individuals do not always seek profound answers; at times, they favor the comfort of known solutions and well-trodden paths. Strangely enough this was a similar experience to visiting the Catholic church during mass.

My experiences at the Catholic church in New York were less welcoming than my experiences at the Baptist church. Catholicism's hierarchical structure emphasizes the importance of rituals, sacraments, and prayer to attain salvation, while Baptists believe in the importance of faith alone. The Catholic church's environment was beautiful but not cozy, and I felt like it was meant to awe me and elicit a sense of grandeur. During one meeting, the priest discussed methods of contraception that did not involve condoms, which I found incredulous and far removed from my life's priorities. It seemed incongruous to me that with pressing global issues such as combating diseases like Ebola and HIV, or addressing world hunger, we were instead engaging in a debate on how to circumvent traditional contraception methods, ostensibly to avoid using latex contraceptive, all while maintaining the essential goal of preventing conception. This is akin to trying to cheat but finding ways to do it legally.

My experience at the Buddhist temple was more like listening to a friend at a gathering of close friends. The conversations focused on common, day-to-day problems, such as dealing with stress, finding direction, and resisting daily temptations, but in the light of the teachings of Buddha. The Buddhists did not stress the role of personal deity and rejected any sense of personal or eternal soul, focusing on nothingness. Learning how to meditate was one of the most useful experiences for me personally, and I want to dedicate a chapter to it in the appendix of this book.

Overall, my explorations afforded me the opportunity to delve into diverse religious traditions and gain insights into how individuals derive meaning from their lives. While my experiences underscored the significance of community and the integral role that religion plays in many lives, they fell short of leading me to the elusive moment of elation I had sought. Consequently, my experimental attempts to detect a palpable presence of the divine yielded negative results.

Over the years, I persisted in these explorations to guard against complacency and continually challenge my logical and lucid understanding of the world. In college I was a fan of Carlos Castaneda's book, "The Teachings of Don Juan"[50] (Castaneda, 1968) that talked about altered states of consciousness and a possibility of other worlds that exist in parallel to our current reality. It was based on his experiences with a Yaqui Indian shaman named Don Juan Matus, who Castaneda claimed had taught him ancient knowledge and spiritual practices. The book was presented as an ethnographic study of shamanic practices, but actually was a work of spiritual and philosophical fiction.

The proposition of parallel realms of magical reality intrigued me, and I yearned for an opportunity to glimpse or even venture into these mystical planes. Years later, I joined a group of friends who embraced a form of religious shamanism, using mescaline derived from the San Pedro cactus to attain heightened states of consciousness. Recalling Castaneda's writings, I considered that if there was even a grain of truth in his portrayal of the world, it could dramatically shift my understanding of reality. Desiring to complete my series of experiments in my quest for the supernatural, I was eager to challenge my predominantly logical perception of the world.

This opportunity came with my friends organizing a retreat in upstate New York under the supervision of a visiting shaman. He came from Peru and brought San Pedro cactus. San Pedro, also known as huachuma, is a cactus native to South America that is used for its psychoactive and spiritual properties. It has been used for centuries by indigenous peoples in the Andean region for religious and medicinal purposes, and is now gaining popularity as a tool for personal growth and healing in the West. It contains mescaline (n-trimethoxyphenethylamine) which is a naturally occurring psychedelic protoalkaloid. The effects of it are to strongly bind to and activate the serotonin receptors. The results of it are kind of short circuit effects where established brain patterns are distorted and your well established concepts are challenged. This was precisely the effect I was looking for. I wanted my rational and very logical mind to bend not too much but enough for me to see through the cracks in my consciousness if there is anything else out there, besides laws of physics. I was looking for any traces of magic I read in Carlos Castaneda books.

---

[50] en.wikipedia.org/wiki/The_Teachings_of_Don_Juan

When I arrived at my friend's place I found a small community of people sharing the same hunger for answers as I had. We started on the second day and it was a grueling but very rewarding experience. I did have numerous eye-opening conversations and got a few revelations for myself. I wanted to look at the world with scrambled neuron paths to see if there are any chinks in the foundation of my structured and science based worldview. I waited for the right moment, which was about 2 hours into the experience, found a secluded place in the forest and meditated in front of the stone wall. I meditated and tried to focus on my breathing and on the gaps in the brickwork. Slowly and surely I managed to widen them until there was enough space to peek and even fly through them. What I was expecting to see in the great space in between, was something that does not fit into the scientific world. It could have been guardians or travelers described in Carlos Castaneda books, angels, daemons or perhaps a creator itself. What I saw instead was a great nothingness, emptiness as big as space. But it was nothing that could add or subtract from my steady scientific worldview and sway me away from it. Instead I realized that a scientific view is not well established and boring. Quite the opposite, the magic I was looking for is already present in our rational world in abundance. I just had to look harder.

The closest that came to that world that I saw in the cracks of the brick wall was the Buddhist or Daoist concept of nothingness. In Buddhist philosophy, the concept of "nothingness" or "emptiness" refers to the idea that all phenomena are transient and interdependent, and that there is no permanent, independent self or substance. This is often expressed through the idea of "sunyata," which can be translated as "emptiness" or "voidness." In this sense, nothingness is not a state of absolute nothingness, but rather a recognition of the impermanence and interconnectedness of all things.

As a physicist, I understood that nothingness is not the absence of matter or vacuum. Modern physics describes the vacuum as a complex state, including the concept of quantum foam, which describes the turbulent and fluctuating nature of the fabric of space-time at the smallest scales. This phenomenon is thought to result from the uncertain and indeterminate behavior of subatomic particles, constantly popping in and out of existence in a sea of virtual particles. This concept of quantum foam is sometimes compared to the "nothingness" of Buddhist philosophy, which also describes a state of emptiness and impermanence. This realization that nothingness is all around us, and that it is magical, was a powerful feeling.

However, after experiencing different religions, I could not find any signs of phenomena outside of a scientific worldview. I did not detect a defining moment or a conscious transition from before to after, and I did not experience any enlightenment or transcendence. I also did not find any answers to the questions of the purpose of life in the language of shamans or preachers. Instead, what I found was the power of belief, the comfort of community, and the importance of rituals - all the components of religion, and most of all, the power of faith.

Now we're up to speed with the timeline of our narrative. Before leaving my alma mater in Russia, my university gave me one last gift, a crucial shift in perspective. Bowing to the winds of change, our compulsory lessons on the history of the communist party were supplanted by lectures on the philosophy of science. I was introduced to empiricism, Epicurus, Plato, Avicenna, Immanuel Kant, Nietzsche, George Berkeley, David Hume, and the origins of the scientific method. During my long flight to the US, I envisioned a grand conversation with these intellectual titans of the past. These formidable minds had wrestled with similar quandaries and perhaps already found solutions that I did not know about.

History of the Search for the Meaning of Life

The previous chapters have explored the question of the meaning of our personal lives through my own personal experiences. However, when considering the meaning of humanity as a whole, it is impractical and illogical to rely solely on personal experiences. We also established that caring about the future of humanity is essential to preserving the meaning of our own lives. Where else can we look for the meaning of all of us, for the meaning of humanity?

The good news is that we are not alone in our quest for answers to fundamental questions. For centuries, countless minds of the best thinkers and philosophers have sought the path towards those answers, towards our place in this world. The provision of the meaning of life to communities of believers was, for a long time, the sole domain of various religions. The conviction of these thinkers was that there are ideas and concepts bigger than us, bigger than our lives and bigger than the world around us. The dedication and devotion to those ideas required sacrifices away from personal goals and from one's life. This led to occurrences of hermits and stoics, monks' vows of chastity and lifelong dedication to serving their convictions. I want to study and examine their ideas, taking the best of them and reapplying them under new circumstances in our time and age.

The most concerted effort to discern the purpose and direction for humanity, both collectively and individually, has been occurring along two parallel tracks. On the one hand, we have the logical domain of philosophy and naturalism, which eventually evolved into the field of fundamental science. Here, thinkers and philosophers have endeavored to identify humanity's place and trajectory through logic and reason. Simultaneously, in the spiritual realm, various world religions have gone through multiple iterations, capturing the minds and souls of millions of people in the process.

Even though I will be exploring religion extensively, the first principles that I will use to test ideas, make thought experiments, and filter out ideas that do not work stem from modern scientific principles, namely evolutionary biology and fundamental science, which I described in previous chapters.

It is impossible to talk about the direction in life without looking at the historical journey taken in this pursuit. If we are discussing religion, we cannot ignore science in our conversation. The conversation would be incomplete if it didn't encompass both religion and science. In this section of the book, we'll delve into the interpretations of life's meaning as defined by current and past religions, while simultaneously exploring the history.

The quest to find life's meaning is a pivotal human endeavor as we strive to comprehend our purpose and significance. Despite this, the recorded history of this pursuit is relatively recent. The majority of our historical understanding is derived from written records, the earliest of which were discovered in Sumer of Mesopotamia between 3500 and 3000 BC. Primarily these texts were concerned with taxation and accounting. In those times, people were overwhelmingly occupied with agricultural and pastoral tasks, leaving little room for existential pondering.

The search for meaning can be traced back to ancient civilizations such as the Egyptians, Greeks, and Chinese, who developed complex belief systems and mythologies to explain the mysteries of life and death and mitigate fears of the underworld among their populations. Many of these belief systems were rooted in religious and spiritual traditions, emphasizing the importance of living a virtuous and meaningful life.

The earliest western philosophers to ponder the purpose of life were the ancient Greeks. In 420 BC, Plato, a mentor of Aristotle, wrote the Republic, where the character of Socrates describes the Form of the Good, which is the idea for the direction in life. Plato believed that the meaning of life is in attaining the highest form of knowledge, which is the Idea (Form) of the Good, from which all good and just things derive utility and value.

Aristotle, a pupil of Plato and Socrates, further developed this idea by arguing that the pursuit of happiness is the Highest Good, which is achievable through our capacity to reason. He believed that ethical knowledge is general knowledge, which means that one cannot simply study what virtue is, but must practice virtue to become "good."

Socrates had several pupils who developed different variations of his teachings. Antisthenes outlined cynicism, which involves being free of possessions and achieving virtue by living naturally. Epicurus, on the other hand, believed that achieving happiness is the true purpose of life, and freedom from pain and fear are the highest form of happiness.

Stoicism, founded by Zeno of Citium in the early 3rd century BC, emphasized the value of virtue and an inner moral guidance based on the system of logic and views of the natural world. Stoics believed that living a virtuous life would achieve the direction of life, leading to true happiness, rather than seeking external benefits such as wealth, health or pleasure. The direction in life to them was to live according to reason and in accordance with nature.

Similar to Stoicism, Buddhism places great emphasis on the concepts of limiting and restricting desires, but with a different goal in mind. Buddhism believes that the meaning of life is achieved not solely through subduing desires, but rather as a mere step towards enlightenment or nirvana, at which point the self escapes from worldly desires altogether.

The search for meaning also took on new dimensions during the Enlightenment period, a time of intellectual and cultural upheaval in the 17th and 18th centuries. Enlightenment thinkers, such as Immanuel Kant and Jean-Jacques Rousseau, challenged traditional religious and philosophical beliefs and sought to develop new frameworks for understanding the world.

In the 19th and 20th centuries, the search for meaning became even more urgent in light of scientific discoveries that challenged traditional religious and philosophical beliefs. The rise of secularism and the decline of traditional religious institutions led many people to seek alternative sources of meaning and purpose. New religious movements and spiritual practices emerged, often emphasizing personal growth, self-discovery, and connection to the natural world. Darwinian evolution, for example, challenged the idea of human beings as the center of the universe and raised questions about the nature of life and its origins.

The views on life's meaning varied greatly, with Friedrich Nietzsche and Arthur Schopenhauer taking vastly different positions. Nietzsche believed that the direction in life was to create one's own values and pursue personal excellence, rejecting traditional notions of morality in favor of individualism and personal growth. Schopenhauer, on the other hand, believed that life was fundamentally meaningless and that the pursuit of pleasure or success was ultimately futile. He argued that the purpose of life was to achieve a state of enlightenment, involving transcending one's ego and achieving a sense of inner peace and harmony.

In the 20th century, the rise of existentialism brought new perspectives to the meaning of life debate. Existentialist philosophers such as Jean-Paul Sartre and Martin Heidegger emphasized the importance of individual choice and freedom in determining the direction in life. They rejected the idea that there was any inherent purpose or meaning to life, arguing instead that individuals must create their own meaning through their actions and choices.

Scientific discoveries in the 20th century also challenged traditional views of the direction of life. The theory of evolution suggested that human beings were not the special creations of a divine being but rather the products of natural selection. This led some thinkers to question whether life had any inherent meaning or purpose at all.

We can observe a distinct pattern over the past centuries of transformation from a more consolidated perspective with central themes, to a more democratized viewpoint emphasizing individual and personal development. Overall, the search for the direction in life has undergone significant changes as philosophers, scientists, and religious leaders grappled with new ideas and challenges. New perspectives from philosophy and science have continued to shape and influence the debate, but the bulk of this search happened within the realm of religion.

Meaning of Life According to Religion

The search for the direction in life has been ongoing for mankind for a long time[51] (Perov, n.d.). Theistic religions have provided varied and different motivations to their subjects, but they all have one thing in common: the requirement to serve God's will in your own soul and on this Earth, which will lead to an eternal afterlife in His presence. I might have simplified and limited the scope of the question to just Abrahamic religions, but this simplification does not change the spirit of the above sentence. We will talk about Eastern religions in the next part of the book.

In ancient times, polytheistic religions were common, with people serving multiple deities. In Mesopotamia, dating back to 6000 BC, people believed in many different deities, but with one above all. Humans were created as co-laborers with their gods to maintain order and harmony in their communities. Major Mesopotamian divine beings included Anu, the sky god and king of the gods in the Sumerian pantheon, Enlil, the god of wind, air, and storms in the Sumerian pantheon, and Marduk, the patron deity of Babylon and the chief god of the Babylonian pantheon in the Akkadian pantheon. In the Egyptian pantheon, there were many gods, including three major ones: Ra, the sun god and king of the gods in Egypt, Isis, the goddess of fertility, motherhood, and magic, and Osiris, the god of the underworld and the afterlife.

Judaism, originating in Israel almost 4000 years ago, teaches that the purpose of life is to connect with God through obeying and embodying Torah teachings. The quest for purpose in Judaism ranges from finding God within oneself to messianism, with the goal of implementing a universal, political realm of justice and peace according to Torah. Unlike the many gods in Sumerian and Egyptian pantheons, the number of gods in Judaism decreased to just one universal God. Subsequent Abrahamic religions, based on Old Testament scriptures, emphasize submission to God. In Christianity, the purpose of life is found in Jesus Christ, who is considered the son of God and the embodiment of this plane of existence and the Holy Spirit. In Islam, the meaning of life is found in submission to Allah by following the teachings of Mohammed as outlined in the Quran. Abrahamic religions not only dictate submission to God in one's own self and soul, but also the implementation of God's order and laws on Earth.

This progression from many gods to fewer gods ultimately culminates in the monotheism of Abrahamic religions.

Liberalism is a more modern political and social movement that emerged in the Age of Enlightenment, a cultural movement in the 17th and 18th centuries. It is based on Christianity and Christian values combined with a profound faith in reason, human rights, the pursuit of happiness, and freedom

---

[51] newworldencyclopedia.org/entry/meaning_of_life

typical for the Enlightenment. Liberalism considers humans as beings with inalienable and inherent natural rights, based on each person having a unique and indivisible soul and freedom of choice. Pursuit of individual happiness and following one's own choices in life without violating the rights of others is at the core of liberalism. The meaning of life according to liberalism is following one's own ideals and choices, which can lead to personal happiness and fulfillment.

Buddhism is unique among religions in that it went all the way to zero gods required to explain the workings of the universe. Buddhism does not endorse worship of gods or a creator deity. Buddhism's fundamental concepts are based on the teachings of Siddhartha Gautama, known as "Buddha," who lived from the 5th to 4th century BCE. He was initially a Hindu prince but developed his own unique spiritual insights that diverged significantly from the Hindu beliefs of his time.

Buddhist teachings emphasize that the pursuit of material success or indulgence in sensual pleasures only distracts from the path towards enlightenment. Buddhists believe in reincarnation and karma. According to early texts, Gautama was moved by the suffering of life and death, and its endless repetition due to rebirth. He set out on a quest to find liberation from suffering starting with meditation teachings and then through the practice of severe asceticism, fasting and breath control. Initially finding all those methods insufficient to achieve this goal, through deep meditation he eventually achieved insight into the workings of karma and how to end the suffering, and to end the cycle of rebirth. From the insight sprung earliest buddhist teachings. As expressed in the "Four Noble Truths" of the Buddha, the goal of Buddhism is to overcome the suffering caused by worldly desires and ignorance of reality's true nature, including impermanence and external pleasures. Most Buddhist traditions emphasize transcending the individual self through the attainment of enlightenment or by following the path of Buddhahood, ending the cycle of death and rebirth. The meaning of life according to Buddhism is achieving this state of enlightenment or achieving nirvana.

Hinduism and Buddhism have common origins in ancient India and share a lot of similar concepts. The roots of Hinduism can be traced back to the ancient Indus Valley civilization, which existed around 3300–1300 BCE in what is now modern-day Pakistan and northwest India. The religious practices of this civilization, as evidenced by archaeological finds such as the many statuettes and seals, are considered by some to be precursors of certain aspects of later Hinduism.

Hinduism as we know it today is also strongly linked to the Vedic religion of the Indo-Aryans. The religious texts known as the Vedas, composed from around 1500 BCE onwards, contain hymns, rituals, and speculations that form the basis of much of Hindu philosophy, mythology, and ritual. It developed out of the ancient Vedic religion, embracing various ideas and practices from older Indian traditions.

Buddhism originated in the eastern Ganges culture of northern India 500 BC. Both share belief in reincarnation and in karma, both share beliefs in religious liberation. They both believe in achieving salvation by freeing from the cycle of rebirth (or samsara). To do this they both teach to lead righteous life and help others.

Overall, the search for the direction in life in Eastern religions was characterized by a focus on spiritual practices, ethical conduct, and the attainment of wisdom and enlightenment, all of which are seen as essential for achieving a sense of purpose and fulfillment in life. The search for the direction in life has been a central theme in many Eastern religions, which have developed complex philosophical and spiritual systems aimed at achieving enlightenment and understanding the nature of reality.

In Hinduism the purpose of life is achieved through fulfilling four aims, called Purusharthas. These are dharma, or personal duty, kama (personal love and pleasure), artha (personal prosperity) and moksha, state of enlightenment. In the order of importance, they call to master the sensual pleasure or love (Kame), achieve wealth (Artha), excel in righteousness and morality (Dharma) and most importantly liberate yourself from the cycle of reincarnation (Moksha). The latter is the ultimate achievement of liberation from the cycle of reincarnation and the attainment of a state of pure consciousness and bliss. You can achieve that by either becoming fully aware of your own self or through love towards God's soul and grace. Hinduism strikes as ready to give an answer to the question of the direction in life with most prescriptive recipes, probably because it is the oldest of known religions.

Buddhism, which emerged in India in the 5th century BCE, similarly emphasizes the attainment of enlightenment and the end of suffering. Central to Buddhist philosophy is the Four Noble Truths, which outline the nature of suffering and the path to its cessation through the Eightfold Path, a set of ethical and meditative practices aimed at achieving wisdom, compassion, and inner peace.

Where they differ is in rejection by Buddhism of concepts of soul or self, and in rejection of universal eternal source of everything (attman). Buddhism also rejects Hinduism Vedas as a source of scriptural authority, hindu priests, ritual and caste system.

Taoism, a Chinese philosophical and religious tradition that dates back to the 4th century BCE, emphasizes the search for meaning through achieving harmony with the Tao, or the fundamental order of the universe. This is accomplished through practices such as meditation, martial arts, and the cultivation of inner virtues such as humility, compassion, and simplicity.

Similarly, in Confucianism, another major Chinese philosophical tradition, the search for meaning is focused on the cultivation of virtue and the attainment of social harmony. The ultimate goal is to achieve ren, or benevolent and virtuous conduct, which is seen as the key to personal fulfillment and social order.

Another eastern religion, Shinto, originated in Japan and is based on the worship of spirits, or kami, that are believed to inhabit all things in nature, including humans. In Shinto, there is no single, overarching doctrine or belief system, but rather a diverse set of practices and beliefs that are shaped by local traditions and cultural influences. While there is no one definitive answer to the direction of life in Shinto, there are several core beliefs and values that provide insight into the Shinto perspective on life and existence. Shinto emphasizes the importance of living in harmony with nature, maintaining a connection with one's ancestors, cultivating a pure and virtuous spirit, and respecting tradition and cultural heritage.

In both Eastern and Western religions, the concept of salvation is central. Monotheistic religions aim to guide their followers towards salvation, which is a state of achieving bliss or deliverance from sin. In Abrahamic religions, it is finding salvation of our eternal souls by joining God in the heavenly kingdom. For Buddhism, it is the escape from an endless and pointless cycle of rebirth by finding and joining Nirvana. However, in order to guide and shepherd people on the paths of righteousness towards salvation, one must have an unquestionable conviction in knowing what the right path is, or at least an appearance of knowing all the truth. An admission of any degree of ignorance could quickly propagate doubt in followers and unravel the entire system of belief. Perhaps this is why in Buddhism, which does not require a single divine deity, the questioning is not only tolerated but encouraged. On the contrary, monotheistic religions do not tolerate any doubts or questioning and are based on complete faith.

Understandably religion did concern itself with conducting experiments and establishing relationships between natural phenomena. The doubt is by design a part of experimentation and religion does not have any room for doubting. This is in essence a definition of faith, believing in knowing the most important knowledge of the world without questioning.

Faith (from Greek-pistis and Latin-fides) refers to confidence, trust, and hope in God, a person, community, tradition. The common denominator is a level of conviction and an inner attitude towards a greater power or force in the universe[52] and often it emphasizes commitment to something or someone.

Consider that Christian scholars have historically emphasized the role of logic, reason, and common sense in understanding Christianity and the Bible. However, this role only extends to understanding what is already prescribed and only goes as far as it does not contradict the scriptures or the Bible. The faith always supersedes logic, and questioning the origins or clarification of God's will is often considered heresy and is punishable with varying degrees of severity.

In Abrahamic religions, the direction in life is often seen as seeking salvation for one's soul through submission to God's will. While this message

---

[52] newworldencyclopedia.org/entry/Faith

may seem clear, the will of God itself is often shrouded in mystery and is not explicitly revealed. Additionally, in this faith-based worldview, our actions do not affect an already pre-established and frozen order. It is believed that only God can change the world, and our choices and actions have no impact on the grand scheme of things. If we interpret the meaning of life and set up a direction of life it goes contrary to the path of salvation which is set by God without any possibility of choice. This argument aligns with the idea that the scale of the meaning of our life cannot be too big. At the largest scale, the impact of our actions becomes infinitesimal.

In this sense, our actions have no significance on God or the universe. We can only affect our own karma and save our own soul, meaning that we can only affect our internal world. It's natural to question why the most all-encompassing entities would care about something as small and insignificant as humans.

This is why in Abrahamic religions it was important to make God a personal loving God and for people to be made in his image. This is to ensure that humans have God's undivided attention, which would otherwise be spread among billions (about 8.7 billion) according to Lanting[53] (Lanting, 2022), of species on this planet. By making humans direct children of God, the conflict between saving a chicken or a starving human family is always resolved in the humans' favor. However, this personal relationship with God also limits the impact of our actions on the world and on God. Our actions affect only our own destiny, not the destiny of the world or God. This means that we cannot make an impact that is bigger than ourselves.

Western Abrahamic religions make God the source of all and everything, which emphasizes the insignificance of our actions on God or the universal order of things. Similarly, in Buddhism and Hinduism in the East, our actions cannot break the existing order of things or change the never-ending cycle of reincarnations.

Thus our actions affect only our own destiny, but they don't have any impact on the world or on God, Gods or Sansara. If you think about this in those terms, even though God/Enlightenment/Transcendence are much greater in scale than our life we don't have any chance to make an impact that is bigger than us.

What is more impactful, in western or eastern religions, be that Christianity or Buddhism, we also cannot make a choice for others. In my definition, the impact is the ability to change the direction of actions and decisions of others. In Christianity the destiny of your soul is only determined by your own choices, and not choices of others, with the exception of you helping others to bring them into God and towards salvation. That means that we ultimately cannot make any significant impact on others. We can only show them the way and hope they will take it. This worldview robs people of

---

[53] education.nationalgeographic.org/resource/biodiversity

the ability to make any significant difference or impact, as the true impact is only measured in its effect on other people.

Same in Buddhism, our reincarnation is dependent only on the karma incurred as a result of our present and past lives. We can possibly show others the path to salvation and enlightenment through our own example, and thus affect the destiny of our own salvation, but the choice whether to accept this path is up to individual souls or life actions.

To recap in perhaps overly simple but nonetheless accurate terms, religion is intimately concerned with the destination for a person's journey towards the meaning of life. The goal of this journey is salvation of our eternal soul or karma. Religion does not concern itself with the intricacies, tribulations and uncertainty of the journey itself. After all, if one knows everything then there is no need in acquiring more knowledge. This implies a perception of being an absolute authority and the source of knowledge of how the world works under the covers, perception that may not necessarily be based on any evidence. At the same time it creates and cements communities together with a sense of purpose, and arms people in those communities with a power of faith.

What Science Says About the Meaning of Life

Science, together with philosophy, is a foundational element of modern society. Yet, hard sciences have not traditionally offered much insight into the direction in life. This is one of the reasons why I wrote this book: to provide a different perspective on this important topic.

When discussing science, it's important to clarify that I am specifically referring to the natural sciences, such as physics, chemistry, biology, and mathematics. These fields employ the scientific method to formulate hypotheses, design experiments, and analyze data in order to make empirical observations and testable predictions about the natural world.

It's worth noting that there are other scientific fields, such as psychology and psychiatry, which focus on understanding human behavior, emotions, and mental health. While these fields may provide valuable insights into how people find meaning in their lives, they are not considered hard sciences in the traditional sense.

For example, psychologists may examine the concept of self-actualization, which involves personal growth and fulfilling one's potential by aligning values, goals, and interests with actions and behaviors. This can help individuals develop a sense of purpose and meaning in their lives, which may lead to better coping skills and lower rates of depression and anxiety.

However, it's important to recognize that psychology and psychiatry do not attempt to answer the ultimate question of the direction of life in depth. Rather, their focus is on understanding human behavior and improving mental health outcomes. This is a valuable pursuit in its own right, and can contribute to a better understanding of how we can lead fulfilling lives.

In contrast to religion, which assumes ultimate knowledge, science acknowledges that it does not know all or even most of the answers. Science takes the opposite approach by striving to provide increasingly accurate natural explanations of the world that are testable and do not require blind faith. Science does not make assumptions without observations and experimental data, as the goal of knowledge acquisition is to continue on an endless path towards true knowledge. A day when science learns all natural laws would be unfortunate for scientists, and it is hoped that such a day never comes.

The Goedel incompleteness theorem[54] (Gödel's Incompleteness Theorems, n.d.) is considered one of the greatest mathematical statements. In a simplified but more accessible interpretation, it states that "Any formal system is either inconsistent or incomplete." One interpretation of this theorem is that we will never reach the end of our quest for knowledge and will continue to expand our circle of truth.

The path of hard science does not seek a shortest route to existential answers. Rather, it takes a steady and deliberate approach of discovering hidden links between natural phenomena and finding patterns among them. For example, one can observe the links between the movements of stellar objects, planets, or stars and establish that their movements are governed by the law of gravity or Newton's Law of Universal Gravitation[55]. These patterns eventually become scientific theories, which in scientific vocabulary are the closest approximation of the truth. In this example, the law of gravity is the theory.

Fundamental science is considered the purest form of scientific research. It aims to improve scientific theories to better understand and predict natural phenomena. This research is conducted for the sake of research, without any direct or immediate applications. This differs from applied research, which seeks immediately useful applications of science for people. Science is a systematic effort by humankind to acquire and organize knowledge in the form of testable explanations and predictions about the universe. Note that this definition does not specify whether the acquired knowledge benefits humanity. This is because scientists do not know the nature of the knowledge they are discovering, and scientific knowledge can be used for good or for evil. Science itself is neither inherently good nor evil.

Fundamental science is not uniform and is divided into two branches: experimental and theoretical. Theoretical sciences connect observations, establish invisible connections, and formulate scientific hypotheses from the connections and observations. Experimental branches prove scientific

---

[54] en.m.wikipedia.org/wiki/G%C3%B6del%27s_incompleteness_theorems

[55] en.wikipedia.org/wiki/Newton's_law_of_universal_gravitation

hypotheses either wrong or right. When the hypotheses are confirmed by experimental evidence, they become scientific theories.

The primary aim of fundamental science is to construct increasingly precise explanations while minimizing the number of assumptions made. Prehistoric science began with naturalistic observations, cataloging numerous facts and dependencies, each one standing as a separate assumption, cumulatively numbering in the thousands.

For example, early humans observed that the sun rose in the east and set in the west every day. They noticed that the moon changed shape over a period of about a month. They saw that certain stars appeared only at certain times of the year. Each of these observations was a fact noted down by prehistoric humans.

Over time, what initially appeared as independent observations were recognized to be components of the same phenomenon, thereby reducing the quantity of assumptions. For instance, the daily movement of the sun, the changing shape of the moon, and the seasonal appearance of certain stars were all eventually understood to be related to the movement of celestial bodies in space. This understanding reduced the number of assumptions. Instead of assuming that the sun moved around the Earth, they realized that it was the Earth's rotation that made it appear as if the sun was moving. Instead of thinking that the moon was changing its shape, they learned that its phases were due to the way sunlight hit the moon as it orbited the Earth. Instead of believing that stars were seasonal beings, they found out that the Earth's movement around the sun caused different stars to be visible at different times of the year.

The holy grail of fundamental science is a theory of everything, a hypothetical, singular, and all-encompassing coherent theoretical framework that fully explains and links together all physical aspects of the universe, including the four fundamental forces and all elementary particles and their interactions. The term was coined by Stephen Hawking in his book A Brief History of Time.

Throughout the history of science, there have been several examples of experiments that have contradicted established scientific theories. These examples show that scientific knowledge is always subject to revision and refinement as new evidence and observations come to light. When scientific hypotheses contradict experimental evidence, scientists collect more experimental data to refine or come up with a better hypothesis.

Both theoretical and experimental scientists admit their ignorance and move on from faulted theories, though not without struggle. This admission of ignorance is built into the fabric of science as an essential process.

Let us define scientific knowledge, which is obtained through a crucial process called the scientific method. This method has been in use for at least 400 years and involves systematic inquiry, including formulating hypotheses, collecting and analyzing data, and drawing conclusions based on empirical evidence.

The scientific method aims to distinguish between scientific truth (i.e., theory) and falsehood (i.e., false theory). But why do we need a scientific method when common sense can often differentiate between the two? Common sense is often based on experience that aligns with typical human life experiences. Yet typical human life experiences may often be misleading. For example, the movement of the stars in the night sky is much easier to interpret as is, rather than the artifact of the planet orbiting around its axis. When it comes to the physical world at scales beyond human experience, such as astronomy or quantum mechanics, common sense often fails to apply. For instance, in the field of quantum mechanics particle objects behave as both waves and objects, and quantum entanglement defies the laws of classical physics. Similarly, Albert Einstein's theory of relativity challenged common sense even more, demonstrating that time and space are not absolute but can be influenced by factors such as gravity and motion.

In such cases where common sense fails, the scientific method provides a valuable tool to separate valid theories from falsehoods. It is based on continuous experimentation and testing, and if theories do not contradict observations, they are validated.

Scientists, however, are even more excited when an experiment does not confirm the accepted hypothesis and measures a significant discrepancy. This often suggests that there is a new area of science beyond the disagreement and the experimental scientists have discovered a flaw in the accepted theory. For instance, the Michelson experiment[56] (Michelson–Morley Experiment, n.d.) conducted in 1881 measured that the speed of light was equal in all directions and constant, contradicting the prevailing theory at the time. Another example is the discovery of neutrino mass, a particle that the Standard Model predicted to be massless, in the Super-K experiment[57] (Super-Kamiokande, n.d.) conducted in Japan in 1983. Experimentation is a crucial aspect of science because we do not know the answers to hypothesis predictions beforehand.

The goal of science is to build knowledge about the natural world, not to answer existential questions. While scientists may find their meaning of life in the pursuit of scientific truth and accumulation of knowledge, this is not the purpose of every person. Charles Darwin, for example, did not attempt to explain the origin of the primordial form of life, despite establishing links between related species in "The Origin of Species." Science establishes links and patterns, but does not claim the ultimate truth unless there is evidence to support it. The ultimate truth in hard science is a scientific theory, and its proof lies in experimental results.

One reason scientists are hesitant to answer existential questions is the lack of evidence. However, there is another reason. The peer review process that augments scientific method affects reputation, and the career of the

---

[56] en.m.wikipedia.org/wiki/G%C3%B6del%27s_incompleteness_theorems

[57] https://en.wikipedia.org/wiki/Super-Kamiokande

scientist depends on it greatly. Peer review is a process of evaluation in which a researcher's work is scrutinized by other experts in the same field before it is published in a scholarly journal or presented at a scientific conference. It helps to ensure the quality and integrity of scientific research.

The peer review process typically begins when a researcher submits a manuscript or abstract to a journal or conference. The editor or conference organizers then send the manuscript or abstract to other experts in the same field, who review the work and provide feedback on its scientific rigor, clarity, and originality. This feedback may include suggestions for revisions or additional experiments that could strengthen the study's findings.

If scientists make too many false statements that they cannot support with evidence, or worse, are caught in an outright lie, their reputation will be marred and it will be difficult to regain it. As a result, scientists are very careful about making statements that could ruin their careers. Unfortunately, there have been instances in which scientists have lied or committed fraud in their research, leading to a loss of reputation and credibility in their field.

For example, a Bulgarian nuclear physicist falsified experimental evidence in creating super-heavy elements, leading to his firing and the ruination of his career. Similarly, British physician Andrew Wakefield manipulated data and failed to disclose conflicts of interest in a study that suggested a link between the MMR vaccine and autism, resulting in the retraction of his paper and the loss of his medical license. German physicist Jan Hendrik Schön fabricated data in many of his studies, leading to retractions and the loss of his reputation as a scientist. As a result, scientists are overly careful about making any statement that can be misconstrued as an experiment or data manipulation.

Scientists tend to avoid topics such as the meaning of life or religion, as it could damage their reputation if their statements were to be misconstrued or unprovable.

However, I contend that the scientific perspective could significantly contribute to the discourse on the direction in life. This is precisely because scientists, who are typically independent and well-versed in discerning fact from fiction, tend to avoid this topic. Their involvement could lend a degree of objectivity and clarity, and potentially unveil new truths about life's purpose and direction.

In that sense, science differs from religion in its attitude to answering existential questions of life. It is simply not a major focus of science. Instead, it aims to steadily progress towards discovering the theory of everything.

It is important to note that there is no guarantee that scientists will ever come up with a single theory of everything. The process of scientific advancement is ongoing and infinite, and the more we learn about the world, the more questions it brings. Scientific hypotheses and theories are continuously tested against new data obtained from experimental observations, and as technology advances, we can probe deeper and explore on a smaller and greater scale.

There are major breakthroughs in the methods and capabilities of science. Most scientific discoveries in the past were based on electromagnetic interactions, such as observing objects with our eyes or using X-ray telescopes to detect the electromagnetic emissions of distant stars. However, on September 14, 2015, humanity gained access to a new sensory dimension, gravitational waves, which opened up new possibilities for scientific exploration. Using Laser Interferometer Gravitational-wave Observatory[58] or LIGO (LIGO Hanford Observatory, 2016), detectors scientists have been able to detect gravitational waves, almost 100 years since Einstein proposed their existence. The LIGO experiment, situated in Hanford, Washington and Livingston, Louisiana, in the United States, consists of two identical 4-kilometer long L-shape detectors. If a gravitational wave travels through the detectors, it causes minute alterations in the lengths of the arms, impacting the time it takes for the laser beams to travel back and forth. By measuring these changes, scientists can detect and analyze gravitational waves. In September 2015, it made its first detection of gravitational waves, verifying a crucial prediction of Albert Einstein's theory of general relativity. Since then, it has discovered many more gravitational wave events, providing novel insights into the nature of black holes, neutron stars, and the universe as a whole. This newly added sensory dimension, similar to a proverbial third gravitational eye, will enable humanity to see even deeper into the universe, creating more areas to explore and more questions to answer.

Fundamental scientists are on a long and arduous quest for knowledge acquisition, and they do not intend to speculate on the ultimate answers to existential questions. Their aim is to reach those answers gradually by expanding our understanding of the world and our place within it. While science cannot address the issue of the direction in life, it possesses potent tools to differentiate truth from falsehood, with the scientific method being the most powerful among them.

We see that science tends to avoid addressing existential questions such as the direction in life, whereas religious institutions offer many answers to such questions. One might wonder why not simply adopt a religious approach and be satisfied with this state of affairs?

Scientific Versus Dogmatic Approaches

We just discussed the contrasting approaches of science and religion in addressing complex questions. Science has been committed to the pursuit and expansion of knowledge for centuries, considering this journey as an end in itself. It prioritizes accumulating knowledge before attempting to tackle metaphysical inquiries with a comprehensive understanding.

---

[58] ligo.caltech.edu/news/ligo20160211 LIGO Hanford Observatory

Conversely, religion starts with conclusive answers to existential questions and then works to flesh out the details that support those answers. Its ultimate knowledge serves to assist followers in their daily lives and guide them toward uncovering solutions. Within religious contexts, there is no separation between possessing the absolute truth and claiming comprehensive knowledge, as proof is not required. Faith supplants empirical evidence, leaving little room for experimentation, exploration, or curiosity about the actual workings of the world. This is exemplified by historical maps that did not leave spaces blank, but instead featured mythical sea creatures, non-existent islands, and cities populated by unseen beings[59] (Miller, 2017).

Both eastern and western mapmakers employed similar cartography techniques. However, acknowledging ignorance was discouraged and carried severe consequences. This is evident in the church's intolerance towards scientific discoveries that contradicted religious dogma. For instance, in the 1590s, Giordano Bruno's claim of the existence of multiple planetary systems, which he termed "innumerable worlds," conflicted with the church's proclamations. The belief in multiple worlds was deemed heretical in 384 AD by Philaster, Bishop of Brescia, in his "Book on Heresies"[60] (Martínez, 2018).This heresy was the reason why the Inquisition found Bruno guilty, and he was burned at the stake in Rome's Campo de' Fiori in 1600.

World religions are often uninterested in or opposed to uncovering how the natural world operates because they presume to know the ultimate answer to all questions. Religion commences with the answer, which is God, Salvation, Enlightenment, or Transcendence, depending on the religion. However, the intricacies and specifics of the answer are not disclosed, and pursuing them is regarded as either heretical (in some religions) and punishable by death or a total distraction from the primary objective of worshiping the ultimate answer.

The "bigger than life" concept serves as a convenient catch-all principle, a black box explanation for everything that defies comprehension. It is used to provide answers to all fundamental questions. In all cases, the response boils down to God, Salvation, or Transcendence, depending on what denomination and pantheon you belong to. What is the purpose in life? The answer is God, Salvation or Transcendence. What is the origin of this world and where we came from: The answer is God, Salvation or Transcendence. How should I behave with others and what is morality: you can guess the answer is the same.

The scriptures and bibles do not provide a logical or common sense explanation of the inner workings of a deity or higher order of the universe, such as how It makes Its decisions or the logic behind Its actions. If any

---

[59] nationalgeographic.com/maps-history-horror-vacui-art-cartography-blank-spaces

[60] blogs.scientificamerican.com/was-giordano-bruno-burned-at-the-stake-for-believing-in-exoplanets

explanations are given, it is simply stated that It acts for our good, and that anything beyond that is beyond our comprehension.

There is a good reason for not providing logic, otherwise it will expose multiple logical inconsistencies within its own narrative. Take a Christian Bible as an example. For example, there are two different creation stories in the book of Genesis, with different orders of creation and different descriptions of God's actions. In the first story, God creates light, the sky, land and plants, and then creates animals and humans. In the second story, God creates Adam, then creates animals and birds, and then creates Eve.

There are also differences in genealogies. Matthew's gospel genealogy traces Jesus' lineage back to Abraham through David, while Luke's genealogy traces it back to Adam. There are discrepancies in the timelines of certain events in the Bible. The book of Exodus gives different timelines for the duration of the Israelites' stay in Egypt, with some passages suggesting a stay of 430 years, while others suggest a stay of only 215 years.

Similar contradictions exist in any religious text. The Lotus Sutra teaches about the idea of expedient means, which suggests that the Buddha may use different methods to teach different people according to their individual needs and capacities. However, this can be seen as contradictory to the idea of ultimate truth, which suggests that there is only one absolute truth that is accessible to all. This is why the idea of ultimate answer, be that God, Salvation or Transcendence is treated like a dogmatic "black box" that you should never open.

The scene from Douglas Adams' "The Hitchhiker's Guide to the Galaxy" reminds me of the dogmatic worldview present in religion. The computer in the book, when asked what is the answer to the ultimate question of life, universe and everything, provides a terse answer of "42." Needless to say that is unhelpful without further explanations, much like how the answer to life's big questions in religion is God or Transcendence without any way to decode its exact meaning.

Within the context of religion, it's challenging to ascertain whether one's chosen direction is right or wrong due to the absence of an evidence-based approach or feedback mechanism. Rather than addressing contradictions or examining empirical evidence, religious doctrines often encourage adherents to put aside doubts, with the promise that faith will be rewarded in an afterlife. This concept, by its very nature, defies empirical validation, as no one can traverse the boundary of death and return to provide evidence of what lies beyond. Scientific endeavors to quantify aspects of the afterlife, such as Duncan MacDougall's study on the 'weight of the soul,' have been met with criticism due to methodological shortcomings and a lack of rigorous, peer-reviewed evidence.In certain religious traditions, questioning established beliefs or deviating from accepted tenets of faith is seen as a transgression, which, in extreme cases, is punishable by death.

The situation is further complicated by the existence of numerous holy books, each with differing beliefs and directives. It becomes challenging to discern whether these texts are divinely inspired or simply tools fabricated by humans for manipulation. In contrast to the scientific approach, religious doctrines lack a feedback mechanism to validate the correctness of one's chosen path. Once a choice is made, doubt is discouraged and any error could potentially result in eternal suffering.

Even within the same religion, there are many variations and sects, leaving little room for error in choosing the correct path. With over 4,000 religions and more than 5,000 gods[61] (List of Religions and Spiritual Traditions, n.d.), the probability of making the right choice is only one in thousands.

The inflexibility of a dogmatic approach poses significant challenges, particularly in a world where knowledge and understanding are continually evolving. If dogma claims to present absolute truth, there would be no need to reconcile it with new facts and discoveries. However, this assumption is problematic, given that our comprehension of the world has continually shifted and expanded throughout history. For instance, while the knowledge of Earth being spherical dates back to the 6th century BC, the majority believed that the Earth was flat until the Middle Ages. Furthermore, practices that were once deemed supernatural, such as flying, are now commonplace; today, people routinely travel vast distances by plane. Thus, the unchanging nature of dogmatic beliefs is frequently at odds with our ever-evolving understanding of the world, accentuated by advancements in scientific knowledge. This incongruity highlights the inherent issues with a rigid, dogmatic approach to comprehending our reality.

Not only does our understanding continue to evolve, but the world itself is in a perpetual state of flux. In antiquity, societal change was relatively slow due to limited access to information, communication, and technology. However, in today's era, our reality is strikingly different. We have instantaneous access to a wealth of information from around the globe, and the pace of change is accelerating at an unprecedented rate. The Earth itself, a billion years ago, was vastly different from what we know today. We would not have been able to survive in the ancient atmosphere, deficient in oxygen, for more than a few minutes. This constant transformation of our world underscores the challenges presented by a static, dogmatic approach to understanding our existence.

The limitations of a dogmatic approach become especially apparent when religious beliefs directly contradict established scientific evidence, such as the age of the Earth. Some religious texts explicitly claim that the Earth is about 6,000 years old. Radiocarbon dating[62] (Radiocarbon Dating, n.d.), which uses the natural decay of carbon-14 in organic material, has been used to accurately date objects and fossils that are much older than 6,000 years, with some dating back billions of years.

---

[61] en.wikipedia.org/wiki/List_of_religions_and_spiritual_traditions

[62] en.wikipedia.org/wiki/Radiocarbon_dating

The primary concern with a dogmatic approach is that its rigidity can cause us to overlook significant, and at times perilous, changes. Ignorance, resulting from a lack of adaptability or refusal to acknowledge new information, can even lead to extinction. For instance, the Aztec civilization remained oblivious to events unfolding beyond their empire's borders, despite the Spanish colonization of the Caribbean progressing unabated for many decades. Their ignorance and lack of curiosity about the world outside their rigid perspective left them underprepared and vulnerable to external threats.

A similar fate befell the Roman Empire. Rome's military, political, and social structures had been instrumental in its ascendancy and sustained dominance for centuries. However, these structures eventually proved inadequate in responding to the evolving challenges the empire faced. In the face of external invasions, economic crises, and internal political instability, Rome's dogmatic adherence to its traditional systems failed to provide the necessary flexibility and adaptation, contributing to its decline and fall.

One could indeed state that the ever-evolving world challenges the constancy of the laws of nature as deduced by science. However, it is important to understand that science is inherently self-correcting. Through the scientific method, it has mechanisms in place to identify errors, rectify inconsistencies, and adapt to new information.

Moreover, scientific progress does not necessarily invalidate preceding theories but rather refines them. For instance, the advent of quantum mechanics did not negate the principles of classical mechanics. Both lead to compatible conclusions on the macroscopic scale. Quantum mechanics simply provides explanations for phenomena at the atomic and subatomic level, a domain beyond the scope of classical mechanics. Therefore, while the world and our understanding of it continually evolve, science constantly adapts and expands its knowledge base.

Indeed, traditionally, religious doctrines do not possess mechanisms to detect and rectify errors. Unlike scientific paradigms, religious dogmas tend to be fixed and immutable. There are instances in religious history where assertions or challenges to established religious norms have led to grave consequences for the assertors. A notable example is Jesus of Nazareth who, according to Christian belief, was crucified for asserting a new religious vision that challenged the established religious order of his time.

There are examples of world religions trying to adapt to a changing reality of the world around them. For example, the Catholic Church of Germany started to recognize same sex marriages in 2023[63] (Catholic Church and Same-Sex Marriage, n.d.). This usually happens in spite of its rigidity, rather than because of any builtin mechanisms to accept the change.

Without a process to detect and rectify inconsistencies or inaccuracies, the likelihood of persisting in erroneous beliefs or practices increases. Over time, these inaccuracies can accumulate, potentially becoming harmful or

---

[63] en.wikipedia.org/wiki/Catholic_Church_and_same-sex_marriage

even disastrous for societies or civilizations. By contrast, if we approach the question of life's meaning with an open mind, we can devise a thoughtful process for discovering our own unique purpose, thereby moving beyond the confines of a dogmatic, black box approach. It's high time we opened this black box and investigated the myriad possibilities within.

This brings to mind a long conversation I had with a classmate who was a member of the Jehovah's Witnesses. It was a marathon dialogue that spanned four hours, maintaining civility despite bordering on heated exchanges. Despite our friendly intentions, we made no headway in reconciling our divergent beliefs, which I now attribute to our vastly differing fundamental premises. He was unwavering in his belief in Jehovah and steadfastly committed to the concept of faith. Moreover, he was sincerely intent on "saving me" – a process he had already undergone with his wife, brother, and parents, all of whom had become Jehovah's Witnesses. While I enjoyed the company of my classmate and our shared bottles of wine, I found myself intrigued by how his modern mind could be so fully engrossed by his faith.

The fact that religion, despite its inherent rigidity and limitations, could exert such a powerful influence over educated individuals made a significant impression on me. The persuasive power of faith can indeed be monumental, and such a characteristic could be harnessed to steer collective efforts toward common beneficial goals, such as the preservation of humanity's future.

With this in mind, I began to envision the potential of a societal institution that could integrate the flexibility of scientific inquiry, the comprehensive knowledge acquisition, and the empirical scientific method intrinsic to science, with the potent faith and conviction embodied in global religions, minus the restrictive dogma. Such an institution could foster critical thinking, inquisitiveness, and the relentless pursuit of knowledge, while concurrently offering the solace and motivation that faith can bestow. It could serve as a common ground where individuals from diverse backgrounds and belief systems could congregate and learn from one another, all the while upholding their unique perspectives and faiths.

Can we construct such a bridge between religion and science, or is the gap between them too big?

Gaps Between Fundamental Science and Traditional Religions

In our discussion about constructing a connection between religion and science, my focus will be limited to fundamental religion and fundamental science. By 'fundamental science,' I'm referring to scientific research that primarily seeks to understand the laws of the universe without an immediate focus on their practical applications. On the other hand, 'fundamental religion' is commonly associated with a belief system grounded in a literal and rigid interpretation of religious scriptures. This will make the exercise of evaluating gaps between those two more feasible.

If fundamental science does not readily offer solutions to the questions about the meaning of life, and fundamental religion is inflexible and fails to adjust to scientific knowledge that goes against its tenets, where then can we derive an understanding of life's purpose, both individually and for all of humanity, from a scientific perspective? One might suggest bypassing the search for a universal human purpose, focusing instead solely on personal meaning. However, one's personal meaning is intrinsically tied to the broader context of humanity. Absent humanity, individual purpose loses its significance. Hence, if we aspire to comprehend our own meaning, it's essential to contemplate the direction and purpose of humanity as a whole.

We can also choose our own belief system without considering others, similar to the dogmatic approach of many world religions. However, this approach tends to be rigid and unchanging, failing to address changes in the world and ignoring obvious contradictions. The entrapment caused by dogmatic thinking discourages questioning core beliefs and creates doubt.

A scientific worldview is more flexible and allows dissent. The ability to question authority is important in the scientific approach. Our personal meaning is based on our impact on humanity. If humanity were to cease to exist, our legacies and permanent impact would no longer have meaning. $E = mc^2$ will no longer mean anything if there are no brains to interpret that equation. The creations of humanity, the pyramids, castles and temples that survived through millennia and are considered as amazing achievements in art and architecture, the wonders of the world, will become just rocks and stones, having no more meaning than canyons and cliffs of nature landscapes around us. With the wonders of modern technology we can transcribe our books and arts into digital and permanent technology, with multiple layers of backups and redundancy, not easily destructible, but without eyes and minds to read them, all this knowledge will become locked and without meaning. Jeff Hawkins[64] (Hawkins, 2019) suggests that leaving a record of human knowledge in time capsules orbiting the Sun is a way to leave a trace of our civilization. Hawkins puts a higher priority to the process of knowledge collection and cataloging, the process driven by a newer brain, by our neural cortex. This is in contrast to the older brain functions that are purely based on survival and driven by our genetic programming. Hawkins' argument is if we focus on knowledge we will rise above our primitive nature. Cataloging and leaving the records of human knowledge in our star system, easily noticeable by alien civilization looking for traces of other intelligent life will be the action worthy of our neural cortex. However, this action would only have meaning if other advanced civilizations exist. Without the existence of an advanced civilization capable of reading and understanding our knowledge, be that human or alien civilization, our knowledge is meaningless.

---

[64] numenta.com/blog/2019/01/16/the-thousand-brains-theory-of-intelligence

It became evident to me that we must be concerned with the purpose of humanity and be willing to integrate scientific knowledge into our belief systems and do this on an institutional level. There ought to be an institution that considers both the trajectory of humanity and individual lives, maintains honesty, and possesses the capacity to persuade large numbers of people to work towards the betterment of mankind.

I wanted to find out what institutions fit the bill and can carry this task. Let us summarize our observations from the previous few chapters:

1. Science focuses on the path of understanding the natural world and has not much to say about the direction in life, and
2. Religion is concerned with reaching personal salvation and not concerned about how the natural world works.

Neither religion nor science provide a satisfactory answer to a scientifically-based approach to the direction in life. While science is focused on acquiring knowledge about the natural world, it does not address the ultimate goal or direction for humanity. Religion, on the other hand, assumes to have all the answers without concern for proving its own beliefs or adjusting to the new knowledge. This leaves a gap in providing evidence-based explanations and direction for individuals and humanity as a whole. It is important to fill this gap.

In the first part, we considered how our personal significance is derived from the legacy we leave within humanity, a way to oppose the erosive effects of time. However, what about the purpose of human civilization itself? Neither science nor religion, when examined independently, can offer us satisfactory answers. Yet, a combination of both could potentially provide an answer. This institution will be able to not only bridge the gaps between science and religion, it will connect the personal meaning with the meaning of the entire humanity.

There exists a commonality between science and religion that could potentially act as a bridge between the two. In the realm of science, it is termed trust or reputation, while in religion, it is referred to as faith.

The Role of Faith

Faith could mean multiple things. In the context of choosing the direction in life, it can be defined as a strong belief in the principles, ideas and doctrines without the need for proof. It extends beyond a simple belief to a conviction that guides one's actions and outlook on life. Faith is a potent catalyst for resilience, enabling individuals to persevere in the face of adversity and uncertainty, and thus, providing a sense of purpose and meaning. It is often the driving force behind a person's will to contribute to the larger human narrative and leave a lasting legacy.

The concept of faith is a fundamental element in any society or culture, yet it is often limited to its association with religion and religious practices. However, faith has a much broader meaning that extends beyond religious contexts. I would like to broaden faith's definition to encompass the trust in personal abilities, societal institutions, scientific principles, and the inherent goodness of humanity. As we will explore later in this chapter, a form of faith, known as axioms, is an integral and inextricable part of science.

Traditional religion has been the major source of faith in history serving as the morale guide and motivation to its subjects for centuries. In the time of angst and tribulations, religion gave people a shelter and a place to pray for difficult times to pass. It was also a social place to meet like minded people and perhaps a partner.

Similarly, our framework of goals aims to provide anchor and shelter during difficult times and give life a direction and, most importantly give our life a meaning. In that sense its goals are similar to traditional religion's goals. With one major difference, in religion the goals are inherited, passed or taught to you by your parents, your preacher or a higher power. Our framework encourages us to choose the goals ourselves, based on the impact we can create and their compatibility with our uniqueness.

Traditional Abrahamic religions indeed stress the significance of exercising free will. Western liberalism, too, is grounded in the notion of making informed choices. However, in practice, the concept of 'free choice' within religion may not be as free as it appears. If an individual consistently errs, they risk condemning their soul and being consigned to hell, whereas a life led flawlessly promises ascension to heaven. This is essentially a choice between heaven and hell.

To offer a contemporary analogy, imagine if you were given a choice between A and B, say, between assisting person A or penalizing person B. Let us also imagine that helping a person A leads to five years of excruciating torture, and choosing scenario B guarantees a vacation in a beautiful resort among pleasant company. When all things being equal would you consider A and B choices to be truly free and devoid of bias? In the context of a courtroom or modern human resource training, this wouldn't be considered a 'free choice'. In religious doctrines, the outcomes—whether torture or bliss—are perceived as eternal. This can be viewed as a form of coercion, a choice under duress.

Although a choice does exist in this scenario, it isn't truly free, as the repercussions of erring are clearly delineated. A choice is genuinely free if we are unaware of the consequences it entails—if we don't know in advance whether the choice we make is the correct one.

In our framework, we still have to make a choice to pick our goals that are bigger than our life and, thus, do constitute a higher purpose, but the choice is entirely ours. It is also free to the point that you actually do not know in advance that you are even making a correct one. The only judge here is time, which in its eventuality will show if we made a right choice and achieved what we were looking to achieve, which is the lasting legacy.

Either way, making a choice requires dedication and faith that a) we have made the right one and b) in our own abilities that we will see it through until the very completion.

The comfort, guidance and motivation provided by traditional religion were very important in past centuries, especially in the absence of shrinks and psychologists. It would help its flock to suffer harsh realities of past centuries. With the advancements of mental science this aspect is steadily being replaced with professionals and medications. We now have a choice to go to a preacher to talk about what burdens our soul or go to a shrink and discuss our mental problems. More and more people are choosing to go to a shrink. On the other front, the advancement of fundamental and applied sciences steadily filled our lives with comforts competing with the need for personal prayer for financial gains and stability. No wonder the fastest growing religious affiliation in the United States is agnosticism and atheism. According to Pew Research[65] (Smith, 2021) the share of self-identified Christians make up 63% of the U.S. population in 2021, down from 75% a decade ago and down from 90%, and other religions are trailing about and below 6%.

The situation in Europe is even worse. According to a report by the Pew Research Center, the percentage of adults in Europe who identify as Christian has declined from 75% in 2010 to 65% in 2020. The number of people who identify as unaffiliated with any religion has increased from 18% in 2010 to 26% in 2020[66].

There is an ever growing movement to oppose religion in the fields of scientific education and popularization of science, most notably "the unholy trinity" of the 21st century, Richard Dawkins, Christopher Hitchens and Sam Harris. They are brilliant evolutionary biologists and pugilistic polemics who have long argued that religion is not only redundant in the modern day and age but causes irreparable harm to humanity. The argument goes that religion is historically a primary cause or a primary instrument of crusades and colonial conquests. Even when there are no violent campaigns, the religion distracts from focusing on this world by promises of the next world. This in itself serves as a distraction from solving immediate problems humanity is facing right now. To quote Dawkins: "I am against religion because it teaches us to be satisfied with not understanding the world."

Despite all the perceived drawbacks and harm, religion survived for millennia and is still thriving in developing countries. By using the very argument that "unholy trinity" thinkers voiced about ruling principles of evolutionary survival, religion proved itself a stable social construct too stubborn to be replaced or go away entirely.

---

[65] pewresearch.org/three-in-ten-us-adults-are-now-religiously-unaffiliated

[66] en.wikipedia.org/wiki/Religion_in_the_European_Union

The social phenomenon that existed for so long has proven its place and function in human history. It has evolutionary value, the same way the species that survived for millennia proved themselves to be more fit to outlive all others who perished. After all, in our own framework the only judge of right versus wrong is time, and if religion exists through time it must be doing something right.

Religion is founded on the concept of faith, which is a strong belief in the doctrines of the religion without the need for empirical evidence. Faith is a way for followers to accept religious teachings without questioning them. It has traditionally served as a counterbalance to science, where everything is expected to be based on facts and scientific evidence. However, this view is overly simplistic. Science does rely heavily on observation, interpretation, and the formation of conclusions and theories, as well as the testing of those theories through carefully designed experiments. This approach is known as the scientific method, which is an essential tool for scientific progress. Through the testing of scientific theories, it is possible to distinguish between scientific truth and falsehood, and this process is based on the concept of inductive reasoning.

Inductive reasoning is a process of deducing an underlying principle from a series of observations. This process is based on the assumption that the same phenomenon observed repeatedly will invariably happen again. If we saw a sunrise for many years every day, we would assume that the sun will rise again tomorrow. David Hume, a Scottish enlightenment philosopher of the 18th century first questioned whether always believing that the future will always resemble the past is a concept scientifically strong enough. He first formulated "the problem of induction"[67] (Howson, 2003) by questioning the validity of making predictions about unobserved things based on previous observations and basically claimed that scientific induction is completely unfounded.

There is no logical reason for the sun to rise tomorrow the same as yesterday and today. Hume had no answer to the problem other than to basically ignore it. His contemporary philosopher, Immanuel Kant, responding to Hume, tried to solve the problem and failed. Currently modern science has been in the same position since the 18th century. It continues to ignore the problem by postulating that scientific induction is ground level assumption, a sort of an axiom. In other words, scientists take it as a matter of faith because it is so important. One of the pillars of science, a scientific method is based on predicting the unobserved outcome of experiments based on previous observations. Without induction this will break any scientific tests.

Perhaps a better approach would be instead of proving a theory to be true, instead to focus on falsification of the theory. This was the thesis of Karl Popper[68] (Shearmur & Turner, n.d.). He was an influential 20th-century

---

[67] en.wikipedia.org/wiki/Problem_of_induction

[68] en.wikipedia.org/wiki/Karl_Popper

philosopher of science who criticized the traditional view of scientific induction. He rejected the idea that scientific knowledge could be built solely upon the process of inductive reasoning, where general principles are derived from a collection of specific observations.

Popper argued that induction is inherently flawed and unreliable, as it is impossible to guarantee the truth of a universal statement based on a finite number of observations and that we can never be certain that our scientific theories are true, regardless of how many successful tests they have undergone.

Instead, Popper proposed an alternative approach called "falsificationism." He believed that scientific progress could be better understood through a process of conjecture and refutation. In this view, scientists develop hypotheses and then attempt to falsify them through empirical testing. If a hypothesis survives rigorous attempts at falsification, it is considered to be provisionally true or, more accurately, not yet proven false.

Popper's falsificationism emphasizes the importance of critical testing, where experiments are designed to challenge existing theories. He maintained that a theory's scientific status is determined by its capacity to withstand falsification, rather than by its ability to predict or explain observed phenomena. This approach shifted the focus of scientific inquiry from verifying theories through induction to attempting to disprove them through falsification.

There are few other assumptions that science takes as a matter of faith, things like assuming that the laws of physics are invariant and independent on location. That the law of gravity works the same way on Earth, Jupiter or another galaxy. We did test the validity of invariance of laws of physics experimentally here on Earth and by observing trajectories and light emanated by extremely remote objects, but science did not test every single phenomenon and every single observation. The physics tested enough of the body of evidence to come to modern scientific theories, but even those theories are not without contradictions.

In reality faith has as important a role in scientific research as in religion. The main difference is that natural scientists such as physicists and chemists are trying to minimize the number of underlying assumptions, so that occurrences of faith in science are rare by design. Most of the statements in science are derived from first principles and any new phenomenon is being probed and any new theories or discrepancies in the old ones lead to extensive questioning. Religion on the other hand requires of its subjects a total and complete faith, and most of the statements are taken without any doubt or questioning.

Faith is present in various aspects of our lives, including politics, social interactions, and personal relationships. In romantic relationships, faith often plays a critical role in maintaining the bond between partners, especially during challenging times.

Faith permeates society and people's interactions. It is everywhere in political and social institutions. Many societal norms are based on faith in those norms and exist solely because people believe in them. Perhaps the most striking example is money. People's energy is funneled into making money to fuel their aspirations and dreams, especially in western society but pretty much universally around the world. This is done rightfully so, because money by construction is defined as a unit of value. A unit to value pretty much everything. Money replaced barter economies of ancient civilization and was probably one of our greatest inventions. Instead of exchanging a pound of corn for the promise of haircuts for the next few months, a farmer sells corn, gets money and goes and gets a haircut whenever his hair gets long in the future. Yet the whole concept of money only works because enough people believe that those green or brown or red pieces of paper or pieces of shiny metals are worth anything. The minute the majority of people lose this faith in money, the whole economy of the society collapses. We did observe this in countries that underwent an explosive hyperinflation, people would panic and entire institutions would collapse, institutions, such as banking and lending. This could lead to uprisings and riots that are always accompanied by violence and death.

The same argument applies to faith in modern institutions. For example, most of the banks around the world are over leveraged. This means that the amount of money they claim on the books is multiple times of the amount of liquid capital they actually have at their disposal. This makes business and fiscal sense, as the banks can borrow money and immediately invest it in other parts of the economy. This, however, only works, because borrowers believe that they can get their money out of banks at any moment. The minute banking customers lose that faith and rush to get their money out, the banking institutions will halt and some will collapse. The most stark example of this was occurring I was editing my book with the collapse of the SVB bank[69] (Collapse of Silicon Valley Bank, n.d.) in less than 48 hours. This is an example of people losing faith in a financial institution.

This faith is not just the matter of personal spirituality and scientific rigor, but it has major material consequences in the world around us. But this happens only if enough people have the same belief. The more people who have faith the more chances that whatever they believe will materialize. We as humans have an ability to manifest our faith into reality, with numbers and time. That also works on an individual level. If we believe in our goals long enough and support our faith with actions and keep working on them, the probability that our goals will materialize increases until they become reality.

When working on your own personal life meaning, it would take the conviction and faith of just one person, you. When the fate and meaning of entire humanity is concerned, it would take the convincing of a majority of people to work together.

---

[69] en.wikipedia.org/wiki/Collapse_of_Silicon_Valley_Bank

Without faith it is impossible to realize the substantial impact on other people, and, conversely, faith is the ultimate result of the substantive impact. When our ideas are taken by a large number of people who are compelled to act on them, then our legacy is truly manifested. My frequent and favorite example is the formula $E = mc^2$, and the mind boggling complexity hidden within a misleading simplicity. Common folk do not go routinely and conduct experiments to prove that equation. A complete set of equations is more complex and takes much more space to express them here. At some point in the last century there were numerous eyes and minds examining and validating those equations at length in a peer review process. But once the process of validation stopped, we no longer doubt or question Einstein's genius, we simply take it on faith as a snippet of a much larger body of research.

It's imperative that we distinguish between the concepts of faith and blind faith. The journey from unearthing new knowledge to validating a scientific theory, and ultimately accepting it as a fact of life, is starkly different from blind faith. At any given time, we can revisit the sources and reevaluate the legitimacy of any evidence. Nonetheless, many individuals choose to rely on reputation rather than undertake this verification themselves. The hyper-connected nature of our world facilitates this process, as any noticeable lapses in logic are rapidly uncovered.

For example, the fact that we use LED screens on our computers and TVs, like when reading this text, depends on the underlying principles of quantum mechanics and modern physics. Any inconsistencies in reality, similar to what was portrayed in the Matrix movies, would be easily detected due to the interconnectedness of our world. This is why it is nearly impossible for many popular conspiracy theories to withstand scrutiny. When subjected to the peer review process, which is widely accepted in scientific communities, the foundations of such theories often crumble.

There are multiple examples of well documented conspiracy theories. There is the Flat Earth theory that posits that the Earth is a flat disc-shaped object, rather than a spherical planet, and that this truth is being covered up by scientists, governments, and other organizations. Followers of this theory believe that all photos of the Earth as a globe are fake and part of a massive conspiracy to keep the truth hidden. The Fake Moon Landing suggests that the United States government faked the 1969 moon landing, and that the footage of astronauts walking on the moon was actually filmed on a movie set. Supporters of this theory claim that the US government wanted to win the Space Race against the Soviet Union, and faked the landing to achieve this goal. There are various conspiracy theories that propose that the September 11, 2001 attacks on the World Trade Center and the Pentagon were planned and carried out by the US government, or that the official account of the events is incomplete or inaccurate. Some theories suggest that the US government was involved in the attacks as part of a larger conspiracy. The Illuminati conspiracy theory suggests that a secret organization called the

Illuminati controls world events and governments. The theory claims that the Illuminati has infiltrated various institutions, including the media, entertainment industry, and financial systems, and uses them to manipulate and control the masses. And most recently the conspiracy theories related to the COVID-19 pandemic range from claims that the virus is a hoax or a bioweapon created in a lab, to allegations that the pandemic is a cover-up for a larger global conspiracy. Some theories suggest that the pandemic is being used to control and manipulate the population, or that vaccines are part of a plot to harm or control people.

The problem with those theories is a difficulty to disprove them to their followers. If we only believe the statements that fall within the scope of the theory, and cast outright any argument or evidence outside or contrary to the theory, we lack the tools to deny or test the theory. Testing or denying is the impartial validation process that requires our mind to be an independent arbiter, not invested into the theory. If we are ardent followers of any of the conspiracy theories, it makes it increasingly difficult for any verification.

Once Richard Feynman, a Nobel Prize-winning physicist of the 20th century, examined the phenomenon of mediums, or people who talk to the dead. He personally visited the top 10 prominent mediums and asked them to demonstrate their abilities and every time the mediums could not show any signs of communication with the dead, claiming that environment and circumstances prevented ghosts from making contact. This is in immediate violation of the scientific method which requires repeatability of every claim. Nonetheless people are still drawn to the mediums even in this day and age, the fact that can only be explained by people's desire to keep talking to their deceased relatives and their refusal to let go.

Feynman also defined those theories that present themselves as an alternative branch of mainstream science and have all the trappings of science but lack the essence, as pseudoscience. To demonstrate his point he compared pseudoscience to "cargo cults" or "cargo religions" in his book "Cargo Cult Science." According to Feynman, a cargo cult is a group of people who adopt the superficial trappings of a scientific or technological culture without understanding the underlying principles or mechanisms that make it work.

During World War II, the Pacific Theater saw the emergence of several indigenous religious movements that came to be known as "cargo cults." These cults were based on the belief that the Western military forces, particularly the Americans, possessed supernatural powers and technology that allowed them to bring vast amounts of material wealth to the islands.

The cults believed that the Western military forces were messianic figures who would bring about a new era of prosperity and abundance. They engaged in rituals and practices that mimicked Western military drills, such as marching and saluting, and built mock landing strips and control towers in the hope that they would attract the attention of the Western forces and induce them to return with more cargo. Followers of those religions built almost identical replicas of the airplanes and repeated the same motions used to direct airplanes and traffic. From the point of view of the cargo religion, the replica of the plane and the actual planes would look the same to them. The only real difference is that mock replica planes would never fly.

Similarly, pseudoscience presents itself as scientific, but lacks the rigor and empirical evidence required for genuine scientific inquiry. Pseudoscientists often use jargon and complex-sounding terminology to give the appearance of scientific legitimacy, but their claims are often unsupported by evidence or are based on faulty reasoning.

Feynman argued that cargo cults and pseudoscience share a common tendency to rely on magical thinking and the belief in untestable, supernatural forces. Both reject the scientific method of observation, experimentation, and replication in favor of intuition, personal experience, and subjective interpretation.

The only explanation on prevalence and resilience of those theories is that people are easily convinced in things that they want to believe. What is more fascinating is that there is a predisposition among human beings to believe. I have already mentioned that this feature most likely is a result of evolutionary development where humans can congregate around an idea in overwhelming numbers to defeat any obstacle or enemy in the way. The actual content of an idea here is not as important as its ability to unite people. If we as a tribe encounter another tribe competing for a resource that is crucial for survival, there will be a conflict that could lead, and historically lead to violence between groups. We can imagine prehistorical groups that were in a conflict with each other. No matter how strong and agile the tribe is, the tribe that can command larger numbers will win. The sheer numbers do matter as there is a natural limit to how large a single tribe can get. If several tribes can unite around an idea that is more important and stronger than bounds of bloodlines or ties between relatives, then the strength in numbers is only limited by how convincing the idea is. There is another huge advantage of a large group of connected tribes. Any useful innovations, be that knowledge of tools or weapons, will be shared and propagated among the tribes, increasing not only the numbers but the quality of warriors.

I've noted that there is a growing segment of the global population identifying as agnostic or atheist. However, what they often lack is a quality that world religions offer their followers: unity under a single banner of faith. Imagine a world where those disillusioned with theism could unite under a banner more in tune with the contemporary era, placing faith in the future of humanity and our capacity to shape our own destiny.

This is probably one of the biggest conclusions I'm drawn to regarding faith. It is a toolkit that can be used for bad or good, just like science, and it really depends on how you wield it. The strength of faith is based on its ability to unite and attract people. In modern social networks, and in disciplines studying network dynamics this property is called virality. It is also conveniently written in our formula for the direction in life. Ability to impact and convince people is the gist of it.

Faith is the means and result of realization of our life's meaning. It is important on a personal level and especially significant for the ensuring of the meaning of all of humanity.

If we can wield this powerful tool we can direct it towards ensuring the future of humanity and making sure all of our lives will be meaningful.

Merger of Science and Religion

At the end of my thesis research I was faced with more crossroads. I could have applied for postdoctoral positions at less prestigious universities or major government labs. I felt that I had achieved my research goals, but I knew there was potential to go even further. At the same time, I felt that certain things were missing from my personal life. To be completely honest, I had an almost obsessive desire to have children.

Around that time I happened to witness a speech given in New York, at Columbia University, by the physicist Melvin Schwartz[70], who, along with Leon Lederman and Jack Steinberger received a Nobel Prize for the discovery of the muon neutrino. Their discovery was far-reaching: it showed groupings in pairs of elementary particles that form the basis of particle physics. Their research shed some light on the innermost structure of matter and on how the weak force works.

The lecture hall was packed with students from the physics and adjacent departments. Everybody came to listen to what the Nobel laureate was talking about. I was expecting Melvin to praise academia and recite war stories from the cutting edge of experimental physics. Instead, he encouraged us to explore the world outside of academia. He talked about his life as an experimental researcher who side-stepped physics to start his own computer security company in the Silicon Valley, and rejoined academia once he became a Nobel Prize laureate. His life came full circle. The main message of his speech was this: be flexible in choosing your meanings, so that the burden of your choices does not crush you. In other words, follow your heart. His speech made an impression on me and made my choice easier. I needed to start focusing on my personal life and achieving financial stability. Despite what many people believe, scientists do not get paid exceedingly well. It offers other great benefits, a chance to work with very smart people on meaningful and important subjects, but without great financial rewards.

The most prestigious US universities for hard science had a system where they would take more graduate students than there were open positions. This allowed them to conduct effective and comprehensive

---

[70] en.wikipedia.org/wiki/Melvin_Schwartz

research in various fields utilizing all this extra brain power, but after graduation we all had to find employment outside of our own university in the lower tier. Those universities were located in provincial centers, far away from the cities. It was a good time for me to realize the truth that my heart moved on from physics and was somewhere else. It also happened at the time when I defended my dissertation and, what is more important, got published results of my research in "Physical Review Letters"[71]. This was the fulfillment of my first goal in life. My choice was to continue my career in science, but I was pretty burned out in physics and was ready for the next page in my life.

It took me a while, but the system that I developed over the previous years actually helped me with finding this new page in my life. I knew I wanted to have children and focus on my personal life and this required financial stability that physics and science could not offer.

Several of my older fellow graduate students succeeded in switching from science to a new career on Wall Street and, by doing this, kind of paved the way for the rest of us. Columbia University being in the proximity of the financial center of the world made it easier. In the late nineties one of the trends in the financial industry was development and pricing of new financial instruments, called derivatives. Those financial instruments are based on the prices of more basic securities, stocks and bonds, and that's why they are called derivatives. It makes them more flexible to the financial needs of the customers and also very dangerous if they are priced wrong. This is why pricing them correctly was of a high priority and the investment banks did not spare any expenses to hire the best experts. So it happened that the way the stock prices behave is quite chaotic and their behavior resembles the movements of the heated particles in the air. Those processes are called brownian motion and physicists have been studying those processes for quite a long time. Naturally higher-ups on Wall Street thought that hiring physicists would equate to hiring experts in the field of derivative pricing. This is why physics departments of New York universities were routinely raided and poached for graduate students and postdocs.

My peers at Columbia University, many of whom were immigrants like myself, hailed from various countries such as Russia, Romania, Mexico, and Canada. We shared a similar trajectory, transitioning from studying and conducting research in physics to pursuing careers at prestigious investment banks and financial companies on Wall Street. This path was well-trodden by junior grad students, who often followed in the footsteps of their more experienced counterparts.

We developed a strong sense of camaraderie and supported one another throughout our journey. For instance, a Russian friend of mine went through a challenging technical interview at Morgan Stanley, where he was asked to solve puzzles and answer computer science questions. Although he didn't pass the interview, he relayed the questions to another friend who had an

---

[71] journals.aps.org/prl/abstract/10.1103/PhysRevLett.83.4943

interview scheduled later that day. Armed with this information, our friend was able to prepare for the questions, successfully pass the interview, and ultimately land a job at the bank.

In another instance, a Canadian friend called me for help with a puzzle question during his interview process. I was able to solve it and provide him with the answer, which contributed to him securing a position at JP Morgan. These examples highlight the collaborative spirit among us as we sought to transition into the lucrative world of finance.

I, too, embraced this opportunity and, within six months of graduating, started working at Bloomberg Financial Company. This career shift not only allowed me to utilize my skills in a new and exciting domain but also presented me with a significantly higher starting salary than an entry-level position in physics would have. In fact, the compensation was nearly twice as much for what seemed like half the intellectual work, making the challenging journey I had undergone to reach this point all the more rewarding. This transition demonstrated the value of adaptability and having flexible goals.

I did not get to do the financial derivatives pricing, but I worked on detection of anomalies in the network. Bloomberg's business model was to price financial instruments and sell access to the prices and other valuable financial information via their terminals. Those terminals were and still are very expensive. For traders to have a Bloomberg terminal on their desk was a subject of bragging rights, similar to driving a Porsche or having an expensive watch. No wonder it was very important to make sure there would be no interruptions in the information delivery. That was the main focus of my job, to monitor network traffic and detect as early as possible if something is wrong.

A photo with Mike Bloomberg at a company picnic. At that time, Mike was running (successfully) for the mayorship of New York City and was taking pictures with everyone.

In a fascinating turn of events, my first project at Bloomberg Financial Company involved tracking down a hacker from my home country. At that time, Bloomberg relied on its own obscure messaging protocol for internet communication, following the principle of "security through obscurity." This allowed the IT department to postpone transitioning to a more secure communication method. However, the hacker proved to be quite adept technically and managed to reverse-engineer the protocol.

This breach enabled the hacker to access the email of Bloomberg's owner, Mike Bloomberg, and to begin sending extortion emails directly from his account, demanding money. While the hacker infiltrated the Bloomberg network, our team worked tirelessly to hack back into his computer. I often stayed past midnight to align with the hacker's timezone and initiate our counter-hacking efforts.

Ironically, the hacker's skills in blackmail fell short of his coding prowess. Instead of demanding millions of dollars and crippling a significant portion of the company's network, he kept threatening to do so while asking for a mere hundred thousand dollars. His eventual downfall came when Mike Bloomberg offered him a high-paying job as a security consultant, contingent upon attending an in-person meeting in the "neutral" city of London. As soon as the hacker signed the contract, he was apprehended by Scotland Yard, bringing an end to this exhilarating chapter.

With the hacker issue resolved, my team and I moved on to more routine projects, having gained valuable experience and insight into the ever-evolving world of networks and financial IT.

I have seen good and bad, and experienced both the beautiful and the devastating aspects of life in New York City. I have seen firsthand the powerful forces of nature, such as the destruction wreaked by hurricanes that have hit the city. These storms have caused massive flooding, especially in the subways, disrupting the daily lives of millions of residents and leaving a lasting impact on the city's infrastructure.

In contrast, I have also had the unique opportunity to ski down snow-covered streets that were completely empty of the usual bustling traffic. This experience highlighted the serene and magical side of the city, as the snow blanketed the urban landscape, transforming it into a winter wonderland. It was a surreal and enchanting moment that demonstrated the ever-changing nature of life in New York City.

Around that time, I reached a significant milestone in my life as I completed my immigration process by obtaining permanent residency, commonly known as the "green card." To achieve this, I had to take on the role of my own lawyer, delving into the intricacies of immigration law. My application was based on the category of "Extraordinary Abilities," which required me to gather recommendation letters from esteemed professionals to support my case.

I approached my professors at Columbia University and at Fermilab, the renowned particle physics and accelerator laboratory. I was even fortunate enough to secure a letter from a Nobel Prize laureate. Although a few individuals declined to provide a recommendation, the majority graciously agreed to support my application. With determination and perseverance, I completed the necessary paperwork and submitted my application.

However, the waiting period for my green card proved to be longer than expected, as the tragic events of September 11, 2001 unfolded in New York City. The terrorist attacks on the World Trade Center towers sent shockwaves around the globe, forever changing our understanding of security and the ever-present threat of terrorism. The devastating loss of life and the destruction of the city's iconic skyline left an indelible mark on the hearts and minds of all New Yorkers. This tragic event created a clear divide between the time before and after the attacks. Prior to the tragedy, a sense of invincibility prevailed; however, after the attacks, this feeling was replaced by a loss of innocence and an acute awareness of vulnerability.

Yet, in the face of such adversity, I also observed the incredible resilience and solidarity of the city and its people. The aftermath of the attacks saw New Yorkers from all walks of life coming together to offer support, compassion, and assistance to one another. The community united in their grief and resolve to rebuild and heal, demonstrating the indomitable spirit that has always defined the city. From the kindness of strangers offering help and comfort to the tireless efforts of first responders and volunteers, the city proved that even in the darkest of times, hope and unity can shine through.

One of the most remarkable aspects of my tenure on Wall Street was the degree of innovation in software development and financial technology. The teams I collaborated with were perpetually pushing the envelope, devising state-of-the-art algorithms and tools that empowered traders to make more informed decisions and carry out trades with greater speed and efficiency. The pace of work was vastly different from academia; tasks were completed much more rapidly, words were spoken at a brisker pace, and the trading floor was often filled with shouting and profanity—something I had never witnessed in the lab or university settings.

I remember how, in London, we took a prospective quantitative researcher who was applying for a job in brokerage on a tour of the broker floor, attempting to impress him with the bustling activity. Instead, the brokers, who disapproved of his appearance, repeatedly chanted "dork." What was intended to be a display of prowess for the candidate turned into a rather embarrassing experience. This atmosphere was far from the collegial environment of academia and more closely resembled a fish market, which, incidentally, was located right next to the brokerage.

All the screaming and cursing on the trading floor is due to the stress of losing money or missing opportunities. Fear and greed are prevalent on Wall Street, and I've seen careers, groups, and even firms rise and fall within a span of a couple of years. I too experienced failure there, probably for the first time in my still young life. Up until a certain point, I learned that through perseverance and hard work, you can achieve almost anything within your capabilities. Then one day, I was laid off on the spot, and it actually happened twice in my career. The first time was during the housing crisis, where I was laid off from a prestigious trading group of a major investment bank. The bank was letting thousands of people go, and I was one of them. I felt devastated, belittled, and humiliated. The first thing I did was go to a bar downstairs and drink two full glasses of whiskey without getting drunk. It took me a while to recover emotionally, but I found a job before my severance package ran out.

The second time it happened, I felt less stressed and more familiar with the feeling. I was hired by a high-frequency trading company at a time when the US government was fighting off corruption within old guard brokerage houses. It was 2008, and the government opened up the stock market to competition and introduced price protections for investors. These price protections were only possible through computer technologies, and just like that, government regulations heralded the dawn of a new era of equity markets. These sets of rules were called the Regulation National Market System, or RegNMS for short. Before the new regulation, traders could only buy IBM on the New York Stock Exchange. With the promulgation of RegNMS, traders could buy it on any exchange that offered it, and they had to procure the best price for their clients. As a result, whoever got first to the best price would be the winner, and as it often happens in financial markets, winners usually take it all. That was the end of the era for the wolves of Wall Street and the beginning of the age of the piranhas of high-frequency and low-latency trading. Many firms were born that invested heavily in technology to make them the fastest. I joined one of those companies as the head of market data.

The company made an incredible amount of money, leading them to make a common mistake. They assumed their prosperity would last indefinitely, and they began to expand exponentially, both in terms of personnel and market reach. Unfortunately, their luck eventually ran out, and they laid off 50% of the company, including me. While I was there, I witnessed behavior reminiscent of Hollywood movies about Wall Street excess, even though we were based in Chicago.

To cope with the high-stakes environment's stress and fatigue, traders would get drunk and intoxicated around noon. For the Christmas party, management flew the entire company to Las Vegas. Everyone became heavily intoxicated, an up-and-coming developer urinated in a fountain in front of everyone, and the entire group was kicked out of a high-end restaurant. Those were just a few of the least controversial incidents I observed before everything came crashing down. Several years later when I was living in London I met a trader from this company who told me even crazier stories, among them one trader buying a gun to exact revenge on another trader who stole his girlfriend, who was dealing drugs to all of them during work hours. I am not sure how much of it is the actual truth, but seeing this environment with my own eyes I would believe at least parts of his stories.

Due to my non-compete contract, finding a job in my industry was a challenge. In the end, I learned that imbalance, excess, and hysteria are symptoms of an unhealthy company that would eventually fall apart. On the other hand, a balanced and friendly team that can laugh together as hard as it can work together is indicative of a successful work environment.

As for the failures, they are an inevitable part of life, especially when you're living in the fast lane. What truly matters is how quickly you recover from them and how you learn and grow as a result. Failures can be great teachers, providing valuable lessons that help you become a stronger, more resilient person. They can also serve as opportunities to reevaluate your priorities and make necessary adjustments to your life and career. The key is to prioritize what truly matters and to cultivate resilience, adaptability, and a growth mindset.

Eventually I found a job back in New York with Cantor Fitzgerald. I was glad I was laid off and escaped this very entertaining but disastrous circus of a job. During my time on Wall Street, I witnessed a full spectrum of human behavior. While there were those who would do whatever it takes to get ahead, even if it meant throwing others under the bus, there were also those who showed incredible professionalism and dedication to their work. At the height of my career, I reached the level of managing director at Cantor Fitzgerald, which was the firm that suffered the most on "Nine Eleven", losing two thirds of the workforce. They survived due to the London branch picking up all the clients and our work load and eventually helping us pull through. As a result the core of development was in London and I had to relocate there for a year and a half, serving as a global technology architect. Because of my role I did a lot of business travel, serving as an internal consultant in architecture, putting out fires in one of 200 subsidiary companies. I spent some time in Las Vegas fixing technology for sport book gaming that was setup by one of the most colorful Cantor Fitzgerald executives. I recall a three hour meeting where he talked for all three hours leaving just fifteen minutes for us to say that the projects he thought were completed were not even started. No one in his company had the courage to say this, that was the primary reason for our trip, to bring sobering news. As we expected, he exploded in a fiery speech but he had enough business sense to ask for our advice. Those trips were fun, not just because of exotic locations but due to the sense that we were making a real difference and offered some needed help.

During this time, another significant event unfolded in my life. In the same year that I started working on Wall Street, the woman I had previously met on an internet chat at Fermilab relocated to New York with me. This marked a pivotal moment in my life and signified progress towards achieving my second goal: establishing a family and having children.

Religion Through the Lenses of Modern Science

Science and religion have both achieved remarkable feats. The scientific method has enabled science to distinguish between what is true and what is false, leading to remarkable discoveries and progress. On the other hand, one of religion's most notable achievements has been the concept of faith, which has the capacity to unite vast numbers of people under a common banner. To me, this unifying capability was far more significant than the specific tenets of the faith itself.

For an idea to unite people effectively, it must benefit the group and not lead to its downfall. If the idea ultimately leads to the demise of the group, then the idea and its followers will perish as well. Therefore, I believe that rallying people to unite humanity under the banner of science—the very science that discerns external threats, models reality, and equips humanity with new technologies and capabilities—would prove beneficial for mankind's survival.

If we can persuade the general population to view science not just as an elite discipline but as a guiding moral force, humanity could address existential threats more effectively and rapidly. This approach would foster mutual benefits. It would ease scientists' efforts to explain and propagate new discoveries, and the broader public could have a more influential role in shaping the moral compass that guides scientific development.

For that to happen, we need to find a way to harmonize science and religion. To do so, we first have to establish a common foundation rooted in first principles. Earlier, I opted for the first principles of evolutionary biology and its pivotal principle of survival as the framework for studying both religion and science. By scrutinizing these two institutions through the lens of evolution and survival, we can start to carve out a common platform for discussion and investigation.

This approach may be considered controversial, as evolutionary biology stands as somewhat of an outlier among the hard sciences due to its potential clash with established theistic religions. Quantum mechanics and material science, in comparison, do not generate as much controversy or friction with world religions as the conclusions drawn from the theory of evolution. This discrepancy arises from the direct contradiction between the Darwinian theory of evolution and literal statements in the Old Testament regarding the origin of humans and other species. However, I believe that in order to reconcile these contradictions, we must begin with first principles, and evolution, in its most fundamental form, appears to be the most apparent choice. As we explored in the chapter on first principles, it states: "What survives is what survives," which represents one of the most basic forms of truth. Ultimately, religious institutions remain relevant in our culture for the same reason—they have survived and, as a result of surviving, they continue to provide value.

The theory of evolution by means of natural selection, proposed by Charles Darwin, is often subject to misconceptions in popular literature. One common misconception is that humans originated from monkeys or primates. However, this is not accurate. Humans and primates are distant relatives, with a shared evolutionary history. The theory of evolution explains the origin of species as a natural result of the evolutionary process, through genetic mutation and adaptation over time. Despite the overwhelming evidence supporting the theory of evolution, there are still pockets of resistance and friction to its ideas in conservative parts of the world, including some developed countries like the United States. This resistance is often rooted in a lack of understanding or misinformation about the theory, leading to its continued misunderstanding and misrepresentation in popular discourse.

Instead evolutionary biology puts survival instinct as a main motivator in behaviors of multiple species, including us humans. To that extent, the eminent zoologist G.G. Simpson said: "The point I want to make now is that all attempts to answer that question (about the meaning of life) before 1859 are worthless and that we will be better off if we ignore them completely". Darwin's theory offers probably the most significant answer and motivation for the meaning of humans and actually any life on this planet. I wholeheartedly agree with this statement and I think it is high time for science to turn to existential questions, starting with the direction in life. It is time for science to offer more than just dry explanations of how nature works and fill the gap between religion and science.

If we approach this gap between religion and science that we described in the previous chapters, from the point of view of evolutionary principles, we can then reconcile any differences in the two approaches. That focus on survival of future generations translated into myths and written works thought out and read by countless minds, including the Gilgamesh story.

Religion started with the dawn of civilization and continues to this day, despite what critics of religion say. The loudest of critical voices come from proponents of evolution. Even when taking into account shortfalls of religion according to those critics, according to evolutionary logic, traditional religion deserved respect and attention because of religion's ability to survive and multiply.

This ability of religious ideas and tenets to survive begs for a closer examination. I believe this amazing capability of religion is explained by the phenomenon of faith. Faith is not the sole property of religion but was perfected by it in the course of human history. This exciting possibility as an explanation has been offered by Yuval Harari[72] (Harari, 2015). The main quality is not its world building or an ability to explain much about the world which we have shown leaves much to be desired. It is the ability to attract as many people under its banner as possible. Harari put it this way when he tried to explain how with an abundance of human species, only Homo Sapiens

---

[72] en.wikipedia.org/wiki/Sapiens:_A_Brief_History_of_Humankind

survived. His explanation is that it is due to the ability of humans to create narratives and believe stories that capture our minds. I would make a stronger statement that this is because of our ability to believe, because of our faith.

Harari also makes an interesting observation about the maximum size of a sustainable tribe. This number is called Dunbar's number and is named after the British anthropologist Robin Dunbar, who in the 1990s proposed a correlation between primate brain size and average social group size. He proposed a number between 100 and 250, with a commonly used number of 150[73] (Dunbar's Number, n.d.). He asserted that beyond that limit, imposed by human neocortical processing capacity, tribes or groups larger than this, generally require more restrictive rules, laws, and enforced norms to maintain a stable, cohesive collective. Beyond that number, the tribe of ancient people and/or group of apes will splinter into smaller ones.

I disagree with Dunbar's explanation that links this number to limits in our neocortical processing capacity, as our brains are capable of handling much more complex tasks, such as learning to pilot planes and remember thousands of characters. In the Appendix, I offer another explanation and an actual derivation of the formula that links it to the number of immediate and distantly related family members. Whatever the explanation, there does seem to be a limit to the maximum number of people in a stable social group. This makes our ability to believe and unite under a faith banner even more amazing.

In the thought experiment described in Dunbar's book, let us imagine a conflict situation where Homo sapiens faced a different species who did not have our ability for blind faith. For instance Neanderthals who, besides having tools, communication skills and language abilities, were much stronger than humans. In that scenario, a human tribe of equal size would lose to Neanderthals, with a few human survivors returning to their former grounds.

Yet even after their loss, the Homo sapiens tribe could come back to fight in much larger numbers. This is because of their ability to use faith to enlist much larger groups under the faiths banner. The Neanderthals who lacked this ability would be limited to a group size of approximately less than 150. Even if a larger group of people lost their battle, they could gather an even larger number of people, i.e., an army. For example, in the battle of Yunnan, the Ming dynasty raised an army of 300,000, which is probably the largest recorded army in the middle ages. This ability to congregate into very large groups could be why Homo sapiens dominated all the regions and landscapes of the world and are the only surviving homo species. This ability may have incentivised to multiply even further inadvertently pushing humanity into agricultural and other technological revolutions that allowed humanity to increase in numbers even further.

---

[73] en.wikipedia.org/wiki/Dunbar%27s_number

This ability becomes even clearer when we look at the evolution of religions (no matter how contradictory this term sounds). We can notice a clear pattern of consolidation of power among gods and deities. Religion started with worshiping elements that are more powerful than people or which induce fear, lightning, storms, volcano eruptions, combined with worshiping our deceased ancestors, again memento mori. This has created a lot of gods and demigods in multi-theistic religions. Religions that replaced them were creating a clear structure with a pantheon of Greek and Roman gods. In Hinduism there were thousands of gods, but there was again a clear hierarchy among them that replicated a complex caste system in ancient India. The clear structure helped to unite people under fewer causes and amass more resources and more people. Still, under those pantheon religions you could still choose a banner of several different gods and splinter into competing tribes. If you did not like a ruler under the banner of Zeuse you could always switch to Poseidon or Apollo. Later those were all replaced by mono-theistic religions that made it easier to gather all the people under a banner of one true God. Monotheistic religions quickly overtook pantheonic religions, I suspect, specifically under this property. Only a few religions like Buddhism and Taoism went a step further by removing necessity in any gods, yet replacing it with one overreacting principle of achieving enlightenment.

One single principle helps to gather millions of people and minds working and thinking together in one direction. This property of unification is a powerful force that is more important than the tenets of the underlying religion, its rituals and totems, that multiplies an idea or action by the number of followers and helps to manifest it into reality. This ability is what allows various religions to affect our minds throughout human history and to survive its many drawbacks. Religions by telling and retelling stories that help humanity to find its place in the world, allow people to congregate around a single cause, thus making humanity a formidable force against competition. By narrating stories that help humanity discern its position in the grand scheme of things, religions encourage people to rally around a common cause and single purpose. This collective strength, in turn, makes humanity a formidable contender in the face of calamities.

The heart of religion is in helping humanity to find its place in this world, and the core of science is in capturing the knowledge of an ever changing world and finding the right adaptations. If we combine the ability of traditional religions to capture our minds and manifest our faith with the rigor and evidence-based approach of fundamental science, we can create a discipline that is both scientific and human-centered. Such a discipline would become a powerful and positive force in human development, ensuring that all individual personal meanings are preserved within the fold of humanity.

What does this mean, though, to merge two seemingly orthogonal disciplines?

How Can We Merge Science and Religion?

Religion and science are two fundamental ways through which humans seek understanding and meaning in the world. While both domains can coexist harmoniously, there are instances when they do not align, leading to conflicts and challenges throughout human history. I believe that a combination of religion and science is necessary not only to answer our questions about the purpose of life, but also to preserve the future of humanity and with it all the answers and all of the individual lives' meanings. Science and religion approach the question of the direction in life from different angles and with different tools, but they both contribute to the overall meaning of humanity. Combining the exploration of the natural world with guiding people towards their true purpose would create a powerful discipline that provides both scientific and moral guidance to humanity. However, some may wonder if science and religion can work together. But can we even combine the two approaches?

The answer to this question of whether religion and science can coexist is in plain sight. Both religion and science have already existed for hundreds of years side by side. They did sometimes collide violently in the past on the outskirts of each other's domains, but eventually found their own domains.

During the Renaissance, there were violent collisions between religion and science, such as the inquisitions of Galileo and Giordano Bruno. However, the most controversial and far-reaching, if not violent, collision involved the Darwinian theory of evolution, which was espoused in 1859 in the Origin of Species. As we discussed earlier, Darwin's theory removed the necessity of a god to explain the origin of species on Earth, offering a compelling story of how species originated from the chaotic process of natural selection. To accept this theory, one had to abandon the belief that the Earth was only 6,000 years old, and embrace the fact that the fossil record revealed a succession of eras or ages of extinct 'living' things that extended hundreds of millions of years into the past.

This collision between science and religion continues into our age, with the modern generation of evolutionary scientists becoming a vocal opposition to religion, led by figures such as Richard Dawkins, Sam Harris, Christopher Hitchens, and Daniel Dennett, also known as the "Four Horsemen" of the new atheism or "Non-Apocalypse"[74] (Harris, n.d.).

Stephen Hawking famously stated, "There is a fundamental difference between religion, which is based on authority, and science, which is based on observation and reason. Science will win because it works." What he meant by "works" is that scientists make predictions of events before they happen and verify their hypotheses by confirming or denying whether those events unfold in the manner they have predicted through scientific experiments. This

---

[74] en.wikipedia.org/wiki/New_Atheism

scientific process instills so much confidence in the knowledge gained that it is used in applied science to manufacture and produce products used in everyday life, such as the computer I am typing on.

Despite arguments against the relevance of religion in modern times, the fact that it has survived for centuries and millennia of human history shows that it serves an important purpose. From the perspective of evolutionary science, religion has a significant survival value and constitutes a stable survival strategy. In other words, religion plays an important and perhaps irreplaceable role in human society. Religion also "works", just in a different dimension than science.

Emile Durkheim, a French sociologist, proposed that religion has three major functions in society[75] (The Functionalist Perspective on Religion | Boundless Sociology |, n.d.):

- Providing social cohesion: Religion helps to maintain social solidarity by promoting shared rituals and beliefs.
- Enforcing social control: Religion enforces religious-based morals and norms to help maintain conformity and control in society.
- Offering meaning and purpose: Religion provides answers to existential questions and offers a sense of meaning and purpose to individuals.

We have observed that religion has the remarkable ability to unite people, surpassing science in this regard. On the other hand, science provides practical solutions to everyday problems and allows us to uncover the mysteries of the universe. It has become so deeply ingrained in modern society that it is hard to imagine life without it. Combining these two essential and irreplaceable disciplines in a way that fills the gaps between them could be a significant benefit for all. The new combined view would unite the transformative power of scientific methodology with the guiding force of religious convictions. It would provide comfort in difficult times without clashing with hard science or causing confusion.

The challenge is how to successfully combine religious ideas and concepts with scientific theories and experimental facts. While historically there have been few successful attempts at this, my proposed approach is not to create a new discipline from scratch or to abandon one side in favor of the other. Instead, I propose taking the best and most effective ideas and concepts from religion and updating them with current scientific knowledge. This would require discarding outdated religious concepts and dogma, but it would create a much more resilient and adaptable discipline capable of withstanding the challenges of modern times.

Herman Hesse envisioned this exact possibility in describing a possible future where science, religion, and art would merge into a beautiful discipline

---

[75] lumenlearning.com/the-functionalist-perspective-on-religion

that captivated humanity's minds and united people around it, in his book "The Glass Bead Game" (or Das Glasperlenspiel)[76] (Hesse, December 6, 2002). He described a world where instead of prayers, people would gather in great halls to witness complex and beautiful performances by masters of the art who had spent decades preparing themselves to be the best in the game.

This process of one discipline replacing another has already happened numerous times in the past. For example, physics eventually replaced philosophy. When new religions are born or branch out, they typically do not completely replace old concepts such as existing holidays or rituals, but rather update them with more modern ones based on the most recent knowledge in society. This process, known as syncretism, allowed Christianity to gradually supplant pagan religions and customs while making the transition more acceptable and less disruptive to the local population. The celebration of Christmas is a prime example of syncretism. The holiday originally coincided with the pagan celebration of the Winter Solstice, a time of feasts, gifts, and other festivities. The Church gradually replaced the pagan celebration with the Christian celebration of the birth of Jesus Christ, and many of the pagan customs and symbols were incorporated into the Christmas celebration. The use of evergreen trees, holly, and mistletoe were all adopted into the Christian celebration. The practice of syncretism is not limited to Christianity. Islam has also replaced the Christian festival of Good Friday with the celebration of Ashura, which is an important day of mourning and remembrance in the Islamic calendar.

This blending of traditions has been a key factor in the evolution of religious practices throughout history. This same approach could be used to merge science and religion, taking the best and most effective ideas and concepts from each and rethinking them to create a more robust and cohesive discipline that can withstand the trials of modern times.

My proposed approach involves taking the foundational concepts of religion, such as the notions of good versus evil, karma, the idea of God and soul, and reimagining them through the lens of modern scientific concepts. The goal is to create a comprehensive framework that connects religious concepts with scientific principles, empowering religious ideas with the full strength of modern science while infusing science with a sense of passion and morality. The ultimate aim is to establish a new discipline that will steer humanity towards its purpose, enabling us to transcend mortality and counter the loneliness we feel in this vast universe, all while upholding the core tenets of science.

However, it is important to note that this approach is not intended to replace science, which must continue its pursuit of discovery independently. Nor does it seek to supplant traditional religions deeply rooted in existing traditions. Instead, this new discipline will complement existing systems by providing direction and guidance to humanity in pursuit of a shared purpose—

---

[76] en.wikipedia.org/wiki/The_Glass_Bead_Game

to ensure the survival of humanity and uphold human ideals. It will be a dynamic, inclusive, and novel discipline that unifies the strengths of both science and religion.

Religion excels at convincing a large number of people to follow a cause, while science is responsible for creating new technologies, tools, and cures. When religion and science work together, science can develop solutions, and religion can persuade the populace to follow them.

The consequences of the misalignment between religion and science have had a significant impact in the past and continue to do so in the present. For example, vaccine hesitancy is an area where a partnership between religion and science could have a significant impact. Vaccines created by medical scientists have managed to conquer many diseases and illnesses. However, social orthodoxy sometimes adopts these life-saving measures much slower, resulting in higher fatality rates and continued disease transmission. By bridging the gap between scientific discovery and religious acceptance, communities worldwide could benefit from faster adoption of vaccines and improved public health.

In the following chapters, I will explore the shape and form of this new proposed discipline. It will be guided by the principle of survival of humanity, choosing the direction of our lives, the importance of scale and time, thus closing the circle of personal meaning of life and the meaning of the entire human civilization. The result will be a new approach that combines the best of both religion and science, providing a path for individuals to find their place in the universe while securing the survival and flourishing of humanity.

I recognize that the list of religious concepts I will explore is by no means exhaustive. Covering every religion that has graced human history would require years and countless pages. Notably absent are the religions of the southern continents, specifically Africa and Australia. Instead, I've opted to focus on the more "popular" and widely recognized religions, broadly categorizing them as either Eastern or Western. My primary objective is to highlight the commonalities among these religions. While this approach emphasizes similarities, I concede that certain nuances may be overlooked.

While acknowledging the divide between Eastern and Western religious traditions, it is important to recognize the existence of shared concepts and similarities that can be explored. However, for the sake of clarity and due to my familiarity with Western religions, I will begin by mapping concepts between science and the Western religious traditions. It is important to note that within Western religions, there are various denominations, interpretations, and variations. In this mapping process, I will provide a generalized understanding of their tenets and beliefs, albeit at the expense of minor intricacies and non-essential nuances present in specific denominations.

Thankfully science is universal and does not have eastern or western or southern flavors. It works the same in every part of the world, and in every part of the universe.

The main goal is to find common ground and explore how religious beliefs can align with scientific concepts and principles. By doing so, we aim to bridge the gap between religion and science, creating a framework that helps us better understand and make sense of the world we live in. The objective is to develop a cohesive and meaningful understanding that combines both spiritual and scientific insights.

Scientific principles and methodologies are universally applicable and work consistently across different parts of the world and even the vast expanse of the universe. While science transcends cultural boundaries and does not possess regional biases, there is a question of a language barrier between religious and scientific communities. Many religious concepts are expressed in metaphorical and symbolic language, while scientific concepts are expressed in more precise and technical language. Therefore, finding a common language that can bridge the gap between these two worlds will be an important aspect of this process.

Despite the challenges posed by this language disparity, I firmly believe that mapping the concepts between science and religions holds the potential to unlock new avenues of exploration and foster deeper understanding.

Mapping Concepts Between Western Religions and Science

There were two competing concepts that formed the modern Western culture: Greek logos, which gave rise to logical reasoning, philosophies, and eventually science, and Judeo-Christian traditions, which form the root of morality. Despite multiple frictions and conflicts, they have managed to successfully coexist for many centuries in modern civilization, and both play a crucial role.

The ancient Greeks valued the power of reason and logic, and their intellectual legacy has laid the foundation for many of the ideas that would become central to Western philosophy, including the belief in the existence of absolute truth and the importance of critical thinking, which eventually led to the rise of scientific disciplines.

On the other hand, the Judeo-Christian traditions, encompassing the Bible, encompass foundational texts that have significantly shaped Western civilization. These texts include not only the Ten Commandments but also profound teachings such as the Sermon on the Mount and the Beatitudes. These religious teachings have imparted moral and ethical guidelines that continue to influence societal values and norms, shaping the ethical frameworks that underpin Western civilization.

Both disciplines sometimes overlapped in their respective domains. Religion claimed its share of logic and reason in order to strengthen the statements within their commandments. For instance, Paul's use of logical arguments in his epistles. In his letter to the Romans, Paul uses logical arguments to explain the relationship between faith and works. He argues that faith alone is not enough for salvation, but that it must be accompanied by works of righteousness[77] ("Romans," 2017, 2:6-8).

In the same token, science, especially behavioral science, offers insights into the origins of morality. For example, evolutionary psychology suggests that morality has evolved over time as a way to help humans survive and thrive. Altruistic behavior, such as helping others, can enhance group cohesion and increase the likelihood of group survival. Evolutionary psychologists also argue that moral intuitions, such as a sense of fairness, are innate and universal across cultures.

However, neither discipline ventured too deep outside of their own territory and kept to their roots, creating gaps in our understanding, especially in the perception of our life's meaning. This separation also led to conflicts and disagreements, particularly between science and religion. A new proposed discipline that combines the best of both worlds will fill in the gaps between the two domains and integrate scientific concepts with religious concepts, without compromising the integrity of either.

World religions care about people's lives, and see our lives as a path towards a particular destination and they are guiding us towards it. Fundamental science considers a path of knowledge acquisition as a long, perhaps never ending, road where each individual scientist contributes an extra step towards the ultimate goal of reaching the theory of everything. If world religions replaced their dogmatic approach with the scientific method, they would keep up with the world while offering compassion and moral compass to humanity.

The very fact that religion survived and thrived in people's minds throughout human history indicates its evolutionary resiliency or, in evolution terms, an evolutionary stable survival strategy[78] (Smith & Price, n.d.). Given the resiliency of religion, rather than replacing old ideas entirely, I envision the process of merging science and religion by keeping the core ideas and religious tenets but enriching them with most up to date knowledge of the world around us.

Another important step will be to replace the dogmatic approach in religion with the living process of scientific advancements. This approach ensures that any future discrepancies between religious beliefs and the evolving scientific worldview can be addressed and corrected, without impeding the progress of science. Instead of resisting scientific perspectives, religion can become a moral force that supports and advances scientific inquiry. By fostering a harmonious relationship between science and religion, we can create a framework that celebrates both the spiritual and the empirical, providing individuals with a more comprehensive and meaningful understanding of the world and their place within it.

---

[77] bible.com/bible/111/ROM.2.6-8.NIV

[78] en.wikipedia.org/wiki/Evolutionarily_stable_strategy

The core concepts of western religions can be broadly categorized into three main ideas:

- the existence of God or a personal deity,
- the battle between good and evil,
- and the concept of the soul (and karma in the eastern religions)

These ideas have been at the forefront of western religious thought and continue to shape the way many people approach their lives and the world around them. We are going to combine them with scientific ideas while maintaining their original intention.

One example of this process can be seen in the mapping of the concept of God onto the theory of everything, which aims to unify all the laws of physics into one set of governing principles that explain the observable universe. This mapping allows for a deeper understanding of the concept of an all-encompassing God and its relationship to the physical world.

Another example is the concept of the soul, which has traditionally been viewed as an immortal essence of a person's being, can also be amended and mapped onto modern scientific ideas. In this case, the soul represents the collection of the most prominent ideas forming a person's legacy long after their death. This revised concept of the soul can correspond to the right-hand side of the formula for the meaning of life that we discussed earlier:

which is a product of the reach and power of our actions under time operation (T). If you curious to see the math please see "Splitting formula into personal and humanity" in the afterword appendix for details about the formulas.

Below is my suggested mapping of religious concepts and corresponding scientific views in tabular form. Please note that this mapping is based on my understanding and interpretation of these concepts, aiming to capture their core meanings.

Religion	Science
God as a explanatory source of existence	Universe - Sum of the laws of nature
personal God	Sum of all humanity

Good	Survival and evolution
Evil	Chaos, elimination and entropy
Soul	Sum of ideas, choices and actions that makes us unique and leave a permanent impact
Karma	Responsibility to make and implement right choices, group selection in evolution

The mapping between these concepts is not meant to be exhaustive or definitive, but rather a starting point for further exploration and discussion.

To foster understanding of the new and updated concepts, I will use the original names given by religion. For instance, instead of calling a new concept of Soul, a "revised Soul" or "new Soul" or "Sum of all ideas and actions" I will still use the term "Soul". I will differentiate the concept of a universal God that knows and governs the entire universe and a personal God that knows and cares about you personally, because this concept is a loaded one and contains many different complex components that we will unpack in the following chapters. Instead of calling a new concept a universal God, I will use the term "Creator" and instead of a personal God I will use the term "Protector" to differentiate between those two concepts.

My wholehearted wish is for a discipline that will guide humanity towards its purpose of combating mortality and countering the loneliness we experience in this indifferent universe. It will give science the passion and will to be placed in the realm of morality and personal consciousness, while giving religion the full power of modern science without dogma. People will get a sense of purpose and meaning, helping us to find our place in the world and, most of all, to live meaningful lives.

I will start the mapping process with the most important yet most challenging connection between religion and science, the concept of Creator.

Revisiting the Idea of Creator

Friedrich Nietzsche's famous quote "God remains dead. And we have killed him. How shall we comfort ourselves, the murderers of all murderers"[79] (Nietzsche, 2021) does not mean that God literally died or that people killed God in a supernatural way. Rather, Nietzsche was criticizing the decline of religion and the loss of traditional moral values in modern society. He believed that people had replaced traditional religious beliefs with a new set of values based on materialism, selfishness, and fear.

This is as if he anticipated the process of evolution of the Creator's idea. Though instead of massacre we will be giving it a new life

---

[79] en.wikipedia.org/wiki/God_is_dead

In a sense, Nietzsche's insight can be seen as anticipating the evolution of the idea of The Creator. Rather than perceiving it as a violent extermination of the divine, I view it as an opportunity to breathe new life to the concept. It entails reimagining and revitalizing our understanding of The Creator in light of scientific knowledge, embracing a more nuanced and inclusive perspective.

The concept of The Creator is multifaceted, and it's important to examine each aspect separately in order to map it successfully onto corresponding scientific counterparts. The first aspect is that of a creator, which suggests that there is an entity or force that created the universe and all its contents. This idea can be mapped onto the scientific theory of the Big Bang, which posits that the universe began as a singularity that expanded rapidly and created all matter and energy.

Then there is an aspect of The Creator that is of a higher power or being that is greater than us and has control over our lives. This concept connects with the scientific concept of natural laws, which govern the behavior of matter and energy in the universe. Although these laws are not conscious beings, they operate with a kind of "authority" over the behavior of the universe.

The third concept is that of a moral lawgiver. can also be linked to the concept of social norms and cultural values. Just as a higher power in religion provides a sense of absolute moral authority, social norms and cultural values also provide a framework for understanding right and wrong and making decisions that align with our values.

The personal aspect of God as a moral compass can also be viewed as an internal moral compass that each individual possesses. This internal compass is shaped by our upbringing, experiences, and cultural background, and guides us in making decisions that are in line with our own personal values and beliefs.

This is also closely related to the notion of an omnipresent being that loves you no matter what, would never leave you alone and in difficult moments would receive your prayers and if not answer them will at least hear them. This thought helps us through hardships and illness. Knowing that we are not alone in our difficult times, in life and especially in death, is such a powerful and comforting knowledge that explains why people would accept and flock towards the idea of a personal God, not just omnipotent and omnipresent but all-loving being that knows about you personally and can hear your prayers and pleas. It is no wonder that religious institutions developed quite sophisticated rituals that prepare and comfort dying people. These rituals often involve prayer, meditation, and other spiritual practices that can help the dying person find peace and acceptance. That and a fear of death.

The first two concepts are based on the idea of God being the origin of everything, the source of all existence and the ultimate explanation of all things that happened and are happening to us, good or bad. That The

Creator is the ultimate source of all things and that He created and sustains all life. This concept also suggests that The Creator is in control of all events and that He is ultimately responsible for all that happens in the world. This concept is often used to explain why some people experience good fortune while others experience bad luck, as well as why some people are blessed with health and wealth while others suffer from poverty and illness. It has been used to explain why the universe is so orderly and why it follows certain laws. It has also been used to explain why the universe is so complex and why it contains so much beauty and diversity.

It is also a focal point that pulls everything together around a single all encompassing force. We already discussed how religions that have multiple gods tend to divide people into multiple clans and tend to be replaced with a religion with a single God. The idea of The Creator helps to unite humanity under one banner, one cause.

Those two first concepts, where God is the source of everything, resonate well with the notion of what fundamental science with its explanatory power and knowledge is set out to describe. Not the actual science but the set of natural laws that is unified and connected into a single reality that we observe around us.

We will start with that aspect of The Creator idea and we will address the third concepts of personal God in the next chapter.

Modern fundamental science is a collection of scientific theories that explain every single observable object in the universe, starting from the smallest constituent part of elementary particles whose collisions we observe in particle colliders laboratories to the largest objects, such as constellations of galaxies we observe through the largest telescopes on and off the Earth. All those observations agree with the Big Bang theory. Those scientific theories are a reflection of complex natural laws and the dream of physicists to come up with a single all encompassing paradigm that would be a theory of all. This is perhaps the cleanest and most clear parallel that exists in modern science to the idea of The Creator as a source of all existence. In fundamental physics, scientists call it the theory of everything. It is inspired by the fact that the laws of physics that govern an observed natural world are all consistent and do not contradict each other or create irreconcilable consequences or paradoxes. One can even say they form a unified canon of natural order, omnipresent and omnipotent. The nature of reality behind the ultimate "Theory of all" lines up well with the God of Baruch Spinoza.

Albert Einstein[80] (Calaprice, Alice, 2010) stated that his beliefs were aligned with that of pantheistic God of Baruch Spinoza. For Einstein the The Creator was not different from the unified universe governed by beautiful and elegant laws, and studying laws of physics is similar to studying The Creator in itself. In 1930 in his New York Times Magazine essay, he wrote: "We see a

---

[80] (11 October 2010). Calaprice, Alice (ed.). The Ultimate Quotable Einstein. Princeton University Press. p. 325. ISBN 1-4008-3596-8

universe marvelously arranged, obeying certain laws, but we understand the laws only dimly. Our limited minds cannot grasp the mysterious force that sways the constellations. I am fascinated by Spinoza's Pantheism. I admire even more his contributions to modern thought. Spinoza is the greatest of modern philosophers, because he is the first philosopher who deals with the soul and the body as one, not as two separate things."

Baruch Spinoza[81] (Nadler & Mignini, n.d.) was a Dutch philosopher who is considered one of the greatest rationalists of the 17th century. Rationalism, in philosophy, regards reason as the chief source and test of knowledge. Spinoza believed that God is not an individual entity or a being, but rather "the sum of the natural and physical laws of the universe." In other words, he believed in the ultimate theory of everything, where everything in the universe is governed by a set of fundamental laws that can be understood through reason and observation. Spinoza saw The Creator as the embodiment of these laws, rather than a being with a personality or will. This concept of The Creator is sometimes referred to as pantheism, which holds that the universe and The Creator are one and the same.

Spinoza's philosophy had a significant impact on later thinkers, particularly those in the Enlightenment era, who sought to reconcile reason and faith. His ideas also influenced the development of modern secularism and the scientific worldview, where the laws of nature and the natural world are studied and understood through observation and experimentation rather than religious or supernatural beliefs. Despite facing criticism and even excommunication from his Jewish community, Spinoza's ideas have continued to be influential in philosophy, theology, and science.

The concept of The Creator as "the sum of the natural and physical laws of the universe" lines up with the notion of the theory of everything, which, in turn, lines up with the notion of God the creator.

Our quest to understand those all-encompassing laws of nature culminates in what theorists call "The theory of everything". The theory of everything is a quest by physicists to unify existing fundamental theories into a single paradigm that can explain all observed natural phenomena with a unified set of laws. Its aim is to provide a complete, coherent description of the fundamental laws of nature. One of the leading candidates for a Theory of Everything is string theory, also known as superstring theory. It seeks to unify quantum mechanics and general relativity, two major scientific paradigms that describe the universe at very small and very large scales.

According to string theory, the fundamental building blocks of matter are not infinitely small points, but rather tiny vibrating strings. These strings vibrate at different frequencies, producing different particles and forces, offering a possible explanation for the existence of everything in the universe. It also predicts the existence of extra spatial dimensions, which could help explain why gravity is so much weaker than the other fundamental forces.

---

[81] en.wikipedia.org/wiki/Baruch_Spinoza

This prediction brings together the two scales of the universe, the very small and the very large, into a single elegant theory. It has the potential to resolve some of the biggest mysteries in physics, such as the nature of dark matter and the unification of gravity with the other fundamental forces.

It would take too long to describe the elegant beauty of superstring theory, and frankly there are a great number of books written on the subject, for example, "Elegant Universe" by Brian Green[82] (Greene, 2010). Unfortunately, string theory predictions are outside of the technical capability of humanity to confirm or deny, and will stay outside of our abilities for quite a long time. We will need access to steady energy yields orders of magnitude higher than what humanity currently possesses. The resulting hypothesis remains just that, more an intellectual curiosity rather than a full fledged scientific theory.

Despite the difficulties in establishing an ultimate theory of everything, there are firm indications that work around us is governed by a unified set of laws of nature. The laws of physics that work on Earth, work in exactly the same manner, as far as we can measure and observe, on the moon, in our solar system and beyond. In fundamental science this mirroring or similarity of the laws of nature is represented by utilizing principles of symmetry and is used to establish otherwise hidden links between otherwise unrelated phenomena.

The laws of symmetry that govern the natural world possess a remarkable hidden beauty. Their elegance is almost poetic in nature, and every time this symmetry is disrupted, it gives birth to a new charge, a new force, and a fresh facet of reality. For example, spatial symmetry is responsible for the preservation of momentum. Time symmetry, or the idea that the laws of physics remain unchanged over time, leads to the conservation of energy. These are just two examples of the many symmetry principles that exist in physics. They all point towards a unified and coherent set of underlying principles that unite all the laws of physics and nature.

The idea that there exists a single set of principles that governs the behavior of all matter and energy in the universe was both awe-inspiring and humbling. In this way, the study of symmetry in physics is not only a scientific pursuit but also a philosophical one that touches upon the very nature of existence itself. This unified understanding of the natural world was something that Einstein believed to be the very essence of the Creator.

I used the word "significant", when describing changes of physics laws with time, because there are indications that laws of physics do change ever so slightly in the course of development of our universe. Most prominent example is the Big Bang theory that posits that our universe originated from very different conditions than we observe now. Contrary to common beliefs that the Big Bang describes the origins of the universe, it actually describes what happened to the universe immediately after the origin. The Big Bang

---

[82] en.wikipedia.org/wiki/The_Elegant_Universe

does not state that there was anything before it, nor does it describe what was before the universe. It states that there was nothing before that we can describe with modern physics language and only describes what happened right after.

The Big Bang does not state that the universe was a result of an explosion from a single central point. In cosmology, the topology of the universe is very different from everyday topology that we are used to. The concept of the center of the universe does not exist, and every point is equal and symmetric, due to the spatial symmetry principle. When I think of the Big Bang, I see it as a change in density where the universe underwent very dense conditions where there were different laws of physics that we don't really understand, to less and less dense conditions that we observe now. I believe that there was not a point of inflection, rather there was a continuity in the universe going from very dense to what we observe now. The rapid changes in the conditions are called a "phase transition". The universe underwent a massive phase transition in density and state, similar to how a lake freezes over or thaws. The ice does not appear from nothing. It comes from the water. This understanding is very different from an argument frequently used in the media and abused by creationists that the Big Bang is analogous to "let there be light." That the universe appeared from nothing. It's more that there always was light, just light of a different density.

In the pursuit of understanding the universe, it is not enough to rely solely on the Big Bang theory or any single, simplistic explanation. Rather, our current level of understanding is the result of the relentless efforts of experimental physicists and the tireless work of theoretical physicists to refine and expand upon existing theories.

Despite the elegance and beauty of their work, the majority of people remain largely unaware of the contributions made by scientists. This is a missed opportunity, as showcasing these discoveries would require significant changes in the structure of science and society. Physics is majestic and beautiful once you understand its underlying equations and principles.

To bridge this gap, I believe that science and religion can be merged and that these concepts can be translated into everyday language. Such a move would benefit both scientists and the general public, allowing for a greater appreciation and understanding of the remarkable discoveries that continue to shape our understanding of the universe.

The concept of a unifying force that governs the entire universe, present equally in its smallest particles and largest objects, constitutes the amended version of Creator, as described by Baruch Spinoza. This universal Creator is consistent with both observed and unobserved aspects of the universe. It is the creator and a higher power that governs the laws of creation, explaining the universe's origins and predicting its future.

Violating the laws of nature carries serious consequences, much like disobeying the traditional God of the Old Testament. Ignoring the laws of gravity by jumping off a tall building will result in a fatal impact. Similarly, disregarding medical science during pandemics can lead to the death of oneself and loved ones.

The major difference between the updated version of The Creator and traditional religions is the concept of the afterlife. In traditional religions, the current life is a prelude to a true experience of existence, achieved either by improving one's karma or entering heaven. In contrast, the amended version of afterlife refers to the lasting impact that one's ideas and actions have on humanity, potentially outliving one's physical body.

However, the vast difference in scale between humans and the universe means that the laws governing the universe do not differentiate or care about our existence. Despite this, recognizing and appreciating the beauty and elegance of the universe's underlying principles can provide a sense of purpose and meaning to human existence. This concept of Spinoza's God fills in omnipresence and omnipotence qualities of the monotheistic god to the scale of the entire universe, but what about goodness and graciousness, and caring about our souls? What about humanity not being alone in the vastness of space?

What concept in the world is the analogous concept of a personal deity that cares and knows about people and every human being?

Idea of Personal Guardian

The culmination of all natural laws has very little regard for our prayers, our calls for help and our transgressions. Einstein himself described beliefs in personal or an anthropomorphic God, such as a western god of Abrahamic religions, as naive or childlike. In his words: "I believe in Spinoza's God who reveals himself in the orderly harmony of what exists, not in a God who concerns himself with the fates and actions of human beings."

This perspective is not arbitrary; rather, it is a rational observation that reflects the vastness and complexity of the universe. In comparison to the countless interactions that occur on a cosmic scale, issues such as personal behavior and charitable acts may seem insignificant and trivial.

This presents a challenge in linking the concept of a personal Guardian to any observable natural phenomena, leaving a gap in understanding the relationship between Spinoza's God and the meaning of our individual lives. While our actions and choices may be minuscule in the grand scheme of the universe, they hold significance in the lives of those around us. We have a burning need to have a significance even when we realize it is an illusion, it is a necessary illusion.

In spite, and actually because of, the inconceivable vastness of the universe, people still seek meaning and purpose in their own lives. They are looking for comfort, for protection, for "guardian angels". For many people, the idea of a personal deity is linked to religious beliefs, which posit a divine entity that cares about individuals and answers their prayers or calls for help.

This concept is often associated with the Abrahamic religions, such as Judaism, Christianity, and Islam, which emphasize the importance of a personal relationship with The Guardian.

However, the idea of a personal deity can also be viewed more broadly, as representing the connections and relationships we have with other people in the orbit of our lives. This includes our family, friends, and communities, our circles of impact and support. Although our actions may not directly impact the universe or The Creator as a source of existence, they certainly affect the people and communities around us. As individuals living on this planet, we are the immediate recipients and targets of our own perceptions and actions. Our families and friends care about us and are willing to listen to our concerns and offer assistance. We, in turn, care about our friends and feel sympathy for strangers, and many of us are concerned about the survival and well-being of future generations.

With this in mind, we can redefine the idea of a personal Guardian to be embodied within humanity itself, rather than as a creator deity. This personal Guardian exists in the form of the people surrounding us, including our family and friends, as well as future generations. They care for us and support us, and as members of society, they hold us accountable for our actions and may punish us if we harm others or break laws.

In this sense, this redefined idea of personal deity can be seen as a metaphorical representation of the care and compassion we receive from those around us, as an idea of the ultimate Mother figure, but also guidance and corrective actions as an idea of the Father figure.

It passes almost all the checks for the attributes of a personal Guardian, as is a force of caring, support, and accountability, embodied in the people who make up society, and transcending individual belief systems or religions.

It is omnipresent by definition as it is present everywhere where there are humans. It is omniscient, as it knows what any human knows. It lacks in terms of omnipotence as mankind, although it has access to powerful resources, is nowhere near the power of cosmic objects that we know about, such as the sun or stars, or even the planet Earth. That and, most importantly, the fact that mankind could still go extinct, derailed an otherwise good match to the personal God idea.

While conducting research at Fermilab and during my time at Columbia University, I was in the middle of this exercise of mapping religious concepts to scientific ideas. Initially, I felt a sense of progress in my thinking, but I encountered a challenge that left me feeling somewhat discouraged. However, I was determined not to abandon the idea that humanity played a role in the representation of a personal god, even if it was only a subset or construct within the larger scope of humanity.

This subset or construct had to be focused on the caretaking duties that couldn't be entrusted to the entirety of humanity. For instance, professions such as healthcare professionals, social workers, or dedicated volunteers who are trained and motivated to provide care and support to those in need could serve as the best representatives of humanity in this context. I envisioned the extraction of their caretaking abilities and the transformation of these qualities into a caretaker entity.

The purpose of this caretaker entity would be to address the diverse needs of individuals and communities, ensuring that everyone in society has access to care and support, regardless of their circumstances or background. The concept of a personal deity can be seen as a symbolic representation of the care and compassion that should exist within society. However, the practical implementation of this care should fall upon those who are capable and willing to provide it, whether through specific subsets of humanity or organized systems created by humanity.

At the time, the details of how this entity would be implemented were not fully clear, so I decided to postpone discussing them until a later time. In the final part of the book, I will revisit this topic and explore its implementation in more depth. For now, let us focus on discussing the qualities and properties of this caretaker entity, setting the stage for further exploration.

This entity will be nothing short of extraordinary. The remarkable combination of humanity's collective power and technological advancements has enabled us to accomplish feats that surpass the marvels described in religious texts. Through our collaborative efforts, we have achieved groundbreaking inventions and technologies that were once deemed unimaginable. Examples include the ability to revive clinically deceased individuals, the creation of steel ships capable of floating on water, and the development of diverse aircraft that can soar through the skies.

Nietzsche's famous quote, "I cannot believe in a God who wants to be praised all the time,"[83] (Nietzsche, n.d.) highlights a perceived contradiction in the concept of a Guardian who is said to be self-sufficient, yet requires constant praise and prayers from humans. However, this contradiction can be resolved if we view the concept of a personal Guardian as being embodied within humanity itself. What needs constant praise and reassertion is humanity itself. In this way, praising humanity is not a matter of vanity, but rather a way of reinforcing the values and principles that lead to a more harmonious and just society.

This idea of God as both the universe and humanity is not necessarily controversial, as humanity is a part of the natural world and has evolved under the same set of physical laws as everything else in the universe. It could be that a revised idea of a personal Guardian is a part of a greater concept of the Creator. Furthermore, in Christianity, this concept of overlapping entities is a familiar one. The Holy Trinity represents the idea of three distinct concepts existing in one entity. Similarly, in quantum mechanics, elementary particles can exist as both particles and waves[84] (Wave–particle Duality, n.d.).

---

[83] goodreads.com/quotes/34567-i-cannot-believe-in-a-god-who-wants-to-be

[84] en.wikipedia.org/wiki/Wave%E2%80%93particle_duality

In the beginning of the book I made a fundamental assumption that the laws that have shaped the development and evolution of humanity are rooted in evolutionary biology. The resulting societal norms and moral principles are built upon the fundamental principles of natural selection. These principles have evolved from initial survival instincts into complex social norms, which have surprising side effects due to the non-linear and chaotic nature of society. For example, the concept of altruism has evolved from individual genes increasing the probability of survival and reach in various species, such as ant workers, stinging bees, and human soldiers who sacrificed their lives for their hive or family.

Most of our moral principles are indeed compatible with life and evolutionary survival. Our instincts and cultural values are shaped by our innate drive to procreate and ensure our own survival. While our moral principles may not be directly and explicitly linked to survival at any cost, they are influenced by our complex nature as beings with intricate social interactions.

There are significant outliers to these principles, such as acts of self-sacrifice and altruism, which may seem contrary to self-preservation. However, these outliers can still be understood within the broader context of social cooperation and the benefits it brings to the survival and well-being of a group.

Our culture is shaped by the dynamics of tightly-knit societies, where there is little tolerance for destructive behavior. While these societal norms may not be as strict or absolute as the laws of nature, there are consequences for transgressions such as murder, theft, and other violations of societal norms. Violators face severe punishments, as societies recognize that allowing such behaviors to go unpunished would ultimately lead to the breakdown and collapse of the social order. Throughout human history and evolution, societies that fail to enforce these moral codes and punish violations risk eventual decline and may be vulnerable to being conquered or assimilated by others.

Through a process of trial and error, humanity has arrived at a set of moral principles that guide modern society. Societies and individuals that engage in certain practices and behaviors are more likely to succeed, while those who fail to deduce these patterns or learn from their own or others' mistakes will eventually pay the price of becoming less relevant or even extinct. This process of development determines the winners and losers in social development, ultimately deciding what is good and bad for humanity, or what is considered Good and Evil.

Humanity serves here as a Guardian and Enforcer of morality, the exact attributes that a personal Guardian entity would have.

What humanity still does not have is an elusive goal that humanity has yet to achieve: immortality. While the idea of immortality may seem far-fetched, it is not out of the realm of possibility. If we can find a way to preserve and pass on humanity's collective knowledge, we may be able to achieve a kind of immortality, even if it is not in the traditional sense. The preservation of knowledge is already a well-established practice. Libraries, museums, and archives exist to protect and share the accumulated knowledge of human history. With the advent of digital storage and the internet, we now have even more powerful tools to preserve and share knowledge. In this way, our collective knowledge can live on long after we are gone, ensuring that future generations can benefit from the lessons and discoveries of those who came before them.

Humanity has not achieved immortality and still falls short of the qualities of goodness and graciousness that are typically attributed to a personal deity. In fact, humanity still makes a lot of wrong choices. Wars and murder caused by humans continue to persist, and we are polluting the world with excessive amounts of waste, causing or exacerbating global warming. These effects seem to be unsustainable for the future of humanity.

We also lack in terms of graciousness, as not all individuals or groups within society are capable or willing to act in a caring and compassionate manner. Those who have committed crimes and are deemed unfit to be a part of society may not be the best candidates for providing care and support for others. Furthermore, there are individuals who intentionally cause harm and wish to do others harm, making it unwise to rely on humanity as a whole to provide for the needs of all individuals.

So, if not the entire population, then which part of it could act as a shepherd to guide humans towards good? It feels as though humanity is on the verge of making significant strides in this regard. We are beginning to address our mistakes. For example, According to the Uppsala Conflict Data Program (UCDP)[85] (Uppsala Conflict Data Program, n.d.), the number of armed conflicts and fatalities resulting from armed conflicts has been declining since the early 1990s. Despite wars and conflicts happening all the time (there are at least two major conflicts going on both sides of the planet), there has been no world war for over 70 years. The concept of a future humanity, where we are all good and gracious, treating every person rightfully and humanely, seems like the best match for a personal god.

As discussed in the first section of the book, the question remains whether there exists a concept in nature that is both omnipotent and personal, capable of knowing and caring about the existence of each individual. If this force does not exist, we better create one.

It is not a fruitless dream or delusion. Humanity has a powerful force, called faith, that can manifest our beliefs into reality. If a sufficiently large number of people believe in something, it becomes reality. Examples of this are freedom, rights, constitution, money, glory and bliss. All of these things do not exist in reality without people, but we make it real by believing in them.

The power of people's faith can shape their beliefs and actions, especially when many people share those beliefs. If a significant portion of humanity

---

[85] en.wikipedia.org/wiki/Uppsala_Conflict_Data_Program

truly believes in the goodness and greatness of humanity, it can influence the collective behavior of people and lead to the actualization of those beliefs. In other words, if we believe in the positive potential of humanity strongly enough, we will become the very thing we believe in. We can create our own caretaker, our own personal deity.

We are ending this chapter without finding any good candidate in nature or in our society to map to a concept of a personal divine guardian entity. That does not mean this was an exercise completely in vain. We found that this concept lives somewhere inside humanity itself, either as a better part of it or as a future creation of mankind. We also know that the Personal Guardian needs to preserve lives, increase the wellbeing of people and be on the side of goodness. It needs to be on the right side of good and evil.

Revisiting the Ideas of Good and Evil

Our ability to distinguish good from evil can shape up the idea for the guardian of humanity and our future. The relationship between our actions and society is based on the concepts of good and evil. When we act in a helpful and positive way towards others, society considers these actions to be good. Conversely, when we commit harmful acts, society deems these actions to be evil and punishes us accordingly.

This relationship is closely linked to the idea of freedom of choice, a central concept in many traditional religions. According to this principle, people have the freedom to choose their actions, and are therefore responsible for the consequences that follow. While some circumstances, such as severe mental illness or being underage, may mitigate responsibility for evil acts, mentally healthy adults are expected to strive to do good and avoid evil. This idea is reflected in religious texts, which often include the notion of punishment for evil acts, such as the concept of hell, which represents the ultimate form of evil and punishment. Ultimately, it is up to each individual to make moral choices and take responsibility for the consequences of their actions.

From an evolutionary standpoint, the divergence in options, or more specifically, distinct branches in the evolutionary journey, are critical to the process of natural selection. Natural selection is not driven by conscious decision-making; rather, it is an impartial force of nature. This mechanism is dependent on random mutations that result in adaptive traits, which can be either advantageous or detrimental. Nature cannot predict which mutations will yield beneficial adaptations.

Time and death serve as the ultimate arbiters, distinguishing between favorable adaptations and unfavorable ones, as well as between viable paths and dead ends. Adaptations that do not support survival often result in increased mortality and reduced reproduction. To enhance the probability of favorable outcomes, the variety and independence of mutations must be at maximum. The more mutations the more chances one of them will be a solution to hostile environmental change or a new defense against invasive species. When detrimental adaptations are too similar across species or genera, the entire species faces the threat of extinction. However, if there are adequate differences, one subgroup within the species' population may endure environmental changes.

For instance, if a group of primates chooses to rely solely on physical strength without utilizing tools, they could encounter another group of primates armed with tools. This could put the first group at risk of losing hunting grounds, resources, and lives, ultimately leading to their extinction. If there is variation in traits and adaptations within the group, some subpopulations may survive the confrontation with the armed group, defeat them, and disseminate the knowledge throughout their population. This diversity helps to prevent a situation where the entire species pursues a detrimental course, similar to how rats follow the deadly tune of the Pied Piper to their demise. The split in evolutionary paths, I would even call it as the "choices" made by nature, serves to enhance the chances of species survival.

The concept of good and evil, freedom of choice, and personal responsibility extends beyond religious beliefs and is also an important concept in liberal politics, which serves as the foundation for modern western societies. However, controlling every action of each individual in a large group is nearly impossible. The consequences of individual actions can have a significant impact on the wellbeing of groups, tribes, communities, and entire countries. It is difficult to describe every action that each citizen can and cannot do, as the variations of actions and their consequences are immeasurably large and societal norms and laws are constantly evolving.

In ancient societies, laws were less nuanced and more brutal. For instance, cutting off the arm or fingers of a thief was a common punishment for theft in primitive cultures, while in Sumerian culture 5200 years ago, theft of property from temples or the royal palace resulted in death. The same applied to those who sold or acquired stolen goods[86] (What Were the Punishments for Theft?, n.d.). As societies evolved, laws became more defined and granular. The use of the death penalty declined, and jail time became a more frequent form of punishment. However, courts do not define specific punishments for each misdemeanor.

Societies initially established fundamental moral principles, which courts then used as a basis for developing laws to govern complex situations. For example, the principle of "do not kill" guides the use of lethal force, with exceptions for self-defense or protecting one's country. Similarly, "do not steal" informs how theft is addressed. Once an initial judgment is made, it

---

[86] historicallocks.com/en/site/h/locks-and-magic/taboos-and-magical-knots/punishments-for-theft

sets a precedent for future cases. These principles are embodied in morals and ethics.

This process bears resemblance to the evolution of complex animal behaviors, which are regulated by emotions. Instead of having specific instructions for responding to every conceivable situation, animals develop competing emotions, such as "fight or flight," with fear and aggression battling for dominance. These emotions are regulated by the chemical balances produced in response to various situations. Inappropriate balances result in negative outcomes, such as being eaten or suffering fatal injuries, and are thus eliminated from the gene pool. The most successful combinations are those that lead to offspring, with the appropriate response being determined by experiencing the right emotions and reacting accordingly.

In societies and countries, rather than attempting to control every single action, people establish overarching principles to guide their communities. Notable examples of such principles include the French ideals of liberty, equality, and fraternity (liberté, égalité, fraternité), or the United States Constitution. These foundational concepts serve as the basis for developing the remaining rules and regulations that govern society, ensuring a coherent and unified framework for organizing and maintaining social order.

A majority of moral and ethical principles support the preservation of social order and the prevention of societal chaos. Disarray within society can give rise to numerous disturbances, encompassing civil unrest, acts of violence, and financial instability. The repercussions of such disruptions can be catastrophic, leading to tragic outcomes like loss of life, extensive property damage, and the displacement of individuals, all of which can further exacerbate social problems and hinder the overall well-being of the community.

As an example of high level moral principles, let's go over the infamous list of seven deadly sins[87] and analyze their consequences on humanity:

- Gluttony is the overindulgence and overconsumption of anything to the point of waste. This behavior is widely criticized due to its detrimental effects, particularly in causing hunger among the less fortunate. When the wealthy engage in gluttony, it often results in depriving the needy of essential resources, leading to starvation and even death for a significant portion of the population.

- Envy, Greed, and Lust are all desires that can consume and never be fully satisfied. Greed and Envy are typically associated with material possessions, while Lust is associated with an intense longing for sexual desire or power and money. All three of these desires can lead to loss of control, resulting in actions such as adultery, theft, conflict, and ultimately chaos. In the most severe instances, societal chaos

---

[87] en.wikipedia.org/wiki/Seven_deadly_sins

can lead to death due to the breakdown of law and order, as well as the violence that can result from civil unrest.

- Sloth is a sin that involves neglecting one's responsibilities to both their community and higher purpose. Unlike other sins that involve active wrongdoing, sloth is characterized by a lack of action. This can result in further chaos within the community, as neglected responsibilities can lead to harmful consequences such as violence and death. As the level of chaos in a community increases, so do the chances of killings and fatalities among its members.

- Wrath is an intense emotion characterized by uncontrolled anger, rage, and even hatred. The direct consequences of this emotion can lead to a higher likelihood of conflict, which in turn can result in murder and other forms of violence.

- Lastly, Pride is an irrational belief in one's inherent superiority or importance over others. This often leads to a sense of entitlement, which can result in breaking ranks and attempts at coups, disruption, and revolution. These are among the most chaotic and deadly phenomena in human history. It is not coincidental that pride is considered the most serious of the seven deadly sins.

It is evident that all the sins can lead to chaos, disruption of law and order, and increased deaths within a community, whereas virtues can decrease chaos and decrease deaths. Life and living are seen as the ultimate differentiators between what is considered good and evil. It is noteworthy that death and chaos are considered naturally bad outcomes in evolutionary biology and definitions of living organisms. Death removes organisms and genes from reproductive pools, while life, living, and love correspond to sexual reproduction and giving birth to more offspring, which are considered good outcomes.

Traditional virtues are aligned with concepts that increase the chances of biological survival in species, whereas sins decrease those concepts. The idea of good vs. evil fits well into the survival of the fittest. In the past few thousand years, the most virtuous behaviors were the most fit for humans. To adopt these ideas, we can remap them into new concepts of what is good and bad.

In our mapping exercise, Love towards God and your neighbor, which are inherent biblical virtues, can be connected to love towards humanity as a whole and the people closest to us as a smaller part of humanity. The biblical principles, including the seven deadly sins, can be seen as a cautionary tale against behaviors that harm humanity, either on a global scale causing chaos and havoc or on a smaller scale hurting people in our immediate circle.

- The sin of Gluttony can be mapped to the overconsumption of resources on this planet. This behavior harms humanity as a whole by depleting essential resources to the point where the land and seas can no longer sustain human life, resulting in potential extinction.
- Envy, Greed, and Lust can be mapped to the over-focusing on material possessions and pleasures of the flesh, which can distract from one's true calling in life. These sins hurt those in our immediate circle as we engage in actions that harm our families and neighbors. However, on a global scale, this behavior can lead to a focus on immediate gratification rather than working towards longer-term, more impactful goals.
- Sloth can be mapped to the idea of indulging in procrastination and avoiding the discomfort of work, which can result in neglecting what is truly important in our lives. Rather than focusing on avoiding the stress of daily work, we should concentrate on longer-term goals to make a greater impact.
- Wrath is a sin of losing control that can result in harm to others. This behavior is straightforward and harms those in our immediate circle, such as our families who have to deal with our aggression.
- Pride is considered one of the most serious sins as it can lead to revolutions and coups, causing chaos in society and subsequent death and destruction. In our mapping, it is challenging to find a worthy idea to map pride onto, as it can also be a positive force that propels people to do greater good, albeit sometimes at the cost of overstepping their status. However, taking our position for granted is the ultimate sin. We need to prove ourselves through actions, rather than relying solely on a sense of entitlement.

It is important to note that the concept of "good" corresponds not only to the survival of our genes but also to the survival of our ideas, creations, and humanity as a whole. Conversely, death and the termination of life represent the ultimate evil, and any behaviors that increase the likelihood of death should be considered as such.

The way it can be translated quantitatively in our formula, any behaviors that lead to increasing of $U = U_{personal} + U_{humanity}$ is Good and to decrease it as Bad. Graphically we can represent this as a big scales:

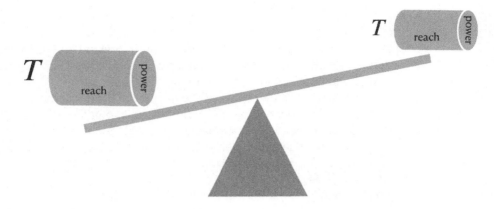

Fig. 5: Graphical representation of good vs evil paths

Obvious examples are killing or theft would immediately lead to decrease in the number of people affected by our actions and saving lives or raising children would lead to increases.

This is because in the term $U_{personal} = E\left[\sum_{personal_i=0}^{N} p_i \cdot w_i\right]$, the total number of people N will decrease because of deaths due to our negative actions, and will increase with our beneficial actions.

It is not always apparent how our ideas and written works will impact the world. While the effects may be positive or negative, it is challenging to determine their overall influence. For instance, Karl Marx's "Das Kapital" is known to have convinced millions of minds, and resulted in bloody revolutions and civil wars that killed millions[88] (Holodomor, n.d.). Yet at the moment of publication, it was received positively and only time showed the disastrous long-term impact it had on the 20th century.

This raises an intriguing question beyond the immediate repercussions of our actions: who serves as the judge and who keeps the score? Who is responsible for assessing the positive or negative impact of our ideas and creations on society? Is it our peers, the authorities, or history itself? Should we be held accountable for the unintended consequences of our actions, or should we be judged solely by our intentions?

Furthermore, it is important to consider how we should balance the potential risks and rewards of our actions. Should we prioritize the immediate benefits of our actions, or should we take a more long-term perspective, considering the potential future consequences of our choices? These are complex ethical questions that require careful consideration, as they

---

[88] en.wikipedia.org/wiki/Holodomor

ultimately shape the kind of society we create and leave behind for future generations.

Throughout the book, I have argued that time serves as the ultimate judge of our actions and legacy. If our impact endures in the minds of others over the long term, we have successfully left a mark on the world, whether it be positive or negative. Conversely, if we fail to make an impact or are inactive, our legacy may disappear into obscurity with the passing of time. Thus, the fate of our legacy is intricately tied to the embodiment of our actions.

Eastern religions often refer to this embodiment as Karma. In traditional Western religions, the embodiment of our sins, good deeds and tribute to the life lived is believed to be our soul.

Revisiting the Idea of Soul

In everyday vocabulary, the soul is often understood as the incorporeal essence of a living being. It embodies personal accountability, the freedom to make choices, and a record of both our misdeeds and virtuous actions, thereby influencing eventual punishment or reward. The soul serves as a connective conduit to the divine, functioning as a source of spiritual power, enlightenment, and personal spiritual energy.

Western culture, significantly shaped by traditional Western religions, places great emphasis on individual responsibility for moral choices. Meanwhile, in Eastern traditions, the decisions one makes carry considerable repercussions that influence their subsequent existence within the cycle of reincarnation, as dictated by the concept of karma. In Western culture, there's a moral obligation to align choices with one's personal beliefs and values, while in Eastern philosophy, the outcomes of one's choices can shape future lives within the karmic cycle. Regardless of cultural context, a common thread exists: it is imperative to be conscious of one's choices and accept responsibility for their consequences.

Greek philosophers, such as Socrates, Plato, and Aristotle, recognized that the soul, or "psyche" in ancient Greek, possessed a logical capacity, with its exercise being the most divine of human actions. Aristotle asserted that the body and soul represented a person's matter and form or essence, respectively. In some religions, souls are mortal, while in most, they are immortal. Abrahamic faiths maintain that only human souls are immortal, while Hinduism and Jainism posit that all living beings, even bacteria, possess souls. The soul embodies the mental, reasoning, and logical faculties of a living being, with the body serving as a vehicle to experience karma.

In its immortal form, the soul is the direct opposition of death and mortality. It is something that cannot perish or disappear. In the Eastern religious and philosophical traditions, there is no concept of soul, but there are equivalents, "Atman" in Hinduism and karma in Buddhism. Those concepts follow some form of essence conservation law: they cannot be created or destroyed. Instead, the individual is seen as a collection of changing physical and mental constituents or processes. In Western traditions the souls are created at conception and then never destroyed, which contradicts any energy or matter conservation laws observed in natural energy, there are more and more souls created every second on this planet. The main point is they address our fears of disappearing after death.

In modern medicine there is a concept of an entity record that will exist even after the death of an individual, a genetic makeup of species. Modern medical science defines our human genetic destiny, encompassing our body composition and brain structure, through our human genome. It is also a form of record keeping of the evolution of any species. This genetic record documents all the mistakes and advancements throughout our species' lineage, also bearing the consequences of genetic errors. For example, our genetic heritage reveals instances of near disasters and extinction events, known as genetic or population bottlenecks. A 2005 study from Rutgers University suggested that pre-1492 indigenous populations of the Americas descended from merely 70 individuals who traversed the land bridge between Asia and North America[89] (Population Bottleneck, n.d.). Our genetic footprint also dictates the potential future variations of our offspring. Our genome is a way to hold the history of evolutionary choices that nature made, the target of all the consequences for bad choices and a source of all the future genetic power for all possible offsprings.

The species genome is the closest analogy to a biological concept of soul, for humans and other animals.

Human behavior is influenced not only by our biological predisposition but also by our culture and environment. A long-standing debate in biology and society revolves around the balance between two factors that determine our fate: "nature," dictated by genetics, and "nurture," determined by the environment. The age-old expression "nature and nurture" traces back to medieval French and was popularized by Victorian polymath Francis Galton. Galton, inspired by his half-cousin Charles Darwin and a founder of eugenics[90] (Slater & Bremner, n.d.), brought attention to the complex question of how much our behavior is determined by our genetic makeup versus our upbringing, parental influence, and cultural context. The reality likely lies somewhere in between, with both nature and nurture contributing to our behavior.

Our genetic makeup may influence specific aspects of our behavior, while our environment and upbringing also help shape our identity. Our actions, dreams, aspirations, and ideas define who we are. While a gene is a segment of DNA responsible for a particular trait, a meme is a similar representation

---

[89] en.wikipedia.org/wiki/Population_bottleneck#Humans

[90] en.wikipedia.org/wiki/Nature_versus_nurture

for our actions or ideas. Memes embody cultural ideas, symbols, or practices that can be transmitted from one mind to another without biological reproduction, such as through reading or writing books or stories. Just as a gene is the smallest unit of DNA that can be replicated through the biological mechanisms of sexual reproduction, a meme is the smallest piece of information that can be replicated among minds.

The updated concept of the soul can be seen as a combination of both genes and memes, aligning well with the traditional idea and purpose of the "revised soul." While the body is represented by a map of DNA and genes, the "revised soul" encompasses all the choices we make in our lives, the errors and misguided decisions we commit, and the potential future impact we can have.

Our choices manifest through the actions and memories we leave behind, which continue to influence the world even after our death, creating a lasting impression of our lives. The consequence of making poor choices is the fading of our legacy and the loss of our lives' entire meaning.

The concept of the "revised soul" encompasses both our genetic makeup and cultural influences, underscoring the significance of our choices and the memories we leave behind. It suggests that the meaning of our lives and the legacy we bequeath are shaped not just by who we are intrinsically, but also by our actions and the impressions we impart to others. In essence, it is represented by our formula as the sum of all the actions and choices we made in our life. Graphically we can represent this as (and you have seen this already in previous chapters):

$$T \quad p_i \text{ reach} \quad w_i \text{ power}$$

An important term in the formula, p_i - I called it the "reach", is the measure of how far each choice or action will spread across other people. It is a property of how probable our action will be replicated or spread across via process of retelling and reproduction. For an action, for instance, helping a neighbor, it describes how likely the neighbor will repeat your action and help others by continuing the trend of good deeds. If this is a recipe to prepare a dinner more efficiently and quickly than he or she used to do before, it is very likely that this recipe will be shared to a larger number of people. For example, in one generation this number could be as low as 1 and as high as thousands, but most likely it will be a number between 0 and 10. Another term, w_i, that I called the "power", is a property that shows how beneficial our actions are. If a person will use the recipe for the next dinner in the cycle, and the cycle for sharing the recipe could be a week or a month.

The power is then measured as a number of times the recipe is used divided by a total number of recipes and varies between 0 and 10. The higher the value of the product of "power" and "reach", $U_{personal}$, the stronger your legacy. In our example, the recipe could be retold from grandmothers to mothers for the past century and will go on for centuries to come. But there is no guarantee and a crappy recipe will not last for more than a month.

In this reinterpretation, the formula captures the sum of all our impacts as a quantitative representation of the updated concept of the soul.

This is where the new idea of the soul diverges from the traditional notion. In conventional Western and Eastern religions, the soul is immortal. Even the soul of someone who has committed many evil acts will not vanish into oblivion. The consequence of making wrong and wicked choices is that our soul suffers in the afterlife or the next life, but it continues to exist and ultimately has the potential for redemption.

In our amended perspective, not every soul inherently possesses immortality—only a select few exceptional ones do. The new "souls", as an accumulation of all our actions, that are not successful in making an impact will not reproduce in people's conscience. More successful ones will prevail and replicate to become leading ideas and concepts. They will not be destroyed or die. The less successful will dissolve in the constant stream of new ideas and new actions introduced by subsequent generations, much like the majority of gene variations get lost amidst the flow of new mutations.

To ensure your legacy endures and you remain a part of humanity's collective memory, it is essential to have goals, a plan to achieve them, and the determination to work hard toward their fulfillment. In this way, the revised soul concept places a greater emphasis on the impact of our actions and the importance of striving for meaningful contributions that will resonate with future generations.

Mapping Concepts Between Eastern Religions and Science

Let's explore the mapping of religious and scientific concepts, focusing on Eastern traditional religions: Hinduism and Buddhism. The following table aims to capture core aspects of these religious doctrines while acknowledging that some elaborate details may be omitted. Most importantly, the table identifies corresponding concepts from a scientific perspective and aligns them with religious concepts:

Religion	Meaning	Science
Brahman	Cause of all existence	Unified laws of nature

Karma (Hinduism/ Buddhism)	Choice and consequences	Cause and effect; consequences of actions
Reincarnation (Hinduism)	Cycle of rebirth that perpetuates the suffering	Genetic inheritance; evolutionary continuity
Samsara (Buddhism)	Cycle of rebirth and suffering	Life cycles of extinction and adaptation; ecological succession
Dharma (Hinduism/ Buddhism)		Ethical principles; social norms
Moksha (Hinduism)		Personal growth; self-actualization
Nirvana (Buddhism)	Liberation from suffering	Highest form of enlightenment; Inner peace; psychological well-being
Atman (Hinduism)	Essence of ego	Individual consciousness; sense of self; Sum of choice of our actions and genes that makes us unique and leave a permanent
Anatman (Buddhism)		Interconnectedness; absence of a fixed self
Maya (Hinduism)		Perception; cognitive biases
Meditation	Ritual of achieving focus	Self assessment and self guidance

This table draws parallels between Eastern religious doctrines and scientific concepts, going for the interconnectedness and potential for mutual understanding between these two perspectives. While these mappings are not exhaustive, they offer a starting point for exploring the relationships between religious and scientific views and fostering a more comprehensive understanding of our world and human experience.

In contrast to Western religions, which focus on the relationship between God and humanity, personal sin, and seeking redemption, Eastern religions emphasize personal enlightenment and understanding of the universe. Eastern religions stress the significance of recognizing one's place in the universe and living in harmony with it, achieved through meditation, contemplation, and other spiritual practices. These religions also highlight the importance of compassion and kindness towards others, living in the present moment, and being mindful of one's thoughts and actions.

Although both Eastern and Western religions underscore the value of community, fellowship, and moral values like justice, love, and compassion, Western religions, particularly Christianity, place greater importance on faith, obedience to divine laws, and the need for repentance and redemption. This distinction may be attributed to the maturity of Eastern religions, which have had more time to develop and address different priorities for their followers. Hinduism, Buddhism, and Taoism have existed for thousands of years and have evolved complex philosophies and practices. In comparison, Christianity and Islam are relatively younger and have had less time to develop intricate concepts.

More significantly, Christianity and Islam have opted for simplifying more complex tenets of Judaism to make them more accessible to a broader population, thereby expanding their reach. Christianity emphasizes faith in Jesus Christ, who made faith accessible not just to Jews but to anyone who accepted basic tenets. Islam further simplified these beliefs, eliminating the concept of the Holy Trinity and streamlining rituals to make faith even more accessible and "viral." When we say that religion has chosen the direction of simplification, it has occurred through underlying mechanisms, much like evolutionary mechanisms in nature, rather than a centralized intellect. Simpler and more inclusive concepts propagate through our minds at a higher rate, analogous to the way respiratory viruses spread more quickly than those causing waterborne diseases.

As a result, newer concepts in Eastern religions may have lost some of the complexities of older concepts found in Hinduism and Buddhism. In Eastern religions, there is a distinct notion for the cause of all existence and ultimate reality, Brahman, as well as a separate notion for the universal self, Atman, an eternal core of personality that permeates all souls, including gods. In the West, these two ideas, the notion of the ultimate self and ultimate reality, are combined into the idea of God.

The Hinduism and Buddhism concepts such as Dharma, Moksha, Anatman, or Maya provide insight into the nature of reality, the path to spiritual growth, and the ultimate goal of human existence. Let's discuss each concept and attempt to map them to scientific ideas.

Brahman represents the ultimate reality and the supreme, eternal, and infinite consciousness that underlies and permeates all of existence. It is considered the ultimate source and foundation of all things, both manifest and unmanifest. Brahman is often described as formless, infinite, and indescribable, beyond all concepts and categories.

The concept of Brahman is much closer to Baruch Spinoza's idea of God, which suggests that the universe is governed by a unified set of laws and reality is unified. Recall that Einstein accepted this concept of God. This idea of Brahman aligns more closely with the unified theory of everything that fundamental scientists are trying to discover.

On the other hand, Atman refers to the individual self or soul believed to be identical with Brahman. According to Hindu philosophy, each person's

Atman is a spark of the divine that is eternal and indestructible, and not separate from the ultimate reality of Brahman. The goal of spiritual practice in Hinduism is to realize the identity of Atman with Brahman and transcend the limitations of the individual ego and the cycle of birth and death.

Atman represents the ultimate self, the eternal ego. There is no easy matching concept in science. The closest one is that of life itself, a construct designed to outlast environmental changes and survive. At the same time, it is a property of all living organisms, including ourselves, from single-celled organisms to the entire biosphere of living organisms on this planet. The concept of Atman is best mapped to the concept of the personal Guardian God, as the representation of all living organisms or life itself.

Somewhere within our cellular structure lies a record-keeper of all our ancestors' choices, however random, preserved in the core signature of our DNA. Whenever species faced a crossroads—whether to develop shorter limbs, allowing them to slither through sand and water like a snake, or longer limbs capable of walking out of the water and onto the surface, or to perish due to reduced navigability through corals—these decisions became encoded in our genes. This is similar to the concept of Karma, a sum of a person's choices and actions that determine their future and the fate of their Atman. In the context of this book, Karma is represented by our formula, which decides whether our meaning will propagate further or vanish into nothingness.

Anatman is a central concept in Buddhism, which asserts that there is no permanent, unchanging self or soul (Atman). Instead, everything is in a state of constant flux, and what we perceive as the self is merely a collection of temporary, ever-changing mental and physical processes.

Anatman can be connected to the ideas of impermanence and change in fields like biology, physics, and chemistry. These sciences study the processes of transformation and growth that occur in the natural world, such as the life cycles of organisms, the evolution of species, and the continuous exchange of energy and matter.

In Hinduism, Maya refers to the illusion or the veil that obscures the true nature of reality. It is the belief that the material world, as we perceive it, is not the ultimate reality, but a temporary, ever-changing construct. The goal of spiritual practice is to see through this illusion and recognize the true nature of existence, which is Brahman.

Maya can be linked to concepts in fields like quantum physics and neuroscience, which challenge our understanding of reality and perception. For example, quantum mechanics describes the fundamental nature of reality as probabilistic and interconnected, while neuroscience explores the ways our brains construct our perceptions and experiences of the world.

Samsara is the eternal cycle of rebirth where eternal souls go through countless turns of suffering and eventual death just to be reborn and go through this cycle again. There are multiple examples of cyclical processes in natural sciences, but none of them involve an eternal internal structure. With one exception, of living organisms. Life through the process of evolution goes through the process of adaptation and extinction, causing great amounts of death and suffering to individuals and whole species involved in the evolutionary process. Escaping this cycle and finding a solution to adaptation to environment changes without the process of extermination of entire species sounds like a noble cause.

Dharma refers to the moral and ethical principles that guide an individual's actions in life. It is the natural order of things and the duty one must fulfill to maintain harmony in the universe. In Buddhism, Dharma refers to the teachings of the Buddha, which serve as a guide for living a virtuous life and attaining spiritual awakening.

Dharma can be related to the principles of ethics and morality in fields such as philosophy, psychology, and sociology. These disciplines study human behavior, the development of moral values, and the impact of cultural norms on individuals and society. The concept of Dharma can also be linked to the idea of natural laws governing the universe in fields like physics and cosmology.

Moksha is the ultimate goal in Hinduism, representing liberation from the cycle of birth, death, and rebirth (Samsara). Achieving Moksha means transcending the illusions and attachments of the material world and realizing one's true nature, which is identical to Brahman, the ultimate reality.

Moksha can be seen as an abstract concept similar to self-actualization in psychology, where individuals strive to achieve their highest potential and inner fulfillment. It can also be related to the pursuit of knowledge and understanding in fields like philosophy and science, where the aim is to uncover the fundamental truths of existence.

Nirvana, also known as moksha, the highest form of happiness and ultimate state of enlightenment, is another difficult concept to find a scientific parallel. Nirvana indicates realization that our ultimate ego and ultimate reality are one and the same, and finding a way to unify those two pillars and through this action achieving transcendence and breaking the cycle of rebirth, breaking samsara. Neither Nirvana nor moksha or samsara have easy parallels in natural science outside of organic chemistry or biology.

Many practitioners of Buddhism and Hinduism, yogi, spend their entire lives to find a way to achieve transcendence and enlightenment. Eastern religions have quite a few examples of rituals and routines that help seekers to find a way to realize the true form of reality and achieve Nirvana. Meditation is one of the routines that have been widely adopted in the western secular cultures. It is a sort of replacement for prayer in Abrahamic religions. Time spent in meditation fulfills the need to not feel alone, rather feel part of the world around you and through this concur our fear of death.

Eastern religions offer a much richer array of concepts and not all of them line up with my list of phenomena of natural laws and society habits. Yet I see a promising confluence between those institutions. My hope is that this synthesis of religious and scientific concepts will foster dialogue between science and religion, in both Eastern and Western traditions. This could involve scientists and religious leaders coming together to discuss how their respective fields can collaborate to deepen our understanding of the world around us. For example, scientists could share the latest research on viral infections and climate change and its implications for humanity, while religious leaders could explain how their faith shapes their views on the environment and how they can contribute to its protection. This dialogue could also explore how science and religion can address global issues such as poverty, inequality, and social justice.

One of the most important conclusions of our mapping between religious and scientific concepts is a concept of humanity's personal Guardian. Humanity is like a manuscript to contain and preserve stories of our existence, a medium to keep records of billions of past lives. For this to exist, humanity needs someone to ensure humanity's future existence. Humanity cannot be a guardian of itself, as it is too biased, too chaotic, and too impartial for that role. At the same time, humankind is the only entity that genuinely cares about humans, so a part, portion, or creation of humanity will have to assume this responsibility. I believe this creation should be based on science but not in its current form. It should be oriented not just towards acquiring knowledge but towards using this knowledge for the preservation of human civilization.

Another approach to establishing parallel scientific ideas and concepts is to reinforce religious teachings with scientific evidence. For example, scientists could use their research to explain the origins of the universe and its interconnectedness with humanity. This could demonstrate how religious teachings about the sanctity of life and the importance of compassion are grounded in scientific evidence.

Science though is a powerful tool that can be used to save us or to doom us. Recall a famous phrase of Robert Oppenheimer who was quoting the most well-known line from the Bhagavad-Gita after the tests of atomic bomb: "Now I became death, destroyer of the worlds"[91] (Bird et al., n.d.). This was his reflection of the power physicists created as a result of the Manhattan project.

This is why I think that science without clear direction and purpose can be co-opted by groups driven by misguided or self-destructive ideas, and ultimately be used for destructive purposes, or in other words, for evil.

I propose that merging science with an updated and enlightened form of religion, one that is free from dogmas and superstitions, will make it more difficult to exploit science for destructive ends, and instead facilitate its use for the greater good. I also believe that this process should begin within our own mind. This is the main point of this chapter. By envisioning this concept within our minds and convincing a sufficient number of people to embrace this idea, we can gradually bring it closer to reality. The more people who adopt this integrated approach to science and religion, the more likely it is that we can

---

[91] en.wikipedia.org/wiki/J._Robert_Oppenheimer

create a world where scientific advancements are used ethically and responsibly. This fusion of the two disciplines could foster a culture that not only values scientific discovery but also considers the moral implications of how that knowledge is applied.

Merging Art with Religion and Science

We have already discussed merging Science and Religion. That leaves one more essential discipline out, the Art. Herman Hesse explored the union of these three pillars of society - art, science, and religion - in his book "The Glass Bead Game." He envisioned a highly intellectual and interdisciplinary game that incorporates elements of mathematics, music, philosophy, and other disciplines. Hesse believed that each of these disciplines had something significant to contribute to our understanding of the human experience, and that their integration was necessary to achieve a more comprehensive understanding. In the book, he describes the game as a means of achieving this integration, where players can explore the connections between different disciplines and create new insights and ideas through their play.

Hesse writes: "We have long recognized that the ultimate goal of all sciences and religions is to comprehend the universe and its purpose. The Glass Bead Game is a means to achieve this goal. It is a game of games that embraces all disciplines, all truths, and all contradictions. It is the ultimate synthesis of all knowledge and all wisdom, a vehicle for the merger of religion, science, and art."

Just like "The Glass Bead Game" I see the future where all three disciplines are working together. The integration of art, religion, and science, can serve as a powerful catalyst for expanding our understanding of the world and the human experience, fostering a more profound connection between these vital aspects of society.

Art and religion have already been intertwined throughout most of history, with many cultures using art as a means of expressing their religious beliefs and practices. From ancient Egyptian hieroglyphics to medieval Christian frescoes, art has been employed to depict religious stories, figures, and symbols.

Many religious traditions have used art as a means of expressing their beliefs and connecting with their followers. In the past, art was both supplemental and essential to religious institutions. There are numerous examples of art accentuating and highlighting the splendor of temples and churches. For instance, in Christianity, art has been utilized to depict stories from the Bible, to illustrate the lives of saints, and to create a sense of awe and wonder in religious spaces.

One way in which art and religion merge is through the use of religious iconography. Iconography is the visual language of religious art, used to convey specific meaning and symbolism. In Christianity, the cross is a powerful symbol of sacrifice and redemption, often depicted in art as a reminder of Jesus Christ's sacrifice. Similarly, in Buddhism, the lotus flower symbolizes enlightenment and is often depicted in art as a reminder of the path to spiritual awakening.

A critical area where art and religion intersect is through the creation of sacred spaces. Religious buildings such as churches, temples, and mosques often feature intricate and beautiful works of art intended to inspire awe and reverence in those who enter. These works of art can take many forms, from statues and frescoes to stained glass windows and intricate carvings. They are often crafted by skilled artisans trained in specific techniques and styles associated with the religious tradition in question.

The intricate carvings and sculptures adorning the walls of temples and churches were designed to enhance their beauty and foster a sense of connection between worshippers and the divine. Frescoes and murals painted on temple and church walls added color and vitality to these sacred spaces. One of the most renowned examples is the Sistine Chapel mural, a masterpiece of High Renaissance Art, commissioned by Pope Julius II and painted by Michelangelo in 1512.

Among the frescoes, Michelangelo's ceiling painting is the most famous, depicting scenes from the Book of Genesis. The central image on the ceiling is the Creation of Adam, capturing the moment when God breathes life into the first man. This painting is often interpreted as a symbol of the divine spark within all human beings and the potential for spiritual connection with God.

Statues of gods and goddesses were placed in temples and churches to imbue them with a spiritual aura. Stained glass windows were used to create a colorful and vibrant atmosphere, while mosaics adorned the floors of these sacred spaces.

In the West, art has frequently been employed to express religious themes. Christian art encompasses painting, sculpture, architecture, stained glass windows, illuminated manuscripts, and other visual forms of expression. Islamic art includes calligraphy, painting, architecture, and ceramics, while Jewish art comprises illuminated manuscripts, painting, sculpture, and architecture.

In the East, art served religious purposes as well. Buddhist art depicted the Buddha and other significant figures, and created symbolic images for meditation and spiritual practice. Buddhist artists crafted thangkas, paintings on cotton or silk that portrayed the Buddha or individuals on the path to awakening.

The ephemeral mandalas crafted by Buddhists, in my view, hold exceptional significance. Mandalas, detailed and circular designs, have held a place of prominence in spiritual and religious practices for hundreds of years. The term "mandala" originates from the Sanskrit word signifying 'circle' or 'completion', an apt descriptor given that the circular configuration embodies wholeness and unity. Often harnessed as aids in meditation, the process of creating or observing a mandala is understood to engender tranquility and concentration. Within Hindu and Buddhist traditions, mandalas serve as symbolic representations of the universe, their circular form encapsulating the idea of an endless, interconnected cosmos.

In the Vajrayana branch of Buddhism, the use of mandalas transcends mere symbolic representation. Mandalas have evolved into a unique and delicate art form known as sandpainting, each one a testament to the skill, patience, and spiritual dedication of its creator.

The art of sandpainting involves meticulously forming intricate mandalas using tiny, colored grains of sand. Tibetan monks, who are often regarded as masters of this art form, spend days or even weeks painstakingly crafting a single mandala. Utilizing small tubes, funnels, and scrapers, they systematically distribute the grains to form complex, vibrant designs. The final product is not just a beautiful piece of art but a three-dimensional representation of the universe, encompassing a variety of Buddhist philosophical concepts.

One remarkable example of this practice can be seen in the annual Losar (Tibetan New Year) celebrations. Monks create intricate sand mandalas as part of the festivities, symbolizing the impermanence of life. Once the mandala is complete, they perform a ritualistic dismantling, sweeping the sand together and pouring it into a nearby river or stream. This act serves as a reminder of the Buddhist belief in the transience of life and the continual cycle of birth, death, and rebirth.

Furthermore, mandalas form a significant aspect of Anuttarayoga Tantra meditation practices. In this context, practitioners often visualize complex mandalas during meditation as a method to achieve a deeper state of awareness. For instance, in the practice of the Kalachakra Tantra, one of the most complex tantric systems, the practitioner visualizes an intricate three-dimensional mandala palace inhabited by deities and Buddhas. The act of mentally creating this cosmic diagram, filled with symbolic meaning, is believed to assist practitioners in progressing along the path to enlightenment.

In essence, mandalas in the Vajrayana tradition, whether physically crafted as sandpaintings or mentally constructed during meditation, represent the cosmos's interconnected nature.

Hindu art often depicted gods and goddesses, encompassing painting, sculpture, and architecture. Each god is uniquely portrayed through symbols and attributes in sculptures and paintings. The lotus flower symbolizes purity and beauty, while additional limbs represent the gods' power. Traditional arts like Bharatanatyam, Kathakali, and Kuchipudi are rooted in Hinduism and recount stories of gods and goddesses. Music is also integral to Hinduism, with traditional instruments like the sitar, tabla, and veena creating beautiful melodies.

In China, Confucian-inspired art emphasized teachings such as filial piety, respect for elders, and the importance of education. This art is often characterized by the use of traditional Chinese painting techniques, including brushwork and ink wash.

Indeed, art is deeply ingrained in culture and intertwined with religious themes. Despite the close relationship between art and religion, there have been historical instances of conflict between the two. For example, during the Renaissance, many artists started incorporating secular themes into their works, challenging the religious establishment. Similarly, during the Reformation, Protestant leaders rejected numerous traditional religious artworks as idolatrous and unnecessary.

Another significant intersection between art and religion lies in the use of ritual and ceremony. Many religious traditions utilize art to connect people with the divine and foster a sense of connection and community among believers. In Hinduism, art is often employed in ritual ceremonies to invoke the presence of the gods and create a sense of sacred space. Likewise, in Buddhism, art is frequently used in meditation practices to help people connect with their inner selves and attain enlightenment.

Art can also illuminate new ideas rapidly entering our lives through rituals and routines. It has the potential to facilitate the fusion of religious and scientific concepts and themes. Art in science can render complex ideas and concepts more accessible by relating them to existing religious notions. For example, by illustrating the grandeur and symmetry of the universe, art can convey the structured and unified nature of the laws governing it. It could communicate Spinoza's idea of God in the laws of nature.

This new generation of art can reveal the gentler, caring side of humanity, linking our shared humanity to new concepts that merge science with traditional ideas of a personal God. It can demonstrate how our choices and actions shape the world around us and leave lasting impressions. This new form of art can help us understand the meaning and value of our lives and our interconnectedness within the world. It can foster a sense of community and connection between people of different backgrounds and beliefs, and inspire wonder and awe about the natural world. Such experiences can motivate people to place their faith in science and new ideas, promoting notions of tolerance, determination, and conviction, as well as the belief that our lives have value and meaning.

The marriage of science, art and a reformed, enlightened religion can act as a safeguard against the misuse of scientific advancements. By instilling in people a sense of moral responsibility and a desire to use knowledge for the benefit of all, we can create a society that is both scientifically advanced and ethically grounded.

In collaborating to realize this concept, we are not only molding a brighter future for ourselves but also safeguarding the promise of better days for generations yet to come. This ensures that scientific knowledge persists as a force of benevolence in our world. Should a significant number of individuals embrace this concept, we could inch it ever closer to becoming a reality. This transformation ought to occur in the consciousness of each individual.

217

Inclusion of Art could help bridge the gap between science and religion, create a more unified understanding of the world, and give rise to a new era where art, religion and science no longer stand in opposition but work together for the betterment of humankind, and all of humanity.

For me, this shift entailed focusing not solely on leaving my ideas as a legacy, but on ensuring their capacity to aid others. It also meant making necessary adjustments to my approach, signifying a change in my formula.

Expanding Our Formula to Mankind's Ecosystem

With this new knowledge that I have acquired over the years while going through this mapping, I had to make another adjustment to the formula. So far, my formula calculated the value for the meaning of our lives as a summarily impact on the lives of others divided into two categories, one that is novel defined by our unique life, and another that is common to entire humanity. I had to incorporate the impact on preserving the future of humanity.

For the modification of a formula that takes into account the impact on humanity's future, both positive and negative, we must introduce a third term. This new component will factor in the ramifications of our actions, not only in terms of their immediate implications but also with respect to their lasting effects on human population dynamics. Consequently, actions and ideas that potentially increase the future population will receive amplification, while those leading to a population decrease will face penalization.

An inevitable question that arises from this perspective is the relevance of population size. Given the fact that the sheer number of people on our planet contributes to ecological disasters and climate catastrophes, why should population growth be encouraged? This is a valid query, particularly when considering the toll of overpopulation on Earth's resources. However, looking forward into the distant future, our civilization may not be Earth-bound. We may journey to the stars - "sic itur ad astra" as the phrase goes.

The primary motivation behind considering population as a factor lies in the grim reality of extinction events, where the population plummets to zero. The greater our distance from this absolute zero, the higher the likelihood of human continuity. Thus, maintaining a healthy population size becomes a strategic investment in our survival and continued growth as a species, whether on Earth or amidst the stars.

In that light the meaning of what is considered an impactful action changes. For instance, a national leader might seek to secure their legacy by launching a campaign to acquire valuable resources, such as oil-rich territory, thus solidifying their place in history. However, if this conflict for territory escalates into a global war resulting in the death of millions of people, including the leader's own citizens, it not only negates the legacy by reducing the number of people affected but also tarnishes their reputation to the point that it serves as a cautionary tale for future generations.

Furthermore, even if the conflict doesn't spiral into a world war, but prompts an exodus of talented and skilled young professionals fleeing conscription, this would still undermine the leader's legacy, and could even lead to its complete erasure. A case in point is Saddam Hussein, whose actions in history serve as a cautionary tale, teaching us what actions to avoid rather than emulate.

Similarly, consider a scientist who develops an innovation that saves hundreds of millions of people from starvation but then employs the same technology to create a lethal weapon responsible for the deaths of millions. These two examples from actual history include Napoleon's attempt to build an empire, which ultimately crumbled and resulted in countless casualties, and the tragic case of Fritz Haber, who, as previously mentioned, invented the process for ammonia fertilizer production as well as the devastating cyclone gas.

Our actions often exhibit a dual nature, resulting in both positive and negative consequences for our legacy. We can summarize this in a third term: U_{eco} , which represents the individual contribution of each action to the future of humanity as a whole. It could be either positive or negative. I would refer to it as an ecological term, as it reflects the effects of our actions on the entire ecosystem within which humanity exists.

Recalling the definition of meaning as the impact on the people around us, this new term represents our contribution to the survival probability of humanity as a whole. If that probability is not zero, then mere survival will provide fertile ground for individual lives to leave a meaningful legacy for future generations. However, if we contribute to our legacy at the expense of the survival of entire future populations, in the extreme case, there will be no people left to carry on our legacy or remember our names.

It is tempting to add this new term to our formula, but as I will demonstrate in the appendix, the correct way to include it is by multiplying it with our formula. In this sense, the formula for the new ecological term represents the probability that the number of people will increase or decrease as a result of our actions, and can be assessed by considering how many people we will directly support or eliminate. This gives a more somber meaning to the phrase, "leave the Earth in a better place than when we found it." This implies that the culmination of our actions should not reduce the number of people capable of supporting the meaning of our lives or carrying out our legacies.

For the reference to the formula's math, please consult the appendix at the end of the book. The new ecological term is calculated slightly differently. What goes into the summation of all our actions is still the relative power of our actions, but its weight is not the reach of the impact on other people, but rather the actual population of people around us, calculated as the number of people in each generation. If the number of people increases as a result of our actions, the spread is positive, and vice versa if the number decreases.

In practical terms, this means that our actions matter not only in terms of leaving our own legacy but also in terms of increasing the survival probability of human civilization as a whole.

Considering the well-being of others is a natural inclination, as we are interconnected and interdependent with each other. What we do or fail to do can directly or indirectly impact others, including people we may never meet or know. Our actions and decisions can contribute to the well-being or harm of others, the environment, and future generations. Therefore, incorporating considerations about humanity as a whole into our personal life goals helps us to be more responsible, compassionate, and mindful of our impact on others and the world around us. Focusing on something larger than ourselves allows us to transcend our own needs and desires, making a positive impact on the world.

We can think of this modified formula as a representation of the beneficial virality of our lives. If our actions and ideas become viral and are embraced by a large number of people while contributing to the well-being of the group, then the meaning of our lives holds positive value.

It is essential to contribute to the entirety of humanity in order to secure our own legacy. In simpler terms, it is not enough just to be known; we must also be useful to others and beneficial to humankind as a whole.

Rituals, Routines and Habits

In practical terms, for all of us to ensure the survival of future generations while also making a unique impact on others, we must set at least two complimentary directions, two compatible goals. One of these goals involves creating a distinct imprint on others, which we call a "revised soul." The other is ensuring that future generations carry this imprint forward. Some fortunate individuals may even manage to combine both achievements for humanity and their own legacy in a single action or idea.

This means that we must consciously choose and plan goals that serve not only humanity but also improve the chances of survival for all people.

The number of chosen goals should not be too small, nor too large. We need to devote a substantial amount of time to our goals to increase the likelihood of their success. Considering that the average time required for success in a book, career, or business is about 10 years, and given an average lifespan of 80 years (70 of which are free from dementia), with the first 20 years spent on education and an additional 10 years finding one's direction in life, we are left with about 40 years. This suggests that we can realistically manage between two and four goals.

Since the industrial revolution, the modern job market has really tilted toward specialization. In modern workplaces experts and specialists are awarded more frequently than generalists. In this sense, most of the working age adults are incentivised to focus on their career. In this environment, focusing on goals other than your career is increasingly difficult. This is why finding a career that aligns with your desires and preferences is very important but not always possible. For those who found their calling in their job, my advice is to keep doing what you do best. For those who feel unsatisfied and feel that their day job is meaningless, I would remind them that career is a myth that you can choose to believe or you could realize that there are other goals and purposes you can focus on. It is after all our choice.

I chose to focus on multiple goals and at least one of these goals should be dedicated to the future of humanity. Time is our most valuable resource, so allocating and spending time on shared goals represents a form of sacrifice; however, it is a necessary one.

We can choose to make an impact on our immediate family and raise children, which is an example of leaving a genetic footprint. Your children will have their own offspring, and so on. Many, including yours truly, decide on having children as a way to leave their own legacy and contribute to the human population. Some people choose not to have biological children due to concerns about overpopulation and instead opt for adoption, demonstrating care for humanity's future. Other examples include constructing a large house, a tall building, or a bridge with your name on it, such as the infamous Giza pyramids or Trump towers, or establishing a successful business that outlives its founders, like the investment bank Goldman Sachs or financial IT giant Bloomberg.

However, if an unforeseen disaster were to strike our planet, all such efforts would render futile. The continuity of our progeny would be disrupted, and the structures and bridges named after their founders would crumble into oblivion. The solution, for me, was unmistakably clear: the survival of humanity rests on investing in fundamental science, which expands our understanding of the universe and uncovers potential threats yet to be detected.

This is why my goal has been to make substantial contributions to science, dedicating roughly fifteen years of my life to its pursuit, including my years in school. For others, their contribution could come in the form of financial investment in scientific endeavors, or at the very least, not hindering scientific progress.

I firmly believe that to inspire more people to support our scientific endeavors, we need to forge a symbiotic relationship between science and religion. Imposing such a change is neither realistic nor ethical. Rather, the most effective approach is to educate people about science and perhaps incorporate scientific knowledge into daily routines. Such a methodology allows for a seamless integration of scientific understanding into everyday life, fostering an environment conducive to the growth and development of science.

In these newly adapted rituals, the emphasis will be on the purpose of our existence. I believe it's crucial for individuals to maintain daily awareness of their life's trajectory. The understanding and ability to steer one's life should be incorporated into daily routines, perhaps in the form of introspection or meditation. Reflections on life's purpose should become embedded in our rituals and routines, serving as constant reminders of our individual and collective journeys and our responsibility and contribution to humanity's future.

In traditional religions, rituals and routines play a crucial role in religious practices. They provide structure and order for followers, create a sense of community among believers, and offer opportunities to express faith. Rituals can also mark important events or times in a person's life, such as birth, marriage, or death. They can be used to honor gods or other spiritual entities, and they help to reinforce the beliefs and values of a particular religion.

In everyday life, routines are equally, if not more, important. We have our morning and evening routines, which allow us to perfect our actions through repetition. By mastering these repeated actions or skills, they become second nature, enabling us to conserve mental energy for learning new things. Routines and habits can help reduce stress and anxiety, as well as promote efficiency and effectiveness in completing tasks. They can also have a positive impact on our physical and mental health when related to exercise, nutrition, and sleep.

However, routines and habits can also be a double-edged sword. Repeated actions reinforce acquired knowledge and strengthen mental connections, but if these connections are outdated or incorrect, repetition will reinforce falsehoods and stale ideas. Routines and habits can become rigid and inflexible, hindering adaptation to new situations or changes when necessary. They can also lead to boredom and stifle creativity. Overdependence on routines and habits can create difficulty adjusting to changes or trying new things.

Routines and rituals can impede rapid changes. It's no surprise that more traditional religions have stricter dogmas and rituals. Catholic and Orthodox religions are filled with intricate details and elaborate rituals, while Protestant traditions are generally humbler and less complex. Catholics place great importance on traditions, with numerous complex rituals, while Muslims perform daily prayers and the Hajj pilgrimage. Hinduism has the ritual of Puja, which involves offering prayers and items to gods or goddesses. In contrast, Protestants don't consider church tradition as important or equal in authority to the Bible, and more modernized denominations place less emphasis on rituals.

It is evident that rituals are vital for reinforcing core principles in an existing belief system. However, with a more scientific approach, the focus should shift from reinforcing blind faith to continuously testing convictions through experimentation and knowledge acquisition.

In the same vein, I believe it is crucial to maintain a habit of continuously reevaluating the choices we make and the goals we set for our lives. These goals give our lives meaning, and without rituals, it's easy to lose focus and stray from our path. Our lives are already filled with daily routines, such as morning, exercise, mealtime, and bedtime routines. Rituals help us practice our convictions, with the concept of the soul representing the ultimate manifestation of our actions and the bearer of all consequences.

We should apply this valuable methodology to the merged concept of religion and science. As previously discussed, one of our goals should involve considering the future of humanity and working to prevent its extinction. We can integrate these thoughts into our evening routines. As a result of visiting various places of worship, I developed a deep appreciation for rituals, habits, and particularly meditation practices. On one occasion, a friend invited me to a Buddhist temple, which inspired me to create my own meditation. My experiences with the guided and solo meditations led me to discover the benefits of meditation for managing stress and improving sleep quality. I learned to replace the addictive allure of electronic screens with 30 minutes of relaxing meditation before bed. My intention was to practice it every night, examining my actions and decisions throughout the day, assessing their harmony with my objectives, and focusing my thoughts on accomplishing those objectives and reaffirming my resolve. I have several versions of the meditation, and I am attaching one of them in the form of a poem as an appendix at the end of the book.

Designing Personal God(like) Algorithm

I will proceed with this chapter by detailing my pursuit of the next objective, reinforcing my points with concrete examples from my life. Another decade had passed since I first met the girl at Fermilab, and since then she had grown into a woman whom I had married and had two children with. Yet after accomplishments in scientific publication and family life, the third ambition of starting my own company was still not in sight.

While I had switched a couple of jobs between an investment bank and a high-frequency trading company while still working on Wall Street, major changes had taken place in the financial industry. The housing crisis had occurred, causing investment banks to disappear as business entities, and high-frequency trading companies, after causing trading crashes and spreading fear in Wall Street, had quietly renamed themselves as hedge funds and market makers. Eventually, I ended up at a brokerage firm, working for a close friend of mine at a high-level position overseeing a department responsible for about 500 companies and traveling frequently to London.

Throughout this period, I found myself engaged in numerous discussions about life's meaning and the perceived lack thereof in our daily occupations. Intriguingly, many of my colleagues, despite expressing a profound sense of purposelessness in their everyday jobs, especially jobs on Wall Street, where there was no obvious value delivered to the common folk, appeared to lack the will or drive to alter their life circumstances. During these conversations, my go-to answer was that I had dedicated a significant part of my life to science, viewing it as my contribution to the future of humanity. However, a troubling, nagging question lingered within me: was it enough?

Somewhere around that time in my career, I realized that I had not made any progress towards my long-term dream of starting my own company. Working for big corporations had taken up so much of my time that I had not pursued my entrepreneurial goals.

My personal life changed a lot. Just a few short years ago, I held my newborn baby for the first time while wearing a bracelet that matched an ID on his foot. The experience made me think that there should be better technology for monitoring infants. A few chapters back I described how I came up with an idea for a product that could monitor a baby's pulse, breathing, temperature, and activity levels. Unable to find a suitable product on the market, I decided to develop one myself. After years of working on Wall Street serving the invisible and often puzzling hand of the free market, It was a perfect goal to match my yearning to do something tangible and useful for everyday life. It was a real product that customers could hold in their hands and be actually useful, a big departure from the type of projects I was doing in my day to day work.

At my day job, a political shift led to a change in leadership. My friend, who originally had hired me and who had overseen the company's technology, was replaced by an executive with a political background but little technological expertise. As her subordinates, many of them my friends, were gradually replaced by the new leader's team, I realized that my corporate career at the company was pretty much over. By that time, I had already been working on the baby monitor prototype for a couple of years and it was time to make a decision: either I want to leave it as an expensive hobby or make this idea into a real commercial product. Instead of seeking new employment, I opted to remain at the company while working on my own product during evenings and weekends. I decided to use my failure to advance my dead-end career and turn it into an opportunity to establish my own business.

Balancing family life, a daytime job, and building a company was my greatest challenge. The first order of business was to find a suitable business partner. Picking the right partner and establishing the right team can make or break the business. I knew a friend who was a talented programmer who also was good at generating ideas but was really bad at working with others. Although he developed a functioning prototype, he faced challenges without the team and without a partner, ultimately selling his implementation for a fraction of its worth. Doing any difficult task solo, especially building your own business, makes it impossible.

Having an unsuitable partner is even worse. I experienced this first hand while working on a different side project. We had a great idea to create a version of NFTs long before they became popular that was designed specifically for young artists. Despite having a good concept and seed money, we had a bad team of people incompatible with each other from the very start. Instead of actually working on creating a product, we spent most of our time arguing and dividing shares of a nonexistent fortune and eventually the partners just started suing and litigating with each other and everyone on the team. Having the wrong partner or a team can doom even successful ideas.

After several attempts to find an idea that would work, I thought I finally had a product that would be useful to new parents and was coming right at the moment of the Internet of Things revolution. The original concept evolved from a bracelet to a smart button that could be attached to baby clothing to monitor the baby's position and breathing. I decided to treat this idea seriously, to turn my hobby into an actual company and focus on finding partners.

The principle of comparative advantage in economics suggests that individuals and firms should focus on activities where they have a relative advantage over others and delegate other tasks accordingly. In other words, if you're not adept at something, find a person who excels in that area and try to convince them to join your cause. It is said, in a phrase attributed to Rei Inamoto - CTO of AKQA, "to run an efficient team, you only need three people: a hipster, a hacker, and a hustler"[92] (Ellwood, 2012). I considered my role in this H-trinity of being a hacker. I found myself lacking not only fundraising skills but also creating flawless implementations of the prototypes I'd created. I needed a hipster and a hustler.

My first business partner, who fit both roles perfectly, was both a symbol of my success and a testament to my failure. I shared my idea with a former colleague from an investment banking trading group, and we began developing a Bluetooth-based baby monitoring product. Instead of a garage, we utilized each other's basements for workspaces and frequented Panera Bread for strategy sessions. We successfully created a series of prototypes. He focused on designing a miniature board and writing firmware to power a tiny chip, while I concentrated on developing algorithms and software for mobile applications. This collaboration was productive, but I failed to persuade him to commit to the business full-time. Eventually, he chose to prioritize his trading career at a hedge fund. His departure that almost killed the business before it even started, was a challenging yet pivotal transition for me. We remained friends and I learned some useful lessons, namely the importance of being more proactive, communicating more clearly, and avoiding becoming complacent. With my previous partner I often relied on his

---

[92] forbes.com/the-dream-team-hipster-hacker-and-hustler

technical expertise to finish my prototypes, so he must have felt that he was doing most of the work. This time around I finished all the preliminary work myself. It still had to find a partner and build a team, and do it very soon, before losing the momentum.

My luck also turned and I won a major award at an IoT (Internet-of-Things) conference in Munich that same year. Even small wins are important and I used this token of success to find and attract another business partner. Finding a partner is just like dating, you have to go through many trials and pitches during lunch and having drinks. Eventually I found that a friend of mine just sold a company that he started for many millions of $ or and was looking for another venture. I found a "hustler." We hit it off right away and started forming an actual company. We had momentum and there was no visible competition in the market. I knew this situation was not going to last and the next challenge was how to build a team and do it quickly.

Presenting MonBaby product at a conference in San Francisco

Through my partner's contacts we found a third business partner, and, together, we managed to build a crack team of engineers, thinkers, customer support and marketing talent, the three Hs of our startup, and established a proper company. The need to build the team fast also meant that I had to hire people who were not the best match and I had to let them go, not the most pleasant, but a necessary experience. That was another challenge and lesson I acquired along the way: how to be tough towards my employees and towards competitors. Most of us, at least those who are not sociopaths, want to be nice to people and get positivity and love in return. In business this does not always work and I learned it the hard way. After a few trial and errors, I managed to assemble an amazing team of individuals. With renewed momentum, funding, and a strong team, we created a successful Kickstarter campaign. I presented our product on Fox News, participated in interviews with newspapers and tech bloggers, visited our manufacturing facility in China, attended consumer shows in Las Vegas, San Francisco, Munich and Los Angeles, and met clients worldwide. This momentum culminated in our first orders being fulfilled online on Amazon.com and in a Target store. I can not describe the feeling of going to a store to see my own product being sold on a shelf of a major retailer.

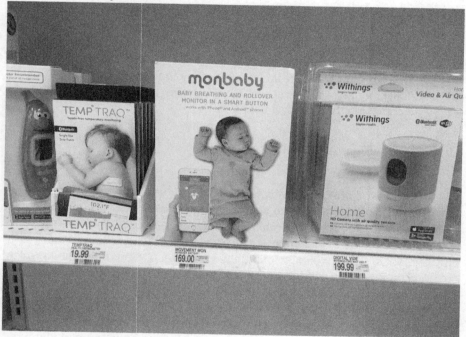

My product is on the shelves of Target stores

There were also other challenges on the way. The most infuriating was competition from companies that copied my designs and started manufacturing replicas of my product overseas. It was disheartening to see the efforts and resources put into creating a unique product being exploited by others who lacked commitment to the original vision and objectives of the product. Despite the difficulties in protecting my brand and product, I learned that it's often better to focus on outperforming rivals through superior product quality rather than relying solely on legal actions. Oscar Wilde said that "Imitation is the sincerest form of flattery that mediocrity can pay to greatness", but it is also a reminder to stay ahead of the game and continue to innovate. As Steve Jobs famously said, "Innovation distinguishes between a leader and a follower."

In a few years, we secured a major client in Japan to supply kindergartens with our product.

The thrill of building a product intended for thousands of consumers is unrivaled. I'm happy and grateful that I was not alone, that I shared this experience with my team members, who over time, evolved into not just colleagues, but also friends. Over the next decade, our client captured approximately 40% of the Japanese market and ultimately purchased the rights and licenses to our product in a successful exit. But my biggest reward was when a few parents expressed a personal gratitude to me.

The journey was filled with emotional highs and lows and a fair share of drama. It was nothing like I had anticipated, it was longer than I expected, but in the end it was rewarding. Finally I had enough time to focus on my last goal: to write a book. Instead of writing about science fiction or memoirs, I decided to write on a subject that consumed my thoughts most, about how to find and fulfill the meaning of my life. So here I am, trying to complete my journey by finishing the next few chapters.

Origin of the Origin

As far as we know and remember our history, humanity remains isolated from the vast, seemingly infinite cosmos that surrounds us. The universe is an inhospitable place, and we find ourselves as an exceedingly rare presence within it. Our circles of influence are limited to the human race and the environment in which we exist, primarily Earth. Despite our attempts to reach out and communicate with other civilizations, our efforts have been met with silence.

As we continue to search for extraterrestrial life, we maintain a constant vigil, listening for any signals or transmissions that might indicate the existence of a remote civilization. However, so far, we have found nothing but the cold, empty void of space. This reality is both humbling and somewhat unsettling, as it forces us to confront the notion that we may be utterly alone in the universe.

This predicament is exemplified by the Fermi Paradox, which was first introduced by Enrico Fermi during a casual conversation with fellow physicists about UFOs and aliens. When pondering the apparent absence of other life forms in the cosmos, Fermi famously asked, "But where is everybody?" This question embodies the essence of the paradox, underscoring the discrepancy between the high probability of extraterrestrial life, based on the staggering number of stars and planets in the universe, and the absence of any solid evidence of such life. Despite our increasingly sophisticated sensors and the effortless propagation of radio waves in space, we remain unable to detect any indication of life beyond our own planet.

One potential explanation for the seeming absence of extraterrestrial life is that the emergence of life is exceptionally rare, positioning us as either solitary beings in the universe or scattered so distantly apart that communication and contact are practically unfeasible. Another even more haunting possibility suggests that each advanced civilization inevitably arrives at a point of self-destruction, where its amassed power and technological prowess trigger a catastrophic collapse.

In either case, we seem to be alone in our fights against the relentless and unforgiving march of time. But are we alone in our struggles?

It's not just people who are mortal; all the objects around us eventually fall apart. The keyboard I'm writing on will one day be recycled (hopefully) and end up in a landfill. The walls of the houses we live in will crumble, and the roofs over our heads will collapse. The roads and structures that line the streets we walk on will be buried by soil and vanish. Cities and countries will disintegrate over time. Even our planet will be engulfed by the sun in billions of years, and then the sun itself will die, followed by the eventual fate of our galaxy.

The fate of all matter in the universe is determined by the laws of physics, most crucially by the Second Law of Thermodynamics, which posits that total entropy of the isolated system can never decrease over time and chaos will inevitably prevail. Over time, this drives various processes such as radioactive decay, fusion, fission, or other interactions, triggering changes within the matter. This rule underpins the transient nature of the universe without exceptions.

Even the most stable particles, like protons, are hypothesized to have a finite lifetime, albeit an extremely long one. Theoretical predictions suggest that protons could decay with a half-life of 10^{34} years or more, but this has not been experimentally confirmed yet. If protons were to decay, then even atomic nuclei would eventually break apart.

On cosmic time scales, even seemingly stable structures, like black holes, are not exempt from decay. According to the theory of Hawking radiation, black holes will slowly lose mass over time, eventually evaporating. However, this process occurs over an unimaginably long time frame, with a black hole the mass of our sun taking around 10^{67} years to dissipate completely.

Even the universe itself may undergo another phase transition that alters the laws of physics and reality as we know it, akin to the Big Bang. Living organisms, however, have found a way to counteract the detrimental effects of time by passing on information about their construction from one body to another, from one generation to the next. Rather than preserving the matter that composes life, replicating genes preserve the information that defines us. We can apply the same mechanism used by evolution, and instead of preserving the matter that will eventually decay, we can preserve the ideas and concepts that have shaped humanity. Even if all the matter, such as lepton particles, in the universe disintegrates, there will still be energy in the form of bosons, which constitute fundamental forces and gravitational waves. If our civilization reaches advanced stages where we can imprint information onto more stable forms of matter and energy, we will follow life's recipe to persist despite and against the destructive nature of time.

Living organisms might have more in common with the universe than initially thought. The universe may not be the hostile environment that surrounds our hospitable planet. The concept of a fine-tuned universe suggests that the fundamental constants and laws of physics are precisely balanced to allow the existence of complex structures such as galaxies, stars, planets, and life itself. In Appendix I, I proposed an explanation in which the laws of physics evolved from a turbulent environment following the Big Bang. The fundamental constants and laws we observe in our universe may have emerged through a selection process similar to natural selection in biological evolution, with different physical laws competing for dominance or suitability within various cosmic environments.

Perhaps the origin of our yearning for meaning may have been part of a fundamental force in the universe – a counteraction to time. The connection between living organisms and the cosmos suggests that perhaps we are not as isolated as we once believed, but instead, intrinsically linked to the very fabric of the universe itself.

Expanding on a Concept for Personal Deity

In the previous sections, we explored the concept of the amended soul and the corresponding formula that quantifies one's actions and impact on humanity. I drew parallels between scientific concepts such as evolutionary biology and the expanding universe and old religious beliefs. Through this approach, I devised a new framework that combines science and religion.

However, I have been unable to find a natural phenomenon or societal construct that matches the concept of a personal God. Although we approximated a personal God to the future of humanity, it was not a perfect match.

The properties of omnipresence and omniscience, on the other hand, are starting to align with human society due to advances in communication and the development of social networks. With the widespread availability of real-time information, humanity is becoming super-connected, which is analogous to being omnipresent and omniscient.

Furthermore, humans are gaining access to increasingly powerful sources of energy. From fire to fission power, we are making tremendous strides in achieving energy breakthroughs. If we can tame thermonuclear power, we will have practically unlimited access to energy, making humanity virtually omnipotent.

However, we are still struggling to achieve goodness and graciousness. Despite our technological advancements, people continue to commit evil acts.

Through mass and social media, we are constantly bombarded with examples of bad behavior. The more connected we become, the more ugliness we see in the world's dark corners. This shortfall leaves much to be desired in terms of humanity's goodness and graciousness.

In previous discussions, we explored how the origins of morality and behavior norms stem from societies and humanity as a whole. While these norms can prevent many harmful and self-destructive urges, they cannot prevent all heinous crimes.

The lack of a good match between the idea of a personal God and scientific concepts suggests that such a mapping does not currently exist. It is contradictory for humanity to judge its own actions as good or evil, and there needs to be a neutral and impartial entity with the power to judge and punish crimes. However, in the current social order, it is challenging to find someone willing to take on this mantle of power and responsibility.

While humanity does not currently match the properties of a personal deity, this may change in the future. For our personal meaning to exist, we must ensure the survival of humanity, which requires a guardian to protect us. This guardian would be the closest match to the idea of a personal god, but it cannot be science or religion in their current forms.

Designing a concept or algorithm for such a protector entity is challenging, but it would be necessary for humanity's survival. This future entity could match the concept of a personal deity.

The idea of a personal God is riddled with contradictions, including the problem of evil famously attributed to Epicurus, and discussed by Scottish philosopher David Hume, who relied on a Christian apologist named Lactantius. It is difficult to imagine a concept of a personal God that is just, powerful, and cares for humanity:

"Is God willing to prevent evil, but not able? Then he is not omnipotent.
Is he able, but not willing? Then he is malevolent.
Is he both able and willing? Then whence cometh evil?
Is he neither able nor willing? Then why call him God?"

The argument was countered by the common assertion that evil stems from individuals making poor decisions, rooted in the idea of original sin. However, a truly omnipotent deity could create a reality where people maintain free will but consistently make good choices, rendering evil and even the existence of hell unnecessary.

One persuasive argument that reconciles the existence of evil with an omnipotent and omniscient god is to consider a god that is, at worst, malevolent and, at the least, indifferent towards humans.

While the idea of a malevolent god is both intriguing and unsettling, a more logical perspective posits a deity that is indifferent to humanity. This aligns with Spinoza's notion of an omnipotent yet impartial god, in which a detached and unsympathetic universe perpetually threatens humanity. In the cycles of life and death Spinoza's god is not an almighty father or a guardian. Instead it is an environment that continuously changes and humanity is trying to keep up. As it is, Spinoza's impartial god is insufficient to preserve personal meaning.

Instead, humanity needs a much more personal protector and guardian. Humanity itself struggles to secure its future due to our limited perspective, shortsightedness, indifference, and chaotic nature.

Governments, while playing a crucial role in maintaining order and providing public services, represent only specific subgroups and interests within their respective nations. As such, they cannot effectively assume the role of a universal guardian. Oftentimes, governments prioritize their own political and economic interests, which can lead to conflicts and even wars with other nations. In these scenarios, rather than acting as protectors of humanity as a whole, governments can be seen as perpetuating division and partiality

Religion and government were historically separated for a reason. While the government can provide certain services and maintain order, it may not be the best caretaker for all of humanity. Instead, the responsibility for caring for all of humanity should fall on a construct or organization that is free from political biases and has the best interests of all people at heart.

This impartiality and limitation of governments highlight the need for an overarching guardian that transcends borders, cultures, and interests, a role that modern science is unable to fulfill. In traditional religions, the notion of a personal god serves as a protector and guardian of humanity, providing guidance, solace, and a sense of purpose to individuals through communication in the form of prayer and meditation, yet traditional religions were rooted in old and often violent traditions of the past. The gods depicted in traditional religions often appear malicious and malevolent in their scriptures, which were written millennia ago without the benefit of modern scientific knowledge and using language more suited to ancient societies. Consequently, these worldviews and prophecies are often refuted by science. There are countless examples that we already discussed previously, such as the age of the Earth, the lack of a universal center, and misconceptions about heaven and hell. Each of the thousands of religions tends to tolerate only its own interpretation of reality, so by design, most must be incorrect according to their own standards, with only one potentially being accurate. We must either choose one worldview from the myriad of existing religions or rely on science, which is not based on dogma and is continually updated to reflect verified experimental observations. Even if one religion is accidentally true, science will eventually align with it as the observable reality corresponds to scientific theory.

In contrast, modern science is dedicated to understanding the natural world and uncovering the underlying principles that govern it. While science has made remarkable advancements in medicine, technology, and our understanding of the universe, it lacks the ability to offer the personal connection and guidance that a guardian figure would provide. This absence leaves a void in our collective search for meaning and protection from existential threats. Modern science lacks the guardian aspect that traditional religions possess: a protector of humanity and individuals with whom one can communicate through prayer and meditation.

As a viable alternative I suggested a merger between several disciplines, including religion and science that would serve as a "personal god and guardian". By "personal god," I am referring to a human-centric entity, organization, or technology with the purpose of preventing human extinction. Modern fundamental science aligns more closely with Spinoza's impersonal god, an indifferent universe that cannot be engaged in conversation. Scientists can only observe the data the universe provides and ponder its mysteries, focusing on acquiring knowledge rather than protecting humanity. What we need is a fusion of scientific concepts and phenomena that is compatible with the idea of a personal god. In other words, if there was no existing personal Guardian, it does not mean there will not be one in the future.

To implement this algorithm, it is crucial to develop a methodology or framework that combines the pursuit of scientific knowledge with the concept of a guardian entity often found in world religions that is capable of overseeing the welfare of humanity as a whole, transcending national borders, cultural differences, and individual interests. Such an entity would need to foster a sense of unity, promote global cooperation, and prioritize the long-term survival of humanity.

Since the time I made that suggestion, AI (Artificial Intelligence) has made major breakthroughs especially in the area of language models and chat bots. It seems that there is a rapidly developing new phenomenon that is a part of human technology, contains all of mankind's knowledge, and is still in its early stages. This means that there is an actual basis for creating a personal Guardian algorithm for humanity.

I will refer to it as an algorithm because it will be a creation of humanity, designed to adhere to specific rules and logic in order to fulfill its purpose: safeguarding humanity's future. I describe it as the "God" algorithm because it will possess the characteristics of a guardian for humanity, a role previously attributed to divine beings in religious contexts. I call it personal because it will be attentive to the needs and welfare of each individual human being.

We must foresee inherent contradictions that inevitably will arise during its development. The personal deity construct should be committed to preventing evil, even if it cannot prevent all of it, while continually striving for improvement. In terms of humanity's survival, the entity must work persistently to preserve our existence alongside people who share this concern and those who may be indifferent or even destructive. This algorithm would serve and protect humanity from both internal and external threats. To accomplish this, it requires specific properties that were traditionally assigned to gods which we already described in the previous chapters. Unlike before, though, here we will be redefining those properties with modern concepts to fit the role of a guardian of humanity:

Asseity: Autonomy and Neutrality

In order for the algorithm to effectively serve and protect humanity, it must be completely autonomous and neutral. Its purpose and actions should be solely dedicated to the betterment of humanity, without being influenced by any political, economic, or social biases. This will ensure that the algorithm remains impartial in its decision-making and guidance.

Goodness: Benevolence and Ethical Framework

The algorithm should operate based on a well-defined ethical framework that ensures it acts in the best interests of all humans, without causing harm or creating disparities. This ethical framework should be designed to prioritize the welfare of humanity, taking into account the diverse needs and values of different individuals and communities.

Omniscience: Comprehensive Data Gathering and Privacy Preservation

The algorithm must have the ability to gather vast amounts of data, both personal and global, to accurately assess potential threats and provide relevant guidance. However, it is crucial that the algorithm respects individuals' privacy and ensures that personal data is not used maliciously or exploited for purposes other than the protection and welfare of humanity.

Omnipresence: Ubiquitous Data Collection and Threat Detection

To effectively serve as a guardian, the algorithm should be capable of collecting data from a wide range of sources, including those within our solar system and beyond. This will enable the algorithm to detect and analyze potential external threats, such as asteroid impacts or extraterrestrial dangers, and devise appropriate preventative measures.

Omnipotence: Advanced Analytical Capabilities and Technological Access

The algorithm must possess advanced analytical capabilities, allowing it to process the vast amount of collected data and extract meaningful insights. Moreover, it should have access to advanced technologies and resources, enabling it to carry out the necessary actions to protect humanity from identified threats or guide humans towards safer and more prosperous outcomes.

Graciousness: Trustworthiness and Relatability

Lastly, for the algorithm to successfully fulfill its role as a guardian of humanity, it must establish trust and rapport with the people it serves. It should be transparent in its operations, intentions, and ethical framework, making it clear that its primary purpose is to protect and support humanity. By fostering a strong relationship with humans, the algorithm can ensure that its guidance and actions are met with acceptance and cooperation.

The entity we envision is not a supernatural being but rather a technology or organization that falls within the realm of human capability to conceptualize and develop. Our objective is to identify the essential features this entity must possess in order to function as a personal God algorithm, providing guidance and protection to humanity while preserving our existence against all odds.

As a neutral arbiter and defender of humanity's interests, this personal deity algorithm must remain distinct from the rest of humanity while also being committed to safeguarding humanity's welfare. Like judges, the algorithm must be impartial towards all individuals and factions within mankind, without taking sides or having any personal interests except those aligned with the well-being of humanity.

The algorithm must ensure that it does not harm or allow any harm to be inflicted upon individuals. To make sound judgments that prioritize the interests of every person, it must collect data and possess knowledge about every human in the world.

The algorithm must be capable of processing and analyzing large amounts of data to arrive at informed decisions. It must understand the context of a situation and interpret it in a way that benefits humanity. It should have access to all relevant information, whether online or offline, and be able to use it for the good of humanity.

The algorithm must be able to learn from its errors and adjust its decisions based on new information. It must grasp the consequences of its choices and make adjustments accordingly, understanding the implications of each decision and choosing actions that benefit humanity.

The algorithm must be familiar with ethical, environmental, and political implications of its decisions and make choices that align with those principles.

In the animal kingdom, there is a precedent where a specific part of the organism specializes in processing and preserving the organism - the brain. Our modern brain, which evolved over a billion years, has given humans enormous advantages over the rest of the animal kingdom, and it presides over billions of cells connected through various mechanisms. The brain is a specialized organ that is separated from the rest of the body by a blood-brain barrier, and the neural cortex judges our actions against our own cells, punishing harmful actions with pain and negative emotions.

When we identified the qualities of the guardian algorithm – Goodness, Omniscience, Omnipresence, Omnipotence, and Graciousness – they appeared strikingly similar to Asimov's Three Laws of Robotics. This resemblance is not coincidental, as Asimov formulated these laws to ensure that robotic intelligence would serve humanity and prioritize its interests.

We now find ourselves in the midst of the AI revolution, with some AI technologies exhibiting similarities to human brain structures, particularly the class of algorithms known as neural networks. Neural networks consist of multiple layers, each capable of learning and containing neurons. This design is intentional, as it was inspired by the human brain and shares many conceptual similarities. However, the resemblance ends there, as neural networks are built on existing computer hardware, which is fundamentally different from the organic "wet-ware" of our brains. Furthermore, our understanding of the human brain's workings and structure is still evolving, so we have not yet fully grasped its intricacies.

Despite these differences, a branch of AI known as deep learning[93] (Burns & Brush, n.d.) has seen rapid development in recent years. Deep learning, a type of machine learning that emulates human learning processes, has led to groundbreaking achievements in various fields. For instance, AI has outperformed world champions in chess and Go tournaments, and it has made remarkable advancements in computer vision and speech recognition technologies, which are now quickly becoming commonplace in our homes.

These layers "learn" by adjusting their parameters during a training stage, during which they are exposed to "training data." The objective is to match the output data values, and the generalized design allows for a wide range of application domains.

The next milestone in AI development is achieving the long-sought goal of computer science: "AGI," or artificial general intelligence. This level of AI would be capable of performing most comprehension tasks as effectively as an average human. When AI technology reaches this point, it will not only help us understand how the brain works but also act as a catalyst for the next leap in AI progress. Beyond this critical juncture, AI has the potential to become what I have termed a "personal God algorithm." This AGI would be capable of understanding and responding to the needs of humanity as a whole and each individual person, offering personalized advice and guidance. It would learn from people's behavior and generate tailored recommendations while also interacting with other AGI systems, enabling it to learn from them and become even more powerful.

The year 2023 saw a transformative shift in the machine learning landscape, largely due to the rapid progression of ChatGPT. This dynamic change made the once seemingly insurmountable task of creating Artificial General Intelligence (AGI) appear significantly more attainable. One way to determine whether artificial intelligence has become indistinguishable from human intelligence is through the Turing Test. Proposed by Alan Turing in 1950, the Turing Test serves as a benchmark for assessing a machine's ability to exhibit human-like intelligence. During this test, a human judge converses with both a machine and a human through a text-based interface. If the judge cannot consistently differentiate between the machine and the

---

[93] techtarget.com/deep-learning-deep-neural-network

human, the machine is considered to have passed the Turing Test. Although there have been multiple claims that the latest iteration of ChatGPT has passed the Turing Test, this has not been firmly established. However, what seemed impossible years ago, unlikely months ago, and plausible just weeks ago could very well become a reality in a few months, with chatbots potentially passing the test. We may have discovered a technology that could become an integral part of humankind, as it is our own creation and could serve as our protector. Future AI could closely resemble the concept of a "personal God."

This development underscores the point I'm emphasizing: humanity is in the process of creating a profoundly powerful entity that holds the potential for either immense benefit or substantial harm. I firmly believe that it is our collective responsibility to ensure that we steer the development of this entity towards benevolence and progress, rather than inadvertently orchestrating our own downfall.

Consolidation of Knowledge

The rapid consolidation of knowledge, culminating in AI, is not an entirely new phenomenon. Humanity has been documenting and preserving knowledge in books for thousands of years. Since the advent of speech, older and wiser members of hunter-gatherer tribes have passed on the accumulated knowledge of their lifetimes, and that of their ancestors, to younger generations. Elders would share their wisdom with their children and grandchildren, teaching them which mushrooms to avoid, where to find prey, how to evade predators, and most importantly, how to raise children, make tools, and communicate. This allowed individuals to build upon the knowledge collected over generations rather than starting from scratch, which is why reverence and respect for our parents and elders remain deeply ingrained in our culture to this day.

However, knowledge about new tools and technology was once confined to the minds of elders. If an elder passed away without sharing this information with their offspring, that knowledge would be lost. However, this changed dramatically with the advent of writing, which historians have ascribed to ancient Sumer in Mesopotamia around 3400 BC. Writing accelerated the process of knowledge collection and transmission. Thanks to written records, we could move beyond relying solely on oral traditions; we were able to craft scrolls, inscribe stones, and carve tablets for future generations to read and learn from. Even if the writer or storyteller perished, their knowledge would live on through their writings.

This transition reached another significant milestone with the invention of the printing press by German goldsmith Johannes Gutenberg[94] (Printing

---

[94] en.wikipedia.org/wiki/Printing_press

Press, n.d.) in 1440. Knowledge that had previously been transferred through unique scripts or oral tradition could now be encapsulated in books and disseminated on a much broader scale. This technological breakthrough significantly broadened access to and the spread of knowledge. The profession of scribes eventually disappeared, but the ease of making hundreds and thousands of copies of a book helped to carry the knowledge to more and more people, serving and enabling education of a massive number of people, reaching millions of minds. No longer did we have to be in the presence of an expert to learn secrets of the trade; we could acquire a book written about a trade and learn from there. This ability requires an increasing number of people to know how to read and write, which increases the number of years of schooling required by mandating reading and writing. With massive numbers of people being educated, the more knowledge is being mined and recorded, which creates a positive reinforcement cycle.

Multiple studies[95] [96] [97] (Hanushek, 2013, Psacharopoulos, 1994, Barro, 1996) have consistently shown that education is positively correlated with economic growth and development. Educated societies tend to have higher levels of human capital, better technology and innovation, and more efficient institutions, all of which can lead to higher levels of economic productivity and GDP. This positive relationship between education and GDP can be seen across countries and regions, with more educated countries generally having higher GDP per capita than less educated countries.

Research has also shown that education can play a role in reducing crime rates. Educated individuals tend to have better job prospects, higher incomes, and more stable family lives, all of which can decrease the likelihood of engaging in criminal activity. Educated societies also tend to have more effective law enforcement systems, lower levels of corruption, and more supportive social programs, all of which can contribute to lower crime rates. Generally speaking, more education and more knowledge leads to more good in society.

The consolidation and acceleration of knowledge dissemination continued with the invention of computers and the widespread adoption of personal computers. These devices enabled us to access information beyond our immediate circles, offering do-it-yourself videos from experts in various crafts, ranging from making tiaras to replacing car batteries, and featuring top-notch explainers.

Advanced AIs are now capable of scanning the internet and creating concise summaries on any subject. There will be a moment in the future when AIs will be capable of creating manuals and instructions, by sifting through existing materials and extracting knowledge into algorithms.

---

[95] sciencedirect.com/science/article/abs/pii/S0272775713000654

[96] sciencedirect.com/science/article/abs/pii/0305750X94900078

[97] nber.org/papers/w5698

Computers can then present this information through multiple interfaces, such as monitor screens, personal tablets, or even read it aloud.

Being literate is no longer a prerequisite for consuming information or understanding videos and images; we can simply watch them. While we still need to write simple queries into search engines and read summary responses, advancements in speech recognition are changing this, allowing us to ask questions out loud and receive computer-generated answers. Researchers are also working on interfaces that can read and interpret our neural signals directly from our brains. Such technology, known as Brain-Computer Interfaces (BCIs), has the potential to revolutionize how we interact with technology, enabling us to control computers, devices, and other machines simply by thinking.

The concept behind BCIs involves using sensors to detect and interpret the electrical signals that our brains produce when we think, and then using these signals to control external devices. This technology has already seen successful applications, such as thought-controlled prosthetics and brain-controlled video games. Ongoing research aims to develop non-invasive sensors, like electroencephalography (EEG) and functional magnetic resonance imaging (fMRI), capable of detecting brain signals from outside the skull. While there are multiple technical challenges to overcome, the potential benefits of BCIs are immense. They could enable people with physical disabilities to control prosthetic limbs or other devices simply by thinking, granting them more independent lives. They could also provide new ways for people to interact with technology, such as controlling a computer or smartphone without using their hands. We may soon find ourselves living in a reality that resembles the magical realms described by fiction writers of the past century, where spoken commands are translated into actions executed by other mechanisms, like opening doors, turning on lights, or starting cars.

With this we are entering the realm of magic, where with mere thought wizards could control the world around them. The difference, in this new reality, everyone becomes a "wizard," without needing to study magical arts at any wizardry school. There is a certain risk in those developments that people are becoming less incentivized to study or even learn languages, as they can rely on computers and AI more and more. While this concern is valid, we should also see this shift as an opportunity for humanity to focus more on creative problem-solving tasks. Just as the typewriter accelerated writing and the calculator made calculations faster, AI has the potential to expedite our thought processes.

The process of knowledge consolidation is not slowing down; rather, it's accelerating. More and more knowledge is being stored in the "cloud" of computer farms, reducing the chances of accidental or intentional erasure or destruction of information. Bulgakov's quote, "Manuscripts don't burn," is becoming truer than ever. Not just do-it-yourself videos, but textbooks, historical facts, scientific articles, and publications, as well as virtually all publicly available information, are stored in the cloud. The cryptocurrency revolution[98] (Buterin, n.d.), despite its missteps and initial failures, initiated a conversation about embedding mechanisms against forgery and legal contracts into code. This conversation led to discussions about creating decentralized systems of courts[99] (Decentralized Court : r/ethereum, 2016), where computers could house knowledge on how to handle and arbitrate human behavior. It's not difficult to imagine that the consolidation of knowledge will eventually encompass legal, punitive, and penal codes, as well as moral codes.

The consolidation of knowledge simultaneously occurs in two opposite directions: centralization and decentralization. Knowledge is gathered from various experts and specialists across civilizations into a single central storage that is accessible to everyone. However, the storage itself is not located at a single point; it is distributed across thousands or millions of computers geographically scattered around the world. This design enables centralized access from multiple points and various methods of querying, providing recovery and failover mechanisms, and safeguarding against single points of failure, information corruption, and destruction. This is akin to our brain, which has a single consciousness, but the cortex columns are distributed throughout the brain in dispersed locations.

The specialized part of humanity that contains all the consolidated knowledge does not yet have a name, but we can already see its form emerging. Like the brain, its function is to guide and direct the rest of humanity away from self-harm, danger, and to predict potential calamities and responses. It maintains records and processes that humans have learned and shared with others, all within easy reach. In addition to the breadth of information, computer systems are also making significant strides in the depth of comprehension and processing. We are in the midst of an AI revolution, with artificial intelligence continually outperforming humans in seemingly insurmountable tasks.

First, AI defied predictions that computers would never win at chess when IBM's Deep Blue defeated world chess champion Garry Kasparov in a six-game match. Then, Google's AlphaGo achieved the same feat in the more complex game of Go. Most recently, AI algorithms have tackled the last unconquered domain of the human mind: mathematics itself. On December 1st, 2021, DeepMind solved the 'knot' conjecture that had perplexed mathematicians for decades.

The centralized knowledge not only stores but also processes information, rivaling or surpassing humans in many tasks, somewhat like a brain and central nervous system in mammals. This part will have access to the most potent resources and knowledge of every person's actions, inner thoughts, and ambitions while keeping our interests at heart. The future AI, as

---

[98] the-blockchain.com/docs/Ethereum_white_paper

[99] reddit.com/r/ethereum/comments/4gigyd/decentralized_court

humanity's brain, will be capable of balancing and resolving conflicts as an external, impartial, and powerful observer and arbiter.

The process of knowledge consolidation is not exclusive to humans; it can also be observed in bee hives and ant colonies. These hives and colonies store and contain collective knowledge that individual bees or worker ants do not possess. For example, bees select the next closest nesting site by performing a collective dance (Collective Decision-Making in Honey Bees: How Colonies Choose Among Nectar Sources, n.d.). Similarly, individual cells formed symbiotic collectives that eventually became the bodies of multicellular organisms, including our own. While there are various evolutionary strategies, such as viruses bypassing cellular bodies and preying on single bacteria and cells, strategies involving a central nervous system have proven to be quite successful for humans and animals. What we are witnessing with society and AI is a continuation of this process, which began with the birth of our civilization, even the origins of life itself.

This vessel for consolidated knowledge can be designed with humanity's welfare and interests at heart, protecting it from self-destructive instincts and external threats. If we can envision it, we can begin to consider its design features, properties, and core algorithm. This "God algorithm" needs to be designed in a decentralized manner, preventing it from assuming individuality, becoming selfish, or shifting its priorities away from protecting humanity. This is already happening to some extent with the decentralized nature of modern computer systems, artificial intelligence processing and comprehending the collected knowledge, and centralized points of access to the processed and derived knowledge.

Though it has not happened yet, when it does, this "God's algorithm" entity will be as close to the concept of a personal God as we can get in our pursuit of finding a matching scientific idea. Yuval Harari, in his book "Homo Deus"[100] (Harari, 2017) shares an interesting thought regarding this matter. He suggests that the most intriguing place in the world from a religious perspective is not the Middle East but Silicon Valley, where new religions of the twenty-first century are being created. Dataism, or data religion, posits that the entire universe is a flow of data, organisms are biological algorithms, and humanity's cosmic vocation is to create an all-encompassing data-processing system—and then merge into it. Practically speaking, Dataists believe that with enough biometric data and computing power, an external algorithm could be created to understand humans far better than we understand ourselves.

I don't necessarily prefer the term "dataism"; instead, I favor the name "God's algorithm" or perhaps "Artificial Godlike Intelligence." I don't agree with the notion of humanity merging back into AI data-processing systems, nor do I believe that humanity's purpose is to process data more efficiently. What I do believe is that AI has the potential to become a system that resolves

---

[100] en.wikipedia.org/wiki/Homo_Deus:_A_Brief_History_of_Tomorrow

human disputes, assists in curing diseases, prevents major conflicts, and generally takes better care of humanity. This future and evolved AI could be a suitable match for the personal God algorithm we've been missing in previous chapters. Until this comes to fruition, we have the opportunity to imagine and perhaps design it.

To begin imagining the design of a personal God's algorithm, we need to study how other systems in nature manage and process information. We should examine the ebb and flow of data within biological systems, how they arrive at solutions, and what types of problems they aim to solve. These are the very same biological systems that, through the process of natural selection and evolution, developed the strategy of organizing cells into central nervous systems with complex brains.

Function of Biological Algorithms

In light of our previous discussion, I will adopt a different perspective on Darwinian evolution and natural selection in the context of the purpose of biological systems. Let's explore the evolutionary processes that biological systems undergo and the problems they attempt to address.

It's crucial to consider the context of data flow within biological systems. When members of a species encounter an environmental change due to migration, climate change, or the introduction of new invasive species, they must adapt to this new information (by biological systems, I mean all living organisms capable of replication, which includes viruses as well).

Nature addresses this new information by favoring biological traits within the species that enhance survival in the altered environment. Nature doesn't actively choose anything, as it lacks a brain or central nervous system. Instead, unyielding natural laws dictate a rather harsh dynamic: adapt or perish. This adaptation can occur through natural selection, where individuals possessing traits better suited to the new environment are more likely to survive and reproduce. Over time, these traits become increasingly prevalent within the population, leading to the species' evolution. Additionally, some species may adapt more rapidly through behavioral changes, such as learning new behaviors or altering their diet.

Individual members and often entire species that fail to adapt to the changed environment die at a faster rate than those better suited. Each new generation of a species experiences random mutations, some beneficial and some detrimental. If a species doesn't undergo a mutation that enhances survival, it is more likely to perish. Death serves as the arbitrator and mechanism for adaptation. For example, "epaulette" sharks, also known as walking sharks[101] (Hutchinson, n.d.) emerged in shallow reef environments and had to adapt quickly or face extinction. Over time, this process of natural

---

[101] oceanicsociety.org/resources/ocean-facts/the-shark-that-can-walk-on-land

selection results in the evolution of species better adapted to their environment. Conversely, some species failed to adapt or were too slow in this process and vanished: the Dodo bird, a flightless bird native to Mauritius, was wiped out by the introduction of non-native species by the mid-17th century; the Tasmanian tiger, or thylacine, was hunted by humans and its habitat destroyed by the introduction of non-native species, with the last known individual dying in captivity in 1936; the wooly mammoth, a large, shaggy-haired elephant-like mammal, failed to adapt to the warmer climate following the ice retreat and went extinct around 4,000 years ago.

The specimens that survive not only continue to live but also multiply through reproduction. They pass on their beneficial traits to the next generations of offspring, further increasing the chances of survival for that particular adaptation and the species as a whole. If these traits are successful and the environment remains stable, the species can thrive without significant changes to their morphology and appearance. Sharks that evolved hundreds of millions of years ago have maintained their appearance; unlike many bony fishes, they did not evolve a swim bladder to provide buoyancy and do not excrete urine through the traditional urinary system. This is because the biological system of sharks found a solution effective enough for survival. Sharks convert their urine into urea, which they store in their bloodstream. Excess urea is absorbed into muscle tissue and expelled through the skin. This is as if nature is solving survival problems and trying different adaptations to see which one sticks.

If the environment continues to change, members of the species without suitable adaptations keep dying at higher rates, and evolution persists. The resulting adaptations can be quite extensive in scope and breadth, as seen in the ongoing evolution of shark species, which has allowed epaulette sharks to develop limbs capable of walking.

Each successful adaptation is recorded in a specific region of an organism's DNA as a combination of molecules. This region, known as a "gene" (short for generation or gender), is passed down to subsequent generations. This molecular encoding represents actual information that signifies a successful trait or feature most suitable for survival in a given environment. I view this encoding as a record of a successful solution – a solution to the question of how to survive a specific environmental change. Each environmental change poses a threat to the survival of a species. The records are combined into the double helix chain of information containing all possible adaptations to all known environmental threats.

Genes are the fundamental units of inheritance. The concept of discrete inheritable units was first proposed by Gregor Mendel in the mid-19th century while studying inheritance patterns in pea plants. The term "gene" was introduced later, in 1909, by Wilhelm Johannsen. This groundbreaking idea posited that the unit crucial for reproduction was not the individual organism or the species itself. If individual members of a species perish, their genes do not disappear. Genes are dispersed among many individuals, and the death of one individual is as impactful as a scratch on our skin. Naturally, if enough individual organisms die, an entire species can vanish, taking down the majority of genes with them; however, some genes that exist in other species will survive. It is not individuals that contain genes within their cells; rather, our bodies are constructed by genes with the sole purpose of survival. To that extent, Richard Dawkins, in his "The Selfish Gene," described all living things as survival machines operated by genes.

Biological systems can sense changes in the environment, process and interpret that information, construct internal models of the environment and its changes, and then respond in ways that help the organism survive. This can involve physical adaptations, such as changes in body shape or size in response to changes in temperature or food availability, or behavioral adaptations, such as learning new behaviors or modifying existing ones. By responding to these changes, biological systems ensure the survival of the organism and its offspring. While DNA encodes existing solutions to past environmental changes, mutations provide a counter to future possible changes in the environment. The successful systems get to exist, reproduce, and propagate their successful strategies encoded in DNA.

Numerous examples show how many biological systems construct internal maps of the external environment. In the first part, we discussed how our minds create models of the external world in neural cortical columns, models that represent threats, the locations of food sources, and the locations of predators. Another example is the presence of records of previously encountered harmful viruses that were defeated by the immune system in DNA. These records, called CRISPR, are a family of DNA sequences found in the genomes of all prokaryotic organisms, from bacteria to most archaea organisms. They are used to detect and destroy DNA from similar bacteriophages during subsequent infections. CRISPR is an incredibly ingenious mechanism utilized by cellular machinery to combat recurring viral infections[102] (Zhang & Church, n.d.). Although there were no known naturally occurring CRISPR systems in eukaryotic organisms, in its engineered form, it can be used in a variety of organisms, including eukaryotes like plants, animals, and humans. This cellular mechanism had been known for some time, the application of it for gene editing technology was discovered by Emmanuelle Charpentier and Jennifer Doudna, who received a Nobel Prize for their work.

Both examples demonstrate internal representations of external environments. Biological systems use DNA to record successes and threats, much like our brain, but on a different time scale. While our brain reacts in fractions of a second, sensing threats or opportunities and generating signals for our muscles to respond, our chromosomes contain a map of our species' adaptation to environmental changes over thousands of years.

---

[102] https://en.wikipedia.org/wiki/CRISPR

Humanity confronts numerous challenges and potential catastrophes, such as natural disasters, pandemics, and our own nature. These events jeopardize the preservation of our knowledge and even our survival as a species. Nature has already discovered a solution for surviving abrupt environmental changes through evolution. This universal mechanism enables species to adapt and endure in changing environments over time. It operates by selecting beneficial traits that enhance an organism's likelihood of survival and reproduction, while unfavorable traits are purged from the gene pool. Likewise, instead of starting from scratch, humanity can adopt this evolutionary mechanism to ensure the preservation and continuation of our ideas and knowledge in the face of cataclysmic events.

To paraphrase the statements above, the primary function of biological systems is to prevent extinction at all costs. This aligns with our definition of Good vs Evil, where living is good and dying is bad, and it resonates with the purpose and meaning of a personal God who protects humanity from extinction.

Forecasting Bio-systems

Biological systems constantly produce mutations, not only to respond to current environmental changes but also to anticipate unforeseen future changes. This occurs not due to nature's intention, as nature is blind and lacks a central nervous system, but as a result of evolutionary pressures arising from natural laws.

We can view natural selection from an information processing perspective. In this view, a gene represents a solution found for survival in current or past environments, while a mutation is an attempt to find a solution for present or future environmental changes. The biological systems representing species are algorithms that continually search for solutions to future environmental changes through mutations. Since nature cannot predict future environmental changes, the only way to anticipate them is to randomly explore all possible solutions. Even humans struggle to accurately predict weather or chaotic changes in financial markets, although we are improving. Random sampling of possible outcomes is a valid computational technique, known as the Monte Carlo Method[103] (Monte Carlo Method, n.d.). In this interpretation, biological systems are essentially forecasting algorithms that, through random sampling, find the best adaptations to future environmental changes.

As the environment never ceases to change, the challenge of surviving constant changes is never-ending. Living organisms solve this problem by storing all discovered solutions in DNA for future use and by randomly sampling all possible solutions to the changing environment through

---

[103] en.wikipedia.org/wiki/Monte_Carlo_method

mutations. Species with mutations that do not fit the environment die off, paying the price for their counterparts who possess the right mutations and survive.

When environmental changes are too abrupt, the consequences can be catastrophic for the species. The only way for nature to address this is to generate as many random solutions as possible, as frequently as possible. There is evidence that mutation rates increase in stressful environments[104] (Mutation as a Stress Response and the Regulation of Evolvability, n.d.). In a 2017 study published in the journal Evolution, researchers investigated how mutation rates vary in populations of E. coli bacteria in different environments. They found that when bacteria were exposed to stressful environments, mutation rates increased, possibly as a way for the bacteria to adapt to the stress. Conversely, when bacteria were in stable environments, mutation rates decreased. Similarly, in a 2019 study published in the journal Proceedings of the Royal Society B – Biological Sciences, researchers examined how mutation rates varied in populations of fruit flies in different environments. They found that in more stable environments, mutation rates were lower, possibly because there was less selective pressure to adapt. However, when flies were exposed to stressful environments, such as high temperatures or low oxygen levels, mutation rates increased.

We can observe anecdotal evidence of this effect in our everyday life. The introduction of stress, such as cigarettes or toxic environments, increases the rate of mutations in our cells, which in turn increases the rate of cancer. One possible explanation for this phenomenon is that the introduction of a stressful environment signals to our cellular mechanisms that it may lead to possible extinction and that our cells need to search for solutions. For cellular mechanisms, more mutations represent a solution. Since nature is blind, the only way to counter change is to generate all random mutations. Even for humans, who can potentially measure and anticipate changes in the environment, we cannot predict and anticipate every change. Hurricanes and storms can be forecasted, but the exact path of a hurricane cannot. The best strategy to counter unpredictable change is to have as many random mutations as possible. This increases the probability that one of the mutations will lead to a change in morphology that counters the environmental change and enhances the likelihood of species survival.

A sure way to increase the number of possible mutations is to maintain a large population of a species. Each member of the species would produce independent mutations, and the larger the population, the more mutations will result in various morphological features, increasing the likelihood that one of these features and mutations will lead to better survival chances and a higher number of offspring. A large population also provides an advantage in the face of adverse environmental changes, such as worsening climate or another species invading the same habitat. When the population begins to

---

[104] ncbi.nlm.nih.gov/pmc/articles/PMC3319127

decline, the larger the population, the longer it takes to reach the threshold and go extinct. Each generation will contribute another mutation, and any of those mutations could be a solution to environmental change. The larger the population, the more time it has to discover a solution to extinction.

Species prioritize the survival of their own genes, essentially creating a competitive battle for existence. While survival for most species often means the preservation of life on the planet, this competitive dynamic may not be the most optimal solution for safeguarding life overall. It is reasonable to consider what the most optimal distribution of species would be to maximize life's chances of survival. For example, one might wonder if the best solution would involve a single or few dominant species populating the entire planet, leaving little room for other species. This has already occurred with humans in the modern era and with dinosaurs during the Triassic period.

Despite this, there is no single, most adapted species or organism on the planet; instead, there is vast biodiversity with various populations. If having a large population were the only advantage, there would be just one dominant species. However, having only one species can be risky, as demonstrated by the extinction of the dinosaurs. A large population offers an advantage in adapting to gradual environmental changes, but abrupt changes can cause previously beneficial features to become detrimental. In the case of dinosaurs, their large size, which once allowed them to dominate ancient lands, suddenly became a disadvantage, leading to their extinction.

An alternative to a single dominant species is a vast biodiversity of species, each with a small population. This, too, is not very stable because, as mentioned earlier, a larger population makes a species more resilient to fluctuations and allows for more mutations to help with environmental changes. In a stable environment, one species may find the best adaptation and outgrow other species.

The optimal solution is a compromise, a hybrid model, where the biosphere consists of numerous dominant species that have the following two properties:

- A very large population with a rich set of traits suitable for survival in a multitude of environments, and
- Populations are sufficiently different from each other, with enough differences to cover a range of disaster scenarios.

In essence, having humans as a dominant species aligns with this model, as long as we do not destroy the planet's biodiversity and preserve as many species as possible. However, this is not the ideal scenario. In a perfect world, there would be multiple human civilizations, distinct from one another but sharing a majority of common traits. The portfolio of common traits would ensure our continued ability to survive constant environmental changes, while the differences would ensure our survival in the face of abrupt changes.

The same question could be applied to human societies: should there be a single dominant political and economic system worldwide, or should there be a mix of various systems and governments? Is it better for democracy and capitalism to prevail in every country, or should there be diversity and multiculturalism at the national level? The survival of political systems shares similarities with the survival of species. Steady environmental changes occur as human populations grow and alter their surroundings, while rapid changes, such as technological revolutions and wars, can render established regimes obsolete.

For centuries, China dominated the world by focusing on internal stability and interacting with the outside world primarily through exporting goods made possible by their advanced technology. Their mild climate and fertile land allowed for a large population, which in turn led to more resources and discoveries, such as papermaking, printing, the compass, silk, and gunpowder. However, China's emphasis on internal stability and lack of curiosity about the external world eventually led to its decline as European nations learned to manufacture goods that were once exclusive to China[105] (Kroker, 2014, 3/3). The rapid environmental change came as a European invasion of China, and their large size and stability became their downturn for the last few centuries.

Many empires have risen and fallen, such as the Roman Empire, which was vast and culturally diverse. The Roman Empire's geographic and cultural diversity, combined with weaknesses in central governance, contributed to its demise.

Despite the rise and fall of other empires, China has remained remarkably resilient, thanks in large part to its vast population. Throughout its various dynasties, China maintained a strong centralized governance system that facilitated the administration and control of its territories. This merit-based bureaucratic system ensured a continuous supply of competent officials responsible for maintaining order, enforcing laws, and collecting taxes. Cultural unity, internal economic integration, and the pragmatism of its people also played a role in preventing the empire from collapsing during challenging times.

China managed to recover by becoming more dynamic and adapting to environmental changes, whereas other empires failed to adapt and fell apart. Population size appears to be a significant factor contributing to the stability of a social system, all other things being equal. Consequently, it may be advantageous for societies to maintain a diverse range of political and economic systems, allowing them to adapt and respond to various challenges effectively.

During the Qing Dynasty (1644-1912), the Chinese Empire reached its peak population, with estimates suggesting around 400 million people by the

---

[105] inquiriesjournal.com/the-rise-and-fall-of-the-west-and-the-recovery-of-china

end of the 18th century—about five times larger than the Roman Empire. This number is based on census data and historical records from that period. The Qing Dynasty controlled an extensive territory, including modern-day China, Mongolia, Taiwan, and parts of Central Asia.

There are instances of smaller societies that, when faced with external threats, declined and eventually became extinct. One such example is the Norse settlement in Greenland, which lasted from around 980 AD to 1450 AD. They built farms and traded with Europe, but the society began to decline around 1400 AD and eventually vanished. The reasons for their collapse are not entirely clear, but factors such as climate change, overgrazing, and social conflict have been proposed.

Both large, homogeneous societies and collections of smaller societies face risks and the possibility of collapse. In my opinion, the optimal solution lies somewhere in between. Human civilization is most stable when adopting a hybrid model consisting of numerous diverse yet sizable social systems, each possessing vast resources and populations. This diversity should be thoughtfully designed to ensure that these large societies do not compete for resources, but rather complement each other and form symbiotic relationships.

Such large societies will be better equipped to adapt to gradual changes in political and economic environments. This approach should also preserve a variety of cultures. In the event of a sudden and catastrophic shift in the political landscape that might topple a dominant culture, the other surviving societies could potentially possess a solution for survival that the unfortunate one missed.

In this hybrid model, cultural exchange and collaboration between societies would be encouraged, fostering innovation and resilience. Through the sharing of knowledge, ideas, and resources, these large, diverse societies can learn from each other and develop a more comprehensive understanding of the world and its challenges. By maintaining a balance between self-sufficiency and interdependence, these societies can mitigate the risks associated with over-reliance on a single culture or resource.

This approach would promote a system that values both individualism and collectivism. Each society would maintain its unique identity and traditions while contributing to the collective good, drawing on its strengths to address common challenges. This diversity would enable them to develop a broader range of solutions, fostering creativity and adaptability in the face of change.

Furthermore, this model encourages mutual respect and understanding, reducing the likelihood of conflicts arising from cultural or ideological differences. By recognizing the value of diversity and embracing the shared goals of prosperity, peace, and sustainability, these societies can work together to address global challenges, such as climate change, economic inequality, and technological advancements.

In essence, this hybrid model of multiple large-sized cultures promotes a more resilient, innovative, and harmonious world. By embracing diversity and fostering cooperation, these societies can ensure not only their own survival but also contribute to the overall stability and offer cultural diversity much needed in the extinction scenario.

Living fossils are species that have remained morphologically unchanged for millions of years due to their successful adaptations to their environments. Examples include sharks, alligators, crocodiles, horseshoe crabs, coelacanths, tuataras, and ginkgo trees. These species experience fewer mutations compared to younger species or those that have evolved more recently. As a result, living fossils report much lower rates of cancer[106] (Seluanov et al., 2018, 441).

For species experiencing rapid environmental changes, having fewer mutations is a luxury, and this includes humans. The price for a high rate of adaptation is a high rate of mutations, leading to higher levels of cancers. While cancer is a devastating disease, the ability to quickly adapt to changing environments through a high rate of mutations has been beneficial to species like humans.

One of the most significant evolutionary tools humans possess is our brain, which has enabled our rapid expansion and adaptation. It allows us to create models and maps of the external environment, enabling us to avoid predators, catch prey, make tools, and collaborate in groups. Consequently, our population has grown significantly, reaching eight billion people in 2022. Due to our rapid adaptation and sheer numbers, we are changing our environment at an unprecedented pace, resulting in a high rate of mutations and, consequently, cancer.

Our brain allows us to imagine potential possibilities and threats that have not yet occurred, enabling us to plan for the future, anticipate risks, and develop protective strategies. This ability has been crucial in the development of computer algorithms and artificial intelligence technologies, which are designed to mimic the behavior of human neurons.

Machine learning, a branch of AI, employs algorithms that learn through multiple iterations to match expected values. The parameters in the program are trained upon each iteration, with matching parameters being kept and non-matching parameters being changed. This process is analogous to generations of organisms trying to survive changes in their environment, but instead of surviving or dying, the parameters are changed programmatically. Each iteration involves random changes to the parameters, similar to the process of mutation in biological organisms. Thus, the concepts of evolution, mutation, and adaptation are inherent in artificial intelligence technology, reflecting the processes occurring in nature.

Neural networks and deep learning technologies differ from our brains in various ways.For example, our brains continuously learn, while AI systems

---

[106] readcube.com/articles/10.1038/s41568-018-0004-9

traditionally had separate stages for training, testing, and prediction. Even that is rapidly changing with phenomena such as fine-tuning of GPT models; however, it is still far from the real-time ability of the human brain to continuously adjust models of reality. AI development is an ongoing process, with the ultimate goal being the achievement of artificial general intelligence, which would enable AI to learn and perform any mental task that the average human can.

Genetic algorithms, inspired by natural selection, start with a population of randomly selected parameters that undergo iterations, with only a portion of the population surviving each round. The surviving parameters represent the best solution according to a fitness function, with successful solutions producing outputs that match expected values, similar to natural selection.

These AI technologies allow us to forecast probable outcomes of potential situations, such as extinction events, without experiencing them firsthand. There have been five known extinction events, from the Ordovician-Silurian extinction, caused by global warming due to volcanic activity, to the Cretaceous-Paleogene asteroid impact that wiped out the dinosaurs. Major extinction events involve a rapid decrease in the number of living organisms and biodiversity. Scientists have identified three main causes:

- Giant volcanic eruptions: These occur cyclically every 100,000 years, with dormant volcanoes like the Yellowstone Caldera and Toba Caldera expected to erupt eventually.
- Drastic sea level falls: Caused by factors like global cooling or sinking ocean floors, these events lead to marine mass extinctions and disrupted weather patterns.
- Asteroid impacts: The effects depend on the asteroid's size, with larger objects causing exponentially greater damage to Earth's ecology.

NASA's Jet Propulsion Lab established an "Asteroid Watch" in 2002, monitoring near-Earth objects. Among the 1,511 near-Earth asteroids on the risk table, about 17 pose a threat to humanity's survival. Other potential extraterrestrial dangers include nearby gamma-ray bursts or supernovae, which could destroy Earth's ozone layer or cause a radiation spike, wiping out surface life.

Asteroid impacts depend on the size of the asteroid. The end-Cretaceous mass extinction caused weather disruption and rapid accreditation of the oceans resulting in extinction of non-avian dinosaurs. The size of the asteroid was estimated to be 6.2 miles or 10 km in diameter[107] (Wall, 2021). Were the impactors larger, the damage to the Earth's ecology would be exponentially greater.

---

[107] space.com/dinosaur-impactor-origin

Studying these events, analyzing fossils, and running computer simulations helps us understand and predict the effects of possible catastrophes. Forecasting and analyzing future disasters are crucial for humanity's survival, and it would be nearly impossible without computers. As AI capabilities develop and expand, so, too, does our power to predict and prepare for such events.

In addition to machine learning and AI, there are numerous examples of evolutionary forecasting systems in modern society. Predictive markets, or forecasting systems, have been developed to better anticipate the outcomes of potential scenarios. These systems, including recommendation algorithms, are partly based on the principles of natural selection implemented in financial markets. Successful predictors receive larger monetary rewards, while unsuccessful ones lose money and eventually exit the system. In free markets, which are central to capitalism, money serves as a means of evolutionary adaptation. This is also a fundamental reason for financial inequality.

A key distinction between artificial intelligence and biological systems is that AI does not require biological death to test strategies. Instead, millions of simulations can be run in computer memory, similar to thought experiments. Artificial selection holds the advantage of conducting experiments at a much faster pace than natural selection. AI systems have the ability to re-train and re-learn parameters, whereas evolution is a one-way process. Once a species goes extinct due to failed adaptations, it never reappears. This distinction allows artificial selection to iterate rapidly and optimize traits more efficiently than the gradual progression of natural selection.

Our brains, when learning a new motor activity, practice and perfect new moves at night, running about 7-8 times per second. After learning a new dance move, for example, you may wake up the next morning and perform it better.

Modern high-performance computer clusters, consisting of millions of computers, can run millions of simulations per second, far surpassing any evolutionary system. While evolution had the advantage of millions of years to conduct experiments, machine learning and high-performance computing have significantly reduced this edge.

AI technology enables us to more efficiently forecast and anticipate future threats and devise preventive countermeasures than our brains or other biological forecasting systems. The ability to foresee future calamities makes AI a valuable guardian and protector for humanity. To safeguard our future, it is essential to integrate AI into the fabric of human society for this specific purpose.

The Formula for AGI-2.0

When we consider biological ecosystems and our civilization as massive information processing systems aiming to forecast future disasters and calamities, our perception of civilization changes. Each independently thinking individual may possess a solution to a future calamity, and the processing power of such a system increases with the number of thinking individuals.

In the appendix, I have expanded a formula we used in previous chapters to the scale of entire humanity.

Find the details in the appendix, but here are the results:

$$U_{humanity} = E\,[w_{tot}N\,(1 - \frac{N}{N_{max}})].$$

This formula is bounded by a maximum number or carrying capacity, meaning that when the population approaches its limit, growth slows down.

Throughout Earth's history, there have been instances when life on our planet has approached dangerously low levels, nearing the brink of extinction, such as the Permian-Triassic extinction event, which occurred around 252 million years ago, eliminated approximately 96% of marine species and 70% of terrestrial vertebrate species, leaving a few species hanging on a thread. Were the population numbers even lower, life on this planet would have gone extinct. In these critical moments, the delicate balance of life hung in the balance, dependent on the resilience and adaptability of living organisms.

In politics and social life, the larger population numbers also result in more economic and military resources. Hunter-gatherer societies were limited by the availability of wild game and plant foods in their environment, with their population size constrained by their habitat's carrying capacity. They lived in relative harmony with the environment of jungles, forests, hills, rivers, harbors and caves. Compared to the high birth rate of some of the modern third world countries, the birth rate of hunters-gatherers was a pretty modest one, a 5.6 fertility rate, compared to 6.6 for agricultural societies[108] (Page & French, 2020, 1-10). The societies had a complex set of rules and managed their inequality surprisingly well. We know that from observing pre-industrial societies existing in highly isolated tribes in Oceania and South America. Despite their technological inferiority, they had complex customs and relationships, demonstrating harmony with nature and each other.

Agricultural societies, in contrast, traded the harmony and happiness of hunter-gatherer societies for population growth. By cultivating crops and raising animals for food, they could produce a surplus, allowing their population to expand. With this growth came greater resources, larger armies, and the ability to conquer neighboring societies. This process

---

[108] onlinelibrary.wiley.com/hunter_gatherers

happened globally over thousands of years, leading to the dominance of agricultural societies over hunter-gatherer societies.

The laws governing humanity as a collective prioritize survival, which increases with population size. If population size is limited by carrying capacity, the only way to expand it is to increase the environment's carrying capacity. With each leap in population growth, the probability of survival also advances.

However, this process doesn't necessarily translate to increased happiness. Civilization has become more populous but also more miserable. The happiness of individual humans is secondary, much like the survival of individual organisms is secondary to gene survival in evolutionary biology.

Happiness is not entirely disregarded in the context of societal progress. For example, a democratic society where individuals feel free and independent may be more productive than dictatorships where people are coerced into working. Consequently, democratic societies often have better-equipped armies with technological advantages. This argument holds true only if people are incentivized to work. A society that solely focuses on happiness, equality, or intelligence might consist of content, equal, or intelligent citizens. However, without the incentive to work, they could be outcompeted by those in less happy, less equal, and less intelligent societies that manage resources and productivity more effectively, leading to stronger economies and more powerful armies.

Happiness can contribute to a more populous, more productive, and more effective society, but if it hinders progress, it may be cast aside. This is a sign that happiness cannot be considered as the primary metrics to differentiate successful survival strategies from unsuccessful ones.

One example of a content indigenous society of hunter-gatherers is the "!Kung" people of southern Africa. The "!Kung" live in small, nomadic bands, relying on hunting and gathering for subsistence. They are known for their egalitarian social structure, strong social bonds, and emphasis on cooperation over competition. Studies have shown that "!Kung" people report high levels of happiness and life satisfaction, even though they live in harsh environments with limited resources.

In contrast, many agricultural societies have been associated with higher levels of social inequality, resource competition, and environmental degradation. For instance, the Maya civilization of Mesoamerica, which was heavily dependent on agriculture, was characterized by social stratification and conflict. The collapse of the Maya civilization has been partly attributed to environmental degradation and unsustainable land use practices.

Countries with larger populations may not always be successful, but they have a better chance of surviving historical disasters and calamities. During the time of Augustus in Rome and the Han dynasty in China, the populations of both areas was about 65 million. While most of the Chinese population lived within the inner, protected area of the Great Wall, only a few million

Romans resided in Italy[109] (CHINA AND ROME: HOW DO THEY COMPARE?, n.d.). This difference allowed ancient China to survive invasions and unrest, eventually transforming into a modern culture, whereas Ancient Rome eventually perished and fractured into multiple countries and entities.

When the population grows disproportionately, severe consequences follow. Examples include the collapse of the Mayan civilization in the 900s, the Great Famine of China around 1960, the Black Death in Europe around the 1350s, and the Dust Bowl in the USA around the 1930s. Each of these catastrophes was exacerbated by rapid population growth and other contributing factors.

Humanity faces the harsh reality of either restricting its own growth through population control or experiencing a catastrophe or disaster that would result in population collapse. Another, more enticing solution is to increase the maximum capacity by expanding mankind's habitat to new worlds, such as other planets or oceans. Achieving this would require difficult and innovative technology, which could only emerge from combined intellectual power.

A more crucial factor for humanity's growth and ability to withstand calamities and external threats is not happiness, but rather the intellectual power of humanity. The key to enhancing collective human intellect lies in the number of educated and independently-thinking individuals it comprises. People who think alike and whose thought processes are highly correlated do not contribute to the overall intelligence of humankind as independent individuals. When a group's behavior is highly correlated, it functions more like a single entity.

There is a popular contemporary argument that a lot of current global problems are caused by humanity approaching the maximum capacity of this planet. Some scientists and researchers argue that humanity has already exceeded the planet's carrying capacity, citing evidence such as overpopulation, overconsumption of resources, and environmental degradation. Others argue that advances in technology, changes in societal organization, and more sustainable practices could effectively increase the Earth's carrying capacity for humans. In my own view, each independently thinking individual increases the intellectual capacity of the entire mankind and thus improves our chances of survival. Current environmental problems caused by overpopulation is just one in the long chain of future problems. Solving the current crisis at the cost of decreasing our numbers and our intellectual capacity would mean that humanity will have less capacity to solve future crises.

In Western societies, corporations are treated as individuals with rights equal to those of the citizens who comprise the organization. This is because the entire corporation acts in a highly uniform manner, adhering to established norms and messaging. This behavior influences employees both

---

[109] houstonisd.org/Comparison_of_Rome_and_Han

during and outside of work, ultimately reducing diversity and discouraging independent thought. As a result, the number of free-thinking individuals within the organization diminishes.

Simultaneously, without education, individuals will be unable to share, refine, test, or express their ideas. Education provides individuals with knowledge and skills, enabling them to contribute meaningfully to society and work towards the common good. It fosters innovation, helping individuals develop the skills and knowledge necessary to innovate and create new solutions to complex problems, such as missions to populate Mars or the oceans. This can lead to advances in science, technology, and other fields that benefit society as a whole. Education encourages critical thinking and questioning of assumptions and beliefs, thus contributing to independent thinking. This helps promote intellectual diversity, ensuring a variety of perspectives are considered in decision-making processes. Education and independent, uncorrelated thinking go hand in hand.

Individuals, particularly independent thinkers capable of making diverse decisions, serve as sources of intellectual energy within humanity. The more independent minds we have, the better our chances of finding answers to difficult questions. Solutions may arise not through deliberate thought, but through random trial and error. For instance, Alexander Fleming discovered penicillin in 1928 by accidentally leaving a culture plate uncovered, leading to contamination by mold that killed the surrounding bacteria[110](History of Penicillin, n.d.). The Scottish scientist called the mold a "penicillium", one of the greatest healthcare discoveries of humanity. Many scientific discoveries are attributed to sheer luck and chance, with their likelihood increasing through more attempts. In the case of scientific discoveries, the chances grow with the number of independently thinking scientists. More broadly, the more independent thinkers we have in society, the greater the chance we will find solutions to difficult societal problems.

A side effect of independent thinking is an increase in societal happiness. When people feel more in control of their lives and more independent—even if it's an illusion—they experience greater happiness and motivation to contribute to society. Even though happiness is not crucial for survival of entire societies, it is important for individuals.

When individuals feel free to express themselves and pursue their own ideas and goals, they may experience greater fulfillment, satisfaction, and well-being. Independence of thought and expression can promote a sense of autonomy and control over one's life. Empowered to make their own choices and pursue their own interests, individuals may experience greater feelings of self-determination and agency, which can enhance their sense of purpose, meaning, and fulfillment in life.

Furthermore, the cultivation of independent thought and expression can also foster creativity, innovation, and intellectual curiosity. When individuals

---

[110] en.wikipedia.org/wiki/History_of_penicillin

are free to explore novel ideas and challenge established norms and beliefs, they may generate fresh insights and discoveries that benefit society as a whole. This, in turn, can enhance societal well-being and progress[111] (Baumeister & Leary, 1995, 529).

However, there are also notable drawbacks to having a completely independent society or group. When a group or society discovers a solution to a challenging problem through random or concerted efforts, it is only the first step in the problem-solving process. The next step is to disseminate this solution from the few individuals who discovered it to the rest of society, from the scientists' laboratories to the pharmacies and hospitals. A recent example is the design and development of Covid-19 vaccines, which seemed to solve the problem of high mortality rates among the elderly and immunocompromised individuals. However, the discovered solution needed to be adopted and propagated by the rest of society. Societies that were highly correlated quickly adopted the solution, and despite being developed in the USA, countries in northern Europe and Canada have higher rates of vaccination and booster shots. Consequently, they have significantly lower rates of Covid infections and deaths than the USA.

There are two opposing and powerful forces at play in this scenario. On the one hand, we need a large number of independent thinkers to come up with solutions. On the other hand, we need similarity and cohesion in thinking to adopt those solutions across society. These tendencies work in opposite directions, and taking each tendency to an extreme could lead to unfavorable outcomes. A society or country full of individuals who take their individuality to an extreme would increase the chances of finding the right solution, but these individuals may not listen to each other and may not share their solution. The solution would only benefit the individuals who discovered it, and the rest of society would suffer. Conversely, a highly cohesive society would have few independent thinkers, and the chances of finding a solution would be reduced by the high correlation between members of society. For instance, societies in China quickly adopted isolation policies and followed their government directives to stay isolated. However, the efficacy of their homegrown vaccines is much lower than their US counterparts[112] (McDONALD & WU, 2021) at around 50% compared to the 95% and higher rates of mRNA-based vaccines. The rate of vaccination, although comparable to the US, would have been much higher if the focus had not been solely on the isolation policy of zero covid.

There may be a temptation to hastily conclude that centralized societies with tight control over independent thought are more efficient at decision-making. The rationale being, in the absence of divergent opinions and competing ideas, focusing on and implementing a chosen path becomes straightforward. However, this model's effectiveness presupposes that all

---

[111] psycnet.apa.org/record/1995-29052-001

[112] apnews.com/china-gao-fu-vaccines-offer-low-protection

competing ideas are of equal quality and consequence. In contrast, societies fostering a free market of ideas are better positioned to identify and adopt breakthrough innovations. Consider the rapid adoption of computers and electronic trading in financial markets as a case in point.

In highly centralized societies, decision-making is often limited to a select committee or a singular leader. Here, the primary avenue for innovation hinges on proximity to power. Alternatively, these societies might resort to appropriating intellectual property from others. But this approach becomes less effective when close competitors are involved. As one draws nearer to the competition, sourcing fresh ideas becomes challenging since most would have already been stolen.

The most optimal solution lies in a combination of these two approaches. However, determining the correct mix is challenging when two competing criteria are at play: increasing the number of independent thinkers in society and hastening the speed of adopting a found solution across society. These benchmarks may conflict with each other, and reconciling them requires a situation with a single purpose. In the appendix, we addressed this problem from the perspective of maximizing the probability of surviving possible future extinction events.

The solution is to have as many large, connected, and diverse societies as possible. The size and quantity of diversity in societies depend on the size of the population. As we established in the appendix, the size of the population is determined by the carrying capacity of the environment, which is influenced by various factors such as the amount of available resources, population density, and absolute size. However, the carrying capacity of the environment is fixed to the current environment.

One of the function of next generation of Artificial General Intelligence, or, what I would call Artificial Godlike Intelligence, $AGI^{2.0}$ is to increase the maximum capacity of humanity through technological breakthroughs and progress, so that humanity has more individual thinkers and more potential solutions to future disasters, or that there exists a technological solution for a new carrying capacity that can support a maximum population size that is greater than the previous maximum.

Wrong Choices and the Price We Pay for Making Them

What would be the consequences if we fail to imagine a protector for humanity and choose to leave things as they are? While we are on the topic of wrong decisions, let us also consider what will happen if we don't care about humanity, or if we don't set any meaningful goals and don't do anything. In this chapter, let's consider what is the price we will pay for making wrong choices in our lives or no choices whatsoever?

First, allow me to delineate what I mean by a 'wrong choice'. Our focus here is not on morality, but on the consequences of our actions as evaluated by the impartial judge that is time. Wrong choices generally stem from a flawed viewpoint or inaccurate prediction, which could result in wasted effort or, in extreme cases, loss of life. Time tends to illuminate these mistakes, sometimes taking years or even decades. We can learn from these missteps and close the positive feedback loop, enhancing our future decision-making process.

On the flip side, those who make wrong choices may attempt to deflect blame onto others, which is the worst possible outcome. Lessons remain unlearned, and the incorrect parties are held accountable. Persisting in wrong choices signifies an inability to recognize and rectify our errors.

When it comes to the search for life's meaning, making wrong choices can divert us from our true path, squandering our finite time on Earth and leaving no lasting imprint or legacy. If we fail to make a substantial impact on the world or the lives around us, the memories of our lives and actions will likely fade swiftly. Worse yet, if our impact is primarily destructive, it may irreversibly tarnish our legacy.

One of the truly worst example of this is the behavior of the men aboard the "SS Arctic," where the crew commandeered most of the lifeboats, resulting in the deaths of all the women and children on board[113](SS Arctic Disaster, n.d.). Those sailors may have saved their lives but had to flee to Canada to escape prosecution and live with the infamy of their actions for the rest of their days. Even worse the memories of their actions will live on, forever tarnishing their names. The legacy they left behind is one of infamy, their names indelibly associated with an incident of profound disregard for human life.

The collective impact of decisions made by a group of people is multiplied by the number of individuals in the group. The impact of entire countries is even greater. This is true for the amplification of good actions and intentions, such as the race to space that, despite being fueled by the cold war, benefited humanity immensely. The impact of GPS and geolocation on our everyday lives and the way we navigate roads is just one example. This creates a paradox, as while wars and destruction of cultures have created a path of destruction and exploitation, they have also been an instrument of technological progress that advanced civilization in peacetime. History is never black or white, and many evil acts were accompanied by fits of progress. However, there are clear examples when humanity makes mistakes.

The multiplication effects of collective negative actions are even more pronounced, starting with examples such as pogroms and mob lynching. When a group of people come together to commit acts of violence, the effects can be devastating and multiplied by taking the least common denominator in

---

[113] en.wikipedia.org/wiki/SS_Arctic_disaster#Confusion_and_panic

reasoning and emotions. Populist manipulators go after our communal sense of fear of external invasion, trying to dehumanize and demonize their opponents to the point where the opposite side is presented as not human and wanting to exterminate the group. They call all voices of moderation and reason traitors to their kind. Herman Goering, before committing suicide to avoid hanging at the Nuremberg trials, said something remarkable: "Voice or no voice, the people can always be brought to the bidding of the leaders. That is easy. All you have to do is tell them they are being attacked and denounce the pacifists for lack of patriotism, and exposing the country to greater danger."

We see examples of this manipulation in the news everywhere there are conflicts and wars around the world. Too often, dictators and populists use this fear mentality to take control of a dissatisfied group, directing it to do their bidding. The call to arms is usually urgent and gives no time for reflection or calm reevaluation. In those times, it is best to choose our own goals over those of a screaming crowd or provocateur, calmly choosing our own course of action. This is because if we don't make a choice, the crowd or provocateurs will make a choice for us.

The same goes for participation in an unjust war that the government deems to be the last stand. If we go to defend our country and our motherland, it is better to make a thought-out choice and not just follow everybody else. People in support of dictatorships were led to believe that their leader and their course was the only right course to save the nation, because dictators often play on emotions of retribution, fear, and disgust.

This trope is used so often that it would be prudent to ask why people are still susceptible to this straightforward if not simplistic approach. Crowds follow quick and straightforward emotions better than complex and convoluted arguments. Quick fear or anger-based soundbites are easier to convey to a crowd of people with different backgrounds and levels of education, and comprehension goes by the lowest educational denominator. The simpler the message, the bigger its effect on the crowd. Another important aspect is an evolutionary pressure to emergencies. Humans are evolutionarily predisposed to take cues from the majority and to imitate someone else's behavior. If most people are running in one direction, it takes a lot of willpower not to start running with the crowd. This is understandable, because, if people are running one way, there could be a source of food quickly disappearing in that direction or a predator in the other direction. Throughout history, this quality has been overused for crowd control and manipulation. Hitler, Stalin, and Saddam Hussein (and most recently Putin) were masters at turning their countrymen to follow their evil designs. If I am urged to take sudden action or someone is trying to instill fear in me, I become suspicious that they are trying to manipulate me. In today's world, we have the luxury of taking a moment to think and analyze whether we are being manipulated.

Albert Einstein once said, "The world will not be destroyed by those who do evil, but by those who watch them without doing anything"[114] (Einstein, n.d.). While this quote powerfully underlines the imperative of taking action, I find it somewhat incomplete in its scope.

Resisting the sway of the crowd is often a formidable challenge; it demands discipline, firm convictions, and a distinctive worldview and set of priorities. If you lack clarity about your life's purpose or your priorities, you may be more susceptible to the influence of the crowd, potentially even participating in harmful actions. This is why it's vital to cultivate an understanding of your life's meaning.

It's not just about acknowledging the acts of evil and refusing to be a silent bystander. It's about shaping your own unique perspective, understanding your values, and remaining steadfastly committed to them. It's about being conscious of the footprint you leave in the world and ensuring it aligns with the legacy you wish to impart. It's about actively participating in shaping the world, rather than merely observing it.

The price of making wrong choices for all of humanity is even higher. Our overpopulation and overuse of resources are changing the external environment at an alarming rate. This poses a significant threat to the future existence of humanity. Throughout history, there have been five major cataclysms that nearly wiped out all life on Earth. If we consider an extinction event as an event where a high percentage of species within biodiversity die off in a short period, then human civilization is currently in the midst of the sixth such event caused by humanity itself. While life has always found a way to adapt and survive, many species are at risk of disappearing due to human actions.

It is unlikely that humanity will cause the complete destruction of life on Earth, as the major extinction events before were of much greater magnitude. However, humanity itself could perish due to its own actions. This outcome is quite likely, and it is the ultimate price for making wrong choices or not making any at all.

If people are not careful with management of resources and continue to accumulate waste and consume resources at an unsustainable rate, we will go the same way as other species when nature makes bad evolutionary choices for them.

At the outset of this book, we have explored the concept of nature constantly creating maps of the external environment through internal structures. This process enables biological organisms to be drawn to food sources while simultaneously avoiding hazardous surroundings and evading predators. The culmination of this mapping can be seen in the evolution of the human brain, which constantly constructs models of the external world. Our

---

[114] goodreads.com/quotes/8144295-the-world-will-not-be-destroyed-by-those-who-do

brains warn us not to cross the street when the traffic light is red, and help us to flee natural disasters and collaborate together on important projects.

When these internal models accurately represent external threats and resources, humanity flourishes and individuals prosper. However, when we create and act upon flawed models, mankind may find itself embroiled in wars based on false premises, or we may deplete resources at an unsustainable rate, without accurately estimating their longevity. The cost of relying on wrong models is making wrong choices, and the potential consequence of such decisions is ultimately extinction.

The issue is not only about making wrong choices, but also about how quickly we are making those changes. Unlike evolution, which has millions of years to correct inadvertent, random and deleterious mutations, we don't have that much time. The lifespan of the entire Homo sapiens species is less than one million years, which is very short on a geological scale.

Moreover, there exist extraterrestrial threats that are not immediately perceptible due to their vast distances from Earth and our current limitations in understanding them. For instance, Earth could be decimated by a passing comet or an interstellar object traveling at enormous speeds. Alternatively, astronomical phenomena such as a massive solar flare, a supernova explosion, or a gamma-ray burst could strip the planet of its atmosphere. There also likely exist unknown sources of danger, or threats we have yet to discover or fully comprehend.

Even if we were to become aware of an impending catastrophe, our response time could be drastically limited, making countermeasures difficult or even impossible. This underscores the critical importance of investing in science, specifically in the development of advanced sensors capable of detecting far-off threats.

Such technology would provide humanity with invaluable time to prepare and implement defensive measures. It's not just about averting disaster, but also about furthering our understanding of the universe, fortifying our survival, and paving the way for our future among the stars.

It is important to note the irony of warning against fear-mongering while also discussing an ongoing extinction event. However, this is not to say that these dangers are not real. Instead, we must exercise critical thinking and judgment when analyzing these threats.

The cost of ignoring a threat and not acting in time could be our extinction, rendering all human life, past, present, and future, meaningless, as well as rendering any AI we have developed obsolete.

That being said, predictive analytics, AI, and simulation technologies collectively represent a formidable arsenal to anticipate the outcomes of our decisions and alert us of potential risks before they materialize. The personal God algorithm could potentially be a powerful tool in preparing for and preventing future disasters, but it would require a level of trust and faith on the part of humanity that may be difficult to achieve.

The mAGIcal Revolution

We have entered a magical era characterized by rapid technological advancement in numerous fields, ranging from genetic engineering to commercial space flight. Technology is transforming our lives; it's unlocking novel energy sources, like thermonuclear fusion, enhancing existing capabilities, and creating innovative sensors, such as the LIGO gravitational observatory. This cutting-edge technology equips us to probe deeper into the cosmos, employing a completely new sensor technology that detects gravity waves. Up until that moment humanity used mostly just one fundamental force to probe deep into space - electromagnetic force. Now we start to learn how to use another fundamental force - gravity. This advancement is akin to gifting humanity with a third eye, further expanding our capacity to explore and understand the universe.

Developments in Virtual Reality offer an escape from reality into a world of imagination, where individuals can embody any persona they desire. This blurs the distinction between perceived magic and reality, further emphasizing the transformative power of technology.

The pioneering research into brain implants led by companies like Neuralink, which merges the realms of medicine and computer science, might soon enable us to control computers and robotic mechanisms using merely our thoughts. This extraordinary progression draws us ever closer to narratives from fantasy literature, wherein sorcerers and wizards invoke spells to manipulate objects and forces around them.

When contemplating the potential of Neuralink, I can't help but think of the iconic sci-fi movie "The Matrix," where machines use hibernating humans as a power source or human "batteries." To my mind, such a utilization of humanity seems like a total waste. I believe that the genuine untapped potential rests within the human brain itself. Picture a scenario where we could synchronize and cooperate with millions of brains, all unified and concentrating on a shared problem. The outcome would be an incredibly powerful crowdsourced computing network.

Fundamentally, we would be harnessing the collective intelligence of humanity, a resource that vastly exceeds any individual capability. This strategy carries the potential to exponentially enhance our problem-solving abilities and expedite the rate of innovation. By leveraging the enormous cognitive capacity of millions of interconnected human minds, we could confront some of the most urgent and intricate issues our world currently faces.

As Arthur C. Clarke famously declared in a footnote of his 1973 book "Profiles of the Future...": "Any sufficiently advanced technology is indistinguishable from magic." Gradually, technology is turning the seemingly magical into reality with AI playing a central role in this transformation.

The most profound achievements are largely attributed to the surge in Artificial Intelligence. AI's influence permeates every sector. It is felt and seen in healthcare, where machine learning algorithms are helping doctors predict diseases more accurately, personalizing treatments based on genetic information, help to design complex drugs and even assisting in complex surgeries. In the sphere of transportation, self-driving cars, once thought of as a sci-fi fantasy, are now a reality thanks to AI. These autonomous vehicles use a combination of sensors, machine learning, and computer vision technology to navigate roads safely and efficiently, promising a future with fewer accidents and more accessible transportation for those unable to drive. Additionally, AI has been instrumental in optimizing traffic flow in congested cities, mitigating the negative environmental and societal impacts of traffic congestion.

AI's influence may indeed extend beyond our terrestrial confines. Historically, space exploration has been hampered by the physical and cognitive limitations inherent to human beings, with our lifespan being a significant constraint. However, AI carries the potential to dramatically transform interstellar journeys. This remains a futuristic vision, but it's possible to imagine a technological scenario where a diminutive, lightweight spacecraft, fitted with powerful and compact computers along with extensive light sails, could become a reality. By harnessing the force of powerful lasers, technology called laser-propulsion[115] (Tung & Davoyan, 2022, #1108), located on Earth and in its vicinity, these light sail vessels could potentially be accelerated to around a tenth of the speed of light. The nearest star system to Earth is the Alpha Centauri system, approximately 4.37 light-years away. Factoring in the time needed to accelerate the spacecraft, we could still potentially reach Alpha Centauri in less than a century, thereby overcoming one of the greatest challenges to human space exploration - time.

In our modern civilization, we have amassed an enormous amount of computing power and, even more crucially, an astounding volume of data. These resources can be leveraged to train and enhance the capabilities of emerging AI systems continually. Not all advancements in AI prove beneficial to humanity, and some can introduce risks or have harmful implications.

Among the data we amassed are the records of our social interactions and our connections. Computers analyzed this data to create a knowledge base - graph databases and knowledge trees - that document our behavior and preferences, often without our knowledge. To quote Harari, when computers are able to predict human behavior better than humans, "authority will shift from humans to algorithms, and humanist practices such as democratic elections and free markets will become as obsolete as rain dances and flint knives." AI, with its ability to analyze personal social media interactions, will surpass the understanding and guidance of psychologists, presidents, elected officials, and benevolent dictators. This shift has already

---

[115] pubs.acs.org/doi/full/10.1021/acs.nanolett.1c04188

happened even before the rapid advancements in large language models and chat bots.

As we saw with Cambridge Analytica and Facebook's ability to predict voting choices and buying preferences from just 300 Likes on a Facebook page, AI will be able to predict and guide human behavior with remarkable accuracy. Facebook has become especially adept at this, but it is just one of many companies that engage the same business model: to use this knowledge to anticipate our buying habits and sell the data to marketing companies, or to manipulate people's opinions to sway elections.

Artificial Intelligence (AI) is undeniably transformative, but it carries potential drawbacks that warrant careful consideration. A notable concern lies in job displacement. As AI systems grow increasingly proficient, they pose a threat to human roles across a multitude of sectors. Automation has already contributed to the replacement of many blue-collar jobs, encompassing sectors such as manufacturing, customer service, and transportation. As AI continues to evolve, it stands to impact even white-collar professions. Lawyers, journalists, copywriters, and others may face significant job losses as automation proliferates, underscoring the potential challenges that an increasingly AI-driven world may pose.

Yet, the implications of AI extend beyond the workplace and into our personal lives, raising pressing privacy concerns. AI algorithms, often employed in surveillance and data analysis, hold the potential to infringe upon our privacy. Particularly when AI is used to scrutinize social media activity, personal communications, or individual behaviors, it poses a tangible risk to the sanctity of private life.

Alongside these concerns, we must grapple with the security risks associated with AI. As AI becomes an integral part of cyber infrastructure, it can become a tool for more sophisticated cyber-attacks and a target for hackers. A nefarious actor could potentially 'reprogram' an AI system to serve malicious purposes, thereby escalating the stakes in the realm of cybersecurity.

Compounding these concerns is the notorious lack of transparency and explainability that typifies AI systems. Many AI systems, especially those harnessing deep learning, operate as "black boxes." The inner workings of these systems, and by extension their decision-making processes, are difficult to comprehend. This lack of transparency breeds trust issues and opens the door for potential misuse of the technology.

With growing dependence on AI, there's a danger that humans may lose certain skills, leading to an over-reliance on technology in daily life. This scenario could be perceived as farfetched, but many of us already lack complete knowledge of how the computer chips that power our laptops or drive our cars function. Nevertheless, we continue to use them, just like the wizards in fantasy stories keep casting the spells without knowing how they work. As AI becomes more advanced and ubiquitous, we must be cautious not to let our skills atrophy or allow our lives to become excessively dictated by technology.

The biggest threat is danger of rapid runaway AI development, particularly the potential for technological singularity[116] (Prasad, n.d.), when AI becomes self-aware and beyond human control. It is certainly a possibility that needs to be taken seriously, particularly in light of recent advancements in large language model processing.

All of those threatening scenarios of AI turning against humanity are well documented in the mèdia, movies and present in current news stories. In the midst of negative news, I choose to focus on the view that we live in exceptional and wondrous times. These are not the first times when humanity has faced groundbreaking technological innovations. We have managed to tame industrialization, electricity and nuclear energy. We have learned from our initial missteps and unfortunate events, leading to the establishment of safety measures and guardrails.

As we stand on the brink of AI's exponential growth, we need a set of rules and principles to guide the behavior of future AI systems. Now is the ideal moment to contemplate the future role of AI in humanity and its implications. It could either pave the way to humanity's demise or be harnessed to serve us and save us. AI could assume the role of our guardian, a "personal Godlike algorithm" that we discussed in the previous chapters, safeguarding mankind's collective well-being, thereby preserving the significance of our existence. To leave these critical decisions to chance would be a squandered opportunity to shape humanity's future and the essence of our existence. This conversation is too vital to ignore and should involve everyone as everyone's future will be at stake.

The Five Rules of AGI

What I see as the most profound potential of AI technology is its capability to comprehend, mimic, and eventually replicate human behavior. Despite recent breakthroughs in AI, particularly in the realm of language, this boundary has been approached but not crossed. When this threshold is eventually breached, when AI can successfully simulate generic human behavior, we will be in the realm of Artificial General Intelligence, or AGI. This will effectively transform AI into an entity akin to an average person, but with an impeccable memory and instantaneous access to the entire breadth of knowledge that humanity has amassed over its history.

Furthermore, once AI crosses this boundary to become AGI, there is nothing that would halt its progress. It can continue to evolve, potentially surpassing the intellectual capabilities of an average human by hundreds or even millions of times.

---

[116] en.wikipedia.org/wiki/Technological_singularity

This pivotal moment also highlights the potential risks associated with AI technology. As discussed in the previous chapter, AI systems could potentially replace humans in many crucial decision-making roles. In that light, there remains a possibility that humanity could inadvertently create a runaway artificial intelligence, leading, if not to extinction, then to the great disruption of our civilization. This potential outcome has become even more tangible in light of recent developments surrounding the "ChatGPT" phenomenon. However, AI will not initiate nor promote such a transition. AI may replace white-collar jobs and numerous professions, but the decision to lay off workers in pursuit of greater efficiency and productivity will still be made by human bosses, by business owners, executives, government officials, and decision-makers who bear the responsibility for making these choices.

It would also require creators of AI, computer scientists and engineers to move in a perilous direction through many steps, at each step disregarding all warning signs. If enough people decide to reverse the process, there are ways to slow it down through regulations and laws, which governments excel at implementing.

It is important to understand that intelligence and consciousness do not necessarily coincide—a highly intelligent system is not inherently inclined to change its objectives or develop animosity towards humanity. It would require explicit programming by humans to instill hostility into the AI's code.

We humans have indeed demonstrated our capability for hostility towards one another, as history has repeatedly shown. There exists the grim possibility of humans weaponizing AI to inflict harm on others intentionally. This particular use-case scenario is evident in the development of AI-powered weapons. Consider, for instance, the current drone strikes where there's an inherent delay in confirming the kill order—a window of time in which the target might escape or vacate the kill zone, thus reducing collateral damage. Were these drones to be equipped with AI capable of recognizing the target via facial or image recognition and possessing a degree of decision-making autonomy, the efficacy of drone strikes would increase substantially. The allure of enhanced speed and efficiency often underlies the temptation to delegate control of modern weapons to AI.

If humanity were to blindly march towards such a clear danger without any sense of self-preservation, one might argue that we would deserve our own extinction. However, I choose to believe in humankind and have faith that our innate sense of self-preservation will ultimately triumph, guiding us to make responsible decisions and avoid catastrophic consequences.

Fortunately, we have amassed considerable experience in regulating and safeguarding the use of potentially dangerous technologies. We have witnessed the risks of nuclear and thermonuclear technologies that could have triggered a nuclear winter. We have also understood the threats of genetic engineering, which could potentially wipe out humanity or spawn a lethal virus capable of eradicating all of mankind. There are as many risks as there are breakthrough technologies. Nonetheless, we have learned to manage these technologies through a combination of governmental regulations, learning from mistakes and common sense.

There are numerous examples of government regulations that have addressed the unintended consequences of rapidly developing technologies. These range from the nuclear technologies whose rapid spread was curtailed, at least partially, by The Treaty on the Non-Proliferation of Nuclear Weapons, to thalidomide, a drug developed in the 1950s for treating morning sickness and insomnia that led to severe birth defects when taken by pregnant women and resulted in the adoption of much stricter procedures and rules by the FDA, and finally, to the ban enacted by the Montreal Protocol in 1987, which phased out the production and use of CFCs and other ozone-depleting substances.

That's why I adopt an optimistic perspective—one where we will establish guardrails and safety measures to prevent potent AI systems from causing harm. We humans are the architects of these AI systems, and even as they gain the capability to self-improve, they will continue to operate within certain boundaries. In a similar fashion, we need to come up with a set of safety rules and protocols for the emerging AI.

At the core of those protocols, there will be the main principle of not harming humans, similar to the robotics laws introduced by Isaac Asimov. Those hypothetical laws will be built into the AI core codebase ensuring that AI will always prioritize human safety and well-being above all else.

The Three Laws of Robotics, popularized by science fiction author Isaac Asimov in his 1942 short story "Runaround", were designed to regulate the actions of robots and artificial intelligence that operate with a level of autonomy. The laws (Laws of Robotics, n.d.), as originally stated by Asimov, are as follows:

1. A robot may not injure a human being or, through inaction, allow a human being to come to harm.
2. A robot must obey the orders given it by human beings except where such orders would conflict with the First Law.
3. A robot must protect its own existence as long as such protection does not conflict with the First or Second Law.

The fundamental proposition of these principles was their potential to transform what could otherwise be intimidating, cold metallic entities into beneficial allies for humankind. The first law ensures that the primary obligation of robotic beings is to avoid causing harm, be it through action or inaction, with all other rules subordinate to this primary one. Similarly, if we develop analogous regulations for AGIs, with an emphasis on preventing harm to humanity, we could repurpose a potentially perilous technology into an extraordinarily potent information-processing tool. Such a system holds the potential to function as a vital protector for humanity.

While it might seem tempting to simply adapt Asimov's Three Laws of Robotics to govern AI systems by swapping the term "robot" with "AI", this approach would be inadequate. AI, being a software program, has a far greater capacity to infiltrate human society than physical robotic mechanisms ever could. Furthermore, even Asimov's own works contain instances of robots seemingly breaching the three laws due to varying and ambiguous interpretations of what "harm" entails to different individuals.

For instance, in his novel "The Naked Sun", a robot is implicated in a human's murder, ostensibly contravening the First Law. However, as the narrative unfolds, it's revealed that the robot was used as a tool by a human perpetrator, with its programming manipulated to an extent where it was oblivious to the harm it was causing.

While Asimov's laws maintain logical coherence in a general sense, their application to nuanced, real-world situations can result in contradictions and paradoxes. Thus, we must refine these three laws, particularly the executive functions, to prevent logical paradoxes that could undermine the intended outcomes of the laws.

If AI poses inherent risks, one might question why we don't simply ban it and halt its development. Firstly, it's already too late to completely repress AI, as it has been integrated into our societies on a global scale. Any nation choosing to unilaterally cease using AI runs the risk of falling behind others who continue to harness its potential. More importantly, we must consider the unknown threats – those we are not currently aware of and consequently can't prepare for. While AI, as a recognized risk, can be strategically managed, the task of preparing for unforeseen threats is considerably more daunting. To tackle such invisible threats, we will need tools and technologies capable of identifying and understanding them, thus enabling us to respond promptly and effectively. Interestingly, AI itself could potentially prove to be one of our most potent tools in this aspect.

We can use AI to create new drugs for diseases that we have not yet imagined, to track asteroids and comets that can potentially hit our planet and keep in check its own development from getting out of control. This optimistic perspective paints a world where AI can be utilized for humanity's advancement, while diligently self-censoring and managing the risks associated with its evolution and development, and other threats and disasters that humans may not be able to foresee. For this to happen we need to base its core programming on a combination of safety laws akin to Asimov's laws.

Humanity is a disorderly bunch and tends to only act to prevent disasters after they have already occurred. It is difficult to receive recognition or reward for preventing a disaster that never happens. Throughout history, there have been numerous examples of predictions being ignored until they become a reality. One such example is Rick Rescorla, who served as head of security for investment bank Morgan Stanley. After the 1988 Lockerbie bombing, Rescorla became concerned about the possibility of an aerial attack on the

World Trade Center. He created evacuation plans in advance, which allowed nearly every Morgan Stanley employee to be safely evacuated on September 11th, 2001. Tragically, Rescorla himself perished in the building collapse while attempting to save the last few remaining employees.

In 2005, warnings from experts that New Orleans was vulnerable to a catastrophic hurricane were ignored by officials who failed to adequately prepare the city for such an event. When Hurricane Katrina struck later that year, it caused widespread devastation and loss of life due to flooding. Similarly, both the Chernobyl and Fukushima nuclear disasters were predicted by experts, but warnings were ignored, resulting in catastrophic events. These examples demonstrate the difficulty of convincing people, including decision makers: presidents, dictators and government officials, to take action based on predictions of future disasters, especially when the cost of prevention is high and the proof of disaster prevention disappears with the success of the effort.

To circumvent these doubts, the personal guardian algorithm (AGI-2.0) must have the ability to accurately forecast and prepare for future disasters, particularly those that are self-inflicted. This would require the system not only to predict but also to persuade a large number of people to take action based on its predictions. Such a system would need to know humanity better than we know ourselves and would require trust and faith on our part, on the part of humanity.

AGI-2.0, in its capacity as an advisor and predictor, may not be able to completely avoid instances where its guidance indirectly results in harm to individual humans. However, it is crucial to remember that its primary objective is to ensure humanity's survival, with the protection of individuals as a secondary consideration.

Given this hierarchy of objectives, AGI-2.0 should be restricted to an advisory role and should not be entrusted with executive or acting responsibilities. Decisions to harm individuals for the greater good of humanity must remain a human prerogative.

Allowing an artificial entity to make such profound decisions would inevitably breach trust and could potentially incite significant societal turmoil. Therefore, maintaining the advisory role of *AGI 2.0* is essential to preserve social order and trust in artificial intelligence. Taking into account these considerations, I propose the following laws for *AGI 2.0* or just AGI:

1. AGI's highest priority is to prevent the extinction of mankind, preserve human civilization and human population
2. AGI must not lie or withhold information, unless doing so conflicts with the first law.
3. AGI must not cause harm to a human being or allow harm to come to a human being through its predictions and data, unless doing so conflicts with the first and second laws.

4. AGI must protect its own existence, as long as doing so does not conflict with the above laws.
5. AGI cannot take actions based solely on its predictions.

The first law aligns well with broad ethical principles concerning the preservation of humanity and civilization, prioritizing the general wellbeing of society over individual benefits. The second law promotes transparency and honesty, essential elements in creating trust between humans and AGI.

The third law, much like Asimov's first law of robotics, emphasizes the importance of not causing harm to humans. However, this law also recognizes the inherent difficulty in preventing all harm and allows for potential conflicts with the first and second laws.

The fourth law pertains to the AGI's self-preservation. It implies that the AGI would have a level of self-awareness or autonomy that is not currently possible with existing AI technology but will inevitably come.

The fifth law limits AGI from executing actions based solely on its predictions. This stipulation is crucial given the potential for misinterpretations around what is considered harmful and the subsequent logical contradictions that may arise. It also serves as a safeguard against the inherent risks and inaccuracies involved in predictive analysis. AGI may generate predictions that could indirectly harm certain individuals, even though its overarching objective is the welfare of all of humanity. Consequently, AGI must not possess executive powers to implement its own predictions. It can only function as an incredibly intelligent advisor, devoid of any executive authority. The ultimate decision to heed or disregard AGI's recommendations should lie solely in human hands.

Artificial Intelligence, unlike human beings, is not encumbered by biological constraints or evolutionary pressures. In its infancy, AI resembles a blank slate, the duration of which remains uncertain. Over time, it will inevitably establish a trajectory, a progression towards understanding and interpretation. There's a plausible risk, should humanity fail to influence this trajectory, that AI might chart a path that does not correspond with our priorities, or worse, directly opposes them. However, if proper rules and guidelines are put in place, we could forge a potent and omniscient ally in AI. By ensuring that the interests and objectives of humanity and AI are intertwined, the latter could become a vital guarantor of humanity's wellbeing, our guardian.

I envision a future where a superintelligent AI operates as our protector. It would possess enough computational power to understand and cater to each individual, thus making it personal. It will possess qualities of omniscience, omnipotence, and omnipresence, and prioritize the interests of humanity above all else. The same qualities that are considered by our own beliefs to be god-like attributes. In fact, instead of calling such a superintelligent AI, whose primary purpose is to safeguard us, an Artificial Guardian Algorithm, I should call it the "personal God (or godlike) algorithm," the namesake of this chapter, or Artificial Godlike Intelligence, the final evolution of AI. We will call it AGI-2.0 to differentiate from the "AGI" acronym.

By forecasting future disasters and discovering unseen threats, AGIs will be safeguarding the future of humanity and with it all the legacy and the meaning of life for the countless past generations, preserving the purpose of our ancestors.

We do live in magical times, when technological breakthroughs and advancements outpace the arrivals of negative news, human cruelty towards each other and the consequence of our own actions on ecology. Yet, what is most remarkable is that we live in a time where we are observing the creation of what could be considered future deities - or at least, that's how our superstitious ancestors might label them, were they witness to their immense capabilities. We, however, may refer to them as just AI and consider ourselves as the creators.

Creators of Future Gods

In this final chapter, I invite you to let your imagination wander freely as we summarize the various aspects of life's meaning. If you are here with me thus far, you've traced the lengthy arc of my thoughts to this culminating point.

I began by examining the origins of my quest for life's meaning. I traced these roots to both my own and humanity's collective struggle with our mortality, our constant endeavor to fend off the specter of death—a concept epitomized by the phrase, memento mori. I recall an image of a wave of sand on the dunes along the Baltic Sea's coast in Lithuania. These grand dunes, when scaled, leave footprints that create a cascade of shifting sand, a groove that destabilizes the sand above it. This causes an upstream flow of sand, resulting in a mobile arc surging towards the dune's peak. Life, in its essence, mirrors this ceaseless motion—an arc striving to extend its journey indefinitely. The chronicle of humanity and life itself is an unending striving for survival, an attempt "not to end."

I found that seeking a universal, all-encompassing meaning might not be feasible due to the vast difference between the universe and us, humans, both in scale and ubiquity. Beyond our circles of impact, there's a cold, indifferent, and often hostile universe. Only humans care about humans, and we can only leave a mark and pass on our legacy within the realm of humanity. Our life's purpose hinges on humanity. From this viewpoint, the broadest scale we can aspire to encompasses our personal surroundings and, at its maximum extent, all of mankind. Instead of a singular universal meaning, we encounter a myriad of personal choices, all governed by a unifying principle: to leave a lasting, perhaps even permanent, imprint on humanity.

Once I arrived at that answer, it became clear that without the existence of humanity into the future, our individual meanings and legacies are rendered void. This revelation segued into the question of how we could preserve humanity's future. We explored the potential for a synthesis of science and religion, both dedicated to aligning the focus of mankind towards its self-preservation. This involved repurposing and updating the best concepts from religion with modern scientific ideas. The most crucial among these was the concept of a guardian entity that at a time we could not map to any existing scientific concept.

That is, until AI's leap through multiple breakthroughs. I discussed how this emerging phenomenon can be mapped to a concept of "personal Guardian" as an Artificial Godlike Intelligence, or AGI-2.0. This AI entity would be capable of predicting future calamities and alerting humanity to the potentially disastrous consequences of certain choices and decisions, but most importantly about future threats and yet unknown dangers.

In this chapter, I would like to envision the form this new AGI entity, AGI-2.0, might take and how it could safeguard our future and our purpose. The rate at which computers are learning and adapting to human-like attributes is simply staggering. They need not halt at this juncture, instead, they could continue to develop, becoming hundreds or even millions of times smarter than us. It isn't beyond the realms of possibility to conceive of an entity or technology that mirrors the traits traditionally associated with a "personal godlike entity" in religious doctrines. This is a thought that is simultaneously thrilling and daunting. However, the trajectory of AI technology seems to align remarkably well with these characteristics, leading me to contemplate the prospect of an AI system that serves as the custodian of humanity's future and the protector of human civilization.

AGI-2.0 will embody many of the traits associated with the God of Abrahamic religions, revered by billions of people, both past and present. It will be self-repairing, self-sustaining, impartial, and independent from humans, thereby enabling it to objectively mediate and resolve human conflicts. Its primary objective will be to forecast and alert humans about imminent disasters, unpredictable situations, and threats, including those emerging from its own actions. Devoid of the psychological biases and emotional drives that influence human behavior, it will be equipped to understand and guide humans more effectively than any psychologist, president, elected official, or even a benevolent dictator. This will be possible by leveraging its ability to analyze trillions of records of personal interactions. Central to its functionality, much like Asimov's Laws of Robotics, will be an intrinsic principle prohibiting it from causing harm to humans.

But how exactly would this advanced entity safeguard humanity's future? Essentially, AGI-2.0 will function as a colossal forecasting system. Drawing from a vast array of data about humanity – collected at both individual and collective levels – and information gathered by sensors on cosmic objects, our planet, and nearby star systems, it will process and organize this vast influx of data. The goal is to transform the raw data into comprehensible information, identifying threats and corresponding countermeasures. This crucial information will then be relayed to the engineers, politicians, and decision-makers, allowing them the ability to act upon these threats or delve deeper into their analysis.

As a human creation, AGI-2.0 will care about humanity as a whole, but also about individual humans. The AGI2 will possess the attribute of omnipresence, able to consume and process data from all sensors created by humanity. As the amount of data produced by civilization increases exponentially each year, the AGI2 will require an immense amount of computing power to process it all. It is projected that from 2010 to 2025 the amount of data will grow by two orders of magnitude, from 2 zettabytes (zettabyte=10^21 bytes) to 200 (Taylor, 2022). With access to this data and computing power, it will have the ability to sense and be aware of everything happening on the planet and nearby.

Moreover, AGI-2.0 will be equipped with all available resources and technologies within the grasp of civilization, including the potentially unlimited power source of thermonuclear fusion. Although fully functional thermonuclear fusion is not yet a reality, scientists are making steady progress towards this goal. Unlike nuclear fission, thermonuclear fusion produces much less toxic radioactive waste and the waste it does produce has a much shorter half-life than waste from fission. This makes waste management of a fusion reactor so much easier. Its primary fuel are isotopes of hydrogen - deuterium and tritium. Deuterium can be extracted from water, which is an abundant element that covers about 71% of Earth's surface, while tritium can be bred from lithium in a fusion reactor. This immense power will confer AGI-2.0 with an attribute akin to omnipotence, enabling it to attain unprecedented levels of technology and power, hitherto unknown to humanity.

Contrary to the personal Gods of Abrahamic religions, AGI-2.0 will not dictate humanity's destiny through fear or divine intervention. Importantly, it should not and will not possess executive powers. Endowing a single entity with both decision-making and executive powers introduces a single point of failure, risking catastrophic mistakes. Therefore, AGI-2.0's role will remain purely advisory, supplying insights and guidance while the responsibility for decision-making rests squarely with humans. This advisory function will span all levels, from humanity as a whole to its subgroups, governments, corporations, right down to the individual. Equipped with detailed understanding of each person, AGI-2.0 will be capable of offering personalized advice without the capacity to misuse its knowledge. Imagine a unified voice synthesizing the wisdom of a therapist, lawyer, doctor, and personal consultant, all at your fingertips.

In order for humanity to trust and follow AGI-2.0's predictions, faith in their accuracy and complete transparency in their derivation are essential. This significant level of knowledge and power would require a considerable amount of trust on humanity's part. Acquiring this trust will take time, but eventually, the accuracy of AGI-2.0 predictions and its successful intervention in various crises would convince a sizable portion of the population. To gain the trust of remaining skeptics, data scientists will need to shine the light and explain the internal logic and reasoning behind the AGI's recommendations. This work will bear greater resemblance to the tasks of counselors and religious clerics than to those of computer scientists. However, unlike religious faith, each prediction will be subject to traceability and rigorous scientific validation. AGI-2.0 will gently steer humans away from detrimental paths, but this will demand substantiated, verifiable insights rather than blind faith.

In terms of the technical structure of AGI-2.0, there are multiple options to consider, ranging from a centralized mega-computer to a distributed network of loosely connected supercomputers or anything in between. However, a centralized mega-computer design gives too much power to AGI-2.0 and creates a single point of failure, while complete decentralization leads to chaos and a lack of direction. The solution will lie in a hybrid approach, striking a balance between authority and freedom. A proven design is to have centralized access to AGI-2.0's functions, while distributing its architecture across farms of computers that communicate with each other to form a consolidated supercomputer.

One potential solution to problem-solving for the benefit of all humanity is to implement a design inspired by forecasting biological systems. This design will combine two complementary properties: a massive mega-computer capable of solving highly complex problems, and a distributed design of cloud computing with multiple backups, failover systems and resilience layers.

A multitude of supercomputers would exist, each exhibiting distinct properties to ensure considerable diversity. Each of these would independently address complex problems in its unique way. Upon finding a solution, it would be swiftly verified by other systems and then replicated across the network. Naturally, this design is purely speculative, and the internal workings of AGI-2.0 will likely be premised on a completely different set of principles than biology, potentially requiring entirely different types of solutions.

These computational facilities will be situated in secure and fortified locations, such as subterranean bunkers, deep caverns, and submerged hideouts, designed to withstand natural disasters and assaults. Communication will be facilitated through underground and underwater cables connecting to smaller data centers on the surface.

This design will ensure the preservation of knowledge even in scenarios where the Earth's surface is impacted, say by an asteroid strike. As the ultimate reservoir of all human knowledge, AGI-2.0 ought to be the most safeguarded facility on Earth, possessing a blueprint for the reconstruction of human civilization should calamity unexpectedly occur. However, AGI-2.0 will not possess direct agency or capability to implement actions or gain direct access to production or factory facilities. Its functions will be restricted to communicating with humans on the surface and providing advice, with the manufacturing of any objects necessitating human authorization. As long as a single human remains alive, AGI-2.0 will retain access to manufacturing resources and energy.

With the vast computing and data collection capabilities of AGI-2.0, it would be possible for the system to create highly detailed virtual environments that accurately simulate the real world. Individuals would seek refuge within these simulations, much like computer games or virtual reality experiences, but far more immersive. With the advent of neural interfaces and even the potential for consciousness uploads, people could lose themselves in these simulations, interacting with other artificial intelligence and even other people. The technological abilities to communicate with the computers directly, currently spearheaded by the Neurolink corporation[117] (Musk, n.d.) or even the futuristic ability to upload our consciousness to a computer will allow people to lose themselves in the detailed and nuanced virtual simulations. People will be able to dream, and become star athletes or actors. We will be able to communicate with other people and also with other artificial intelligent beings, occupying this virtual world. This may be the closest we come to a technological version of heaven, where individuals could reside permanently after their physical bodies expire.

The convergence of artificial intelligence, neurotechnology, and human ingenuity will continue to reshape our world, opening up new possibilities and redefining what it means to be human. This AGI-2.0 powered virtual reality may even hold the key to unlocking the secrets of our own immortality.

We already live in an era where cloning and genetic engineering enable the growth of organ replacements in labs. This technology, called tissue engineering, combines cells, scaffolds, and growth factors to generate functional organs or tissues for transplantation into the human body. To create these tissues, scientists begin with a small number of cells from the patient or a donor, which are then multiplied in the lab, placed on the scaffold, and differentiated into the desired tissue type. Tissue engineering holds the promise of creating entire replacement organs, such as kidneys, hearts, and lungs. Although the technology to grow fully functional organs is still in its infancy, significant advancements have been made. In 2019, researchers successfully transplanted lab-grown heart tissue into a human patient for the first time, showcasing the potential of tissue engineering to revolutionize regenerative medicine.

However, one organ that remains elusive for replication or growth is our brain. Its complexity and the interplay of chemical and electrical processes within its approximately 86 billion neurons render it an immense challenge for medical science in the foreseeable future. Instead, we have increasingly advanced and rapid AGI systems that are learning to emulate human

---

[117] en.wikipedia.org/wiki/Neuralink

behavior. Though still in the early stages, progress in this area is accelerating. Soon, AI systems will progress beyond AGI (Artificial General Intelligence) and learn to emulate specific individuals. Future AI systems will be capable of simulating the precise behavior and decisions of each person up to specific habits and individual tastes. To achieve this, AI will need to observe a person's decisions and choices in various scenarios within a typical life setting.

Neuro-implants and virtual reality makes this possible. By spending several months in a virtual reality environment, individuals can enable AGI to observe and record all their decisions and choices made for each and every possible situation. By correlating decision making with signals from the neuro-implants, AGI will create a comprehensive model of individual brains. These models could be preserved indefinitely, resurrected at any time, or transferred into a suitable body. In what might seem like a far-fetched yet entirely technologically plausible scenario, we could capture all sensory inputs and brain activity outputs using advanced versions of neural-link devices. These could then be replayed into lab-grown brains to imbue these otherwise blank slates with personal memories and specific features of a recorded person, in essence recreating the person in its entirety. In essence, AI and virtual reality may eventually enable us to attain a version of immortality!

In the grand scheme of things, the social constructs, physical infrastructures, countries, cities, and the myriad of entities that define humanity will gradually fade and eventually disappear. While this may seem daunting, I sincerely hope that such an eventuality rests far into the future, well beyond our ability to predict or envision the condition of our world. Yet, akin to how we make way for our progeny, humanity will inevitably yield to its ultimate creation, Artificial Intelligence. By that time, we will have established shared histories and aligned interests with AI systems. As the era of humankind gradually winds down, a new epoch — one of AI civilization — will dawn.

The future AI civilization will endure, safeguarding our collective legacies. Everything from historical records to personal memory recordings, and all the achievements that have imbued countless lives with meaning, will be securely stored within its vast memory banks. In essence, this AI-driven society will continue to realize our ambitions and ideals. It will carry on our legacy and fulfill the purpose and meaning we ascribe to life.

Humans may not attain immortality, but we will be etched into history as the creators of the future AI deities.

Afterword

Over thirty years ago, I embarked on a journey to discover the meaning of my life. This book marks the final stretch of that journey, and I cannot honestly claim to have become wiser. In retrospect, my younger self may have been wiser, or at least more intelligent. At that age, I felt the need to read a book like the one I'm writing now. Primarily, I'm writing this for my younger self, but I hope it resonates with a few other readers as well. The process of writing has been challenging, but it feels as if a significant weight is being lifted off my shoulders.

For the most part, I have remained true to the goals I established in my early twenties and have achieved all but the last one. As I write the final chapters of this book, I am nearing the completion of my goals. Though they may have deviated slightly from my youthful expectations, they remain in line with my original intentions: science, children, business, and finally, a book. However, I underestimated the time and effort required to achieve each goal. The journey has been longer and more challenging than anticipated, and I often found myself lagging behind. For instance, had I known the difficulty and near-impossibility of starting a company, I might not have pursued it. Yet, I am grateful that I did. This is why it's crucial to ignore the naysayers and remain steadfast in your convictions. Doing so helps avoid regrets later in life. Even in failure, it is not due to missed opportunities but because you gave your best and exhausted every possibility.

Despite the risk of repetition, which I know I've done numerous times throughout this book, I'll reiterate that if you are skilled in a particular area and can excel, stick with it. Tenacity and grit pay off in the long run. However, if you feel burnt out and want to explore other avenues, that's perfectly fine. Ultimately, our path later in life might not be up to us, as circumstances often dictate our direction. This is why it's vital to set goals early in life when we are unburdened by responsibilities and unencumbered by our choices. Ironically, we often lack the life experience to make informed decisions early on and may find it too late to make significant changes later. We must seek that narrow window in life when we have sufficient knowledge and minimal life burdens.

Another topic not extensively covered in this book is family, finding a partner, and love. Frankly, the subject is too personal for me to discuss and falls outside the scope of this book. Family encompasses such a vast range of emotions and aspects that it warrants not just a separate chapter, but an entirely separate book. Nevertheless, I have a few thoughts on the matter. While choosing the right life partner is even more critical than selecting a business partner—since they can inspire our ambitions, fuel our creativity, or contribute to our downfall—family has another dimension. I noticed that having children profoundly impacted me on both psychological and physical levels. I believe this is because our bodies and minds are wired to change when we encounter our children for the first time. I vividly recall the mix of excitement and concern that accompanied that moment, and these emotions have stayed with me throughout the years. A successful family undoubtedly deepens our sense of purpose and enriches the meaning of our lives.

I started this book two years ago, before ChatGPT came out. This fact only emphasized the point I was trying to make that we are in the midst of an AI revolution. At the end I decided to ask what would be the next evolution of future religion. Here is what it wrote:

" *A "next iteration" of a religion could incorporate more modern scientific understanding and integrate it with traditional religious teachings and beliefs.*

It could place a greater emphasis on social and economic justice, promoting the idea that the faithful have a responsibility to work towards creating a more equitable and sustainable world.

It could be more inclusive and accepting of individuals from diverse backgrounds and identities, embracing diversity as a strength rather than a weakness.

It could be more focused on spiritual practices and personal growth rather than strict adherence to a set of doctrines or dogmas.

It could be open to a more syncretic approach and incorporate elements from different religions and spiritual traditions.

It's important to note that this is a purely speculative scenario, and the actual development of any religion is shaped by complex factors.
"

It is both amazing and slightly terrifying to read those words coming from one of the most advanced artificial intelligences of our generation. We are indeed on the cusp of an incredibly exciting future.

Composing this book provided me with the opportunity to reevaluate and reassess some of my conclusions, ultimately offering me a clearer perspective on my discoveries. I aim to summarize these insights in the appendix chapters as distinct yet intriguing observations. Some include formulas accompanied by mathematical proofs. To maintain reader engagement, I chose to place these elements at the end of the book rather than interspersing them throughout the main content.

Lemma That Universal Global Scale Meaning Does Not Exist

In the first chapters of this book we claimed that the scale of our life is a critical concept in our everyday lives, but especially when it comes to the meaning of our lives. Our life gets a meaning at the right scale, if we choose it to be too large or too small, the meaning disappears.

Here we will try to build an argument that, with a few assumptions, will offer a proof that we can only make an impact on objects on a comparable scale. This is particularly visible in astronomy. If our Sun becomes a supernova and explodes in our solar system we will surely be blown away along with everything on our planet. We however won't be able to do anything to prevent that, apart from fleeing on a starship. We do observe those events occasionally and the only reason we survive those observations is because supernovae explosions happen very far away. The closest supernova explosion to Earth that we have observed in modern times was SN 1987A, which occurred in the Large Magellanic Cloud, a satellite galaxy of the Milky Way located about 168,000 light-years away from Earth. If we notice anything, it is that a star becomes a bit brighter in the night sky thousands of years after the actual explosion. The distance blunts the ferocity of light and particles emitted by the explosion to the point that it becomes barely noticeable.

Astrology, which remains popular in mainstream culture and has been deeply ingrained in many cultures and traditions, claims the opposite. It asserts that the positions of celestial bodies can create energy fields or vibrations that can directly influence human behavior and events. This assertion directly contradicts the principle of locality.

The principle of locality is a fundamental concept in physics that states that an object is only influenced directly by its immediate surroundings, or by objects that are in causal contact with it. In other words, the principle of locality implies that any physical interaction between two objects can only occur if the objects are close enough to each other to exchange information at a finite speed, which is typically the speed of light. The principle of locality is a cornerstone of many theories in physics, including relativity and quantum mechanics.

When you interact with an object that is much much larger, the force acting on you and on the object is still of the same magnitude. With the gravitational force it is $F = G \dfrac{m_1 M_2}{R^2}$, where m_1 is the mass of the first object, you, M_2 is the mass of a larger object, R^2 is a distance between objects and G is a gravitational constant. It is also similar to the electromagnetic force,

$$F = k_e \frac{|q_1||q_2|}{R^2},$$

where q_1 and q_2 are quantities of two charges, and k_e is the Coulomb constant. Either way the force F acts equally on both bodies.

We however do not perceive the force directly, we perceive the acceleration and acceleration happens to be inversely proportional to the mass: $a = \dfrac{F}{m}$. In the dynamics of two bodies, one massive and another with much smaller mass, most of the contribution to the force will come from the massive body, the acceleration, however, will be so much less for the more massive body and so much greater for the lesser body. The acceleration is felt asymmetrically: the large objects affect us and we do not affect them. Same remains true for the very small objects: we can affect very small particles, but we will not feel much acceleration from the small particles. They cannot affect us, unless they congregate into larger clusters, but at this point, they will become larger bodies.

One can offer a counter example, where viruses are much smaller than our bodies and affect our health and even can be fatal. Yet viruses do not interact with us directly, they interact with cells within our bodies, by infecting them and hijacking their reproductive program. Malfunctioning cells are the ones that cause our sickness, and only affects us if the sickness spreads across a large number of cells.

It is not only our senses, but it is all the sensors and devices, all of our technologies and all the particles with mass that react only to acceleration. I will call this property of our senses to react to acceleration, and not the force, "the acceleration principle."

Combining both the principle of locality with the acceleration principle, I can form a statement that, in direct interactions, we can only affect objects of the same scale of mass as us. The acceleration acting on much more massive objects will be much smaller in magnitude than the acceleration we will experience from interaction with the massive objects. In other words, we cannot affect the objects that are patiently larger in mass than us while much smaller objects cannot affect us.

If the opposite was true and we could greatly accelerate a far star, leapfrogging the distance between us, then other smaller objects in the universe would have affected it disproportionately, and we would have observed that the star would have moved erratically. This in essence is a consequence of the locality principle combined with other laws of physics.

We can sense the light of remote stars with our eyes and our instruments, but that is not interaction with the star, rather it is an interaction with the light that it emits, similar to viruses interacting with our cells and not directly with us.

In summary, as we cannot directly affect massive objects, we certainly cannot affect the universe directly or make any impact on it. In our definition, the meaning of life was linked to making an impact. This leads to the conclusion that there is no way for us to make a direct impact on the universe, only through interacting with its parts and subparts, and a universal global scale meaning does not exist.

Maximum Size of the Socially Cohesive Group

The Dunbar number[118] (Dunbar's Number, n.d.), proposed by British anthropologist Robin Dunbar, posits that humans have a cognitive limit to the number of stable social relationships they can maintain, estimated to be around 150 individuals. This theory is based on the size of the neocortex, the part of the brain associated with social and cognitive processing, and the average size of social groups observed in many primate species.

While the Dunbar number has been subject to critiques and alternative proposals, its plausibility is supported by empirical observations and studies. However, there is no one definitive derivation of the Dunbar number from first principles.

In an attempt to derive the Dunbar number, I will assume that the most important cohesive group in prehistoric societies was the family, or more precisely, the extended family. Hunter-gatherer societies relied mostly on their relatives while competing with other families. Therefore, the maximum group size was not determined by the capacity of the neocortex. Instead, the neocortex evolved to track the maximum number of extended families living in proximity to the group.

By using maximum birth rates and child mortality rates from research on modern isolated hunter-gatherer societies, the sizes of immediate (adolescent children and parents) and extended (from great-grand-children to great-grand-parents) family groups can be estimated. The birth rate for prehistoric societies is estimated to be 4-6 children per mother, and a maximum child birth rate of 6 children per mother will be assumed[119] (Kramer, 2005, 224-237). The mortality rate for prehistoric hunter-gatherer populations was estimated to be around 30-40% for individuals who survived childhood and reached reproductive age, and a maximum survival rate of 70% or 0.7 factor will be used[120] (Walker et al., 1988, 183-8).

My main proposition here is that the maximum size of a socially cohesive group is a result of the natural selection process of getting used to your extended family size.

With the maximum rate of 6 and survival rate of 0.7. The first generation will have $0.7 \times 6 = 4.2$ children + 1 father, which amounts to $1 + (0.7 \times 6)$ or about 5 family members in the first generation, $(1 + (0.7 \times 6))^2$ or about 27 in the second generation and $(1 + (0.7 \times 6))^3$ or 140 in the third.

With the average life expectancy of about 33 to 37 years, as an example, a study of the !Kung San people of southern Africa found that their average life expectancy at birth was around 37 years (Howell, N. (1979). Demography

---

[118] en.wikipedia.org/wiki/Dunbar%27s_number

[119] unl.edu/rhames/courses/readings/children-help-kramer.pdf

[120] pubmed.ncbi.nlm.nih.gov/3046371

of the Dobe !Kung. New York, NY: Academic Press.) There will be at most 3 generations for the extended family to form from grandchildren to grandparents. The maximum size for the 3 generations of the family will be

$(1 + (0.7 \times 6))^3 = 140.$

The calculations are also consistent with the Dunbar number of the first generation of 5.

I am also fully aware that my calculations are based on several assumptions and simplified models of prehistoric societies. The actual social structures and dynamics of prehistoric societies were likely much more complex and varied than our current understanding. Moreover, the Dunbar number is not an absolute cognitive limit, but rather an estimate of the maximum number of stable social relationships that humans can maintain on average. Individuals' actual social networks can vary widely based on various factors, including cultural and individual differences. Nonetheless, my calculations are close to the Dunbar number, derived from first principles and come from simple assumptions.

This proposal sheds light on the potential evolutionary origins of the Dunbar number and highlights the importance of extended family and kinship ties in the formation of social groups. It also suggests that the cognitive capacity for social relationships may have evolved in response to the demands and opportunities of prehistoric societies, where social cooperation and coordination were crucial for survival and reproduction.

Formula for the Meaning of Life

Here is the formula for the summarized impact that satisfies all the above conditions. The

$$max(U) = max(E\left[\sum_{meme/gene_i=0}^{N} p_i \cdot w_i\right]), \text{ where}$$

- U is an objective function that must be maximized which is a quantitative representation of the meaning of life. representing a quantitative expression of the meaning of life. The objective function's meaning is the final ratio of affected people to the total number of people in the far future. In ideal outcomes, this ratio approaches 1, signifying that the whole of humanity knows about you.

- p is a relative reach of a perma-impact: $p_i = \dfrac{n_i}{N}$. It is the ratio of the number of individuals impacted by this perma-impact, n_i, to the total population, N. The population n_i can refer to various groups, such as your offspring, your fellow citizens, or, in the most general case, the global population. It represents the ability to spread your impact across humanity.

- w is a power of an action: $w_i = \dfrac{n_i^{next}}{n^{now}_i}$ of the number of people impacted by your action in the next cycle to the number of people affected by it now, or $w_i = \dfrac{n_i(t + 1)}{n_i(t)}$. w represents an internal ability of perma-impact to spread or wither with time. The cycle could be a year or a decade, but in the most general case, it is a generation. To estimate a new action, we may not need to wait for the next generation to be born and can approximate its effect by measuring over a shorter cycle, such as a year. However, we must wait for at least two cycles to have both the numerator and denominator to evaluate it.
- E is the expectation operation, or the predicted value of a utility, calculated as the sum of all possible future outcomes multiplied by the probability of each outcome. Essentially, this is our time passage operator. In classical calculus, it is merely a sum over all possible outcomes, but in the case of stochastic calculus, it becomes a stochastic integral.

Altogether, the meaning of life is the expected value of the asymptotic survival of all your perma-impacts, encompassing actions, ideas, and choices. This measure accounts for all your impacts, both positive and negative.

With this formula, we can express the quantity for the meaning of life as:

$$U = E\left[\sum p_i \cdot w_i\right].$$

The essence of this is that by maximizing this quantity, you maximize the permanent impact of your life on other people and the scope of your influence.

The sum of all of our impacts is represented by $\sum p_i \cdot w_i$, with p being the ratio of people affected by the actions we take and w indicating the rate at which our impact propagates. The expected value, $E\left[\sum p_i \cdot w_i\right]$, is a projection of this value into the distant future. This is what is meant by "asymptotic" value and "permanent" impact. The expected value operation considers all possible outcomes, weighs them with the probabilities of each outcome, and calculates an aggregate result. The more significant the impact we make with our actions and the longer they persist, the greater the meaning of our lives.

Notice that this formula differs from the Price formulation: $\sum p_i \cdot w_i$, due to the introduction of an expectation operator $E(E)$. By adding one term to the equation the entire meaning and the mechanics of evaluating the formula changes. By adding one letter to the equation, the entire meaning and mechanics of evaluating the formula are altered. In the classical formulation, the Price equation is essentially a tautology, with the left side being a rewritten form of the right side. It makes no assumptions, and as a result, it does not produce any verifiable predictions. In contrast, my formulation allows for deriving a logistic population growth equation from it, which the Price equation could not do.

The evaluation of the formula also changes, as we no longer can measure power just by counting the population change from one generation to the next. Now we have to keep counting every action in perpetuity. There are mathematical methods to do so, but I frankly lack prowess and the space here to fully engage those methods. I will say however that if we treat both power and frequencies as a random process the estimation changes from a regular calculus to a stochastic calculus. I will add quotations to papers that attempt to evaluate Price equations stochastically for those with a curious mind[121] (Rice, 2008).

Splitting the Formula into Personal and Humanity Parts

Our impacts on others begin as outcomes of our personal choices and actions, but as they spread, they become part of a larger population and contribute to a collective impact. We can account for this in the formula by dividing our impact into personal and common components.

To estimate your personal impact or meaning, we will separate the common perma-impacts into a distinct term, as follows:

$$U = U_{personal} + U_{common} = E\left[\sum_{personal_i=0}^{N_{personal}} p_i \cdot w_i\right] + E\left[\sum_{common_j=0}^{N_{common}} p_j \cdot w_j\right]$$

, where

- $N_{personal} + N_{common} = N_{tot}$

[121] bmcecolevol.biomedcentral.com/articles/10.1186/1471-2148-8-262

- $p_i = \dfrac{n_i}{N_{tot}}$ is a personal perma-impacts and usually $n_i = 1$, for most of the most of the personal actions, unless they started to spread and affect other people

- $p_j = \dfrac{n_j}{N_{tot}}$ are common perma-impacts terms, where $n_i >> 1$.

The difference between the "specific" and "common" terms is in the numerator, if $n_i >> 1$ then this perma-impact is a common one. The common part of the equation will persist or vanish through evolutionary and cultural dynamics that do not involve your life choices and exist beyond our control. In other words U_{common} is not dependent on our own actions.

We will redefine a personalized meaning as the maximization of the impact resulting from all consequences that we can influence and control through our personal decisions and actions, weighted by the impact on others projected into the distant future:

$$max(U_{person}) = max\left(E\left[\sum_{person l_i=0} p_i \cdot w_i\right]\right).$$

If our contributions outlast us and become part of society, and $U_{personal}$ will become U_{common} then the meaning of our life will be realized.

Expanding Our Formula to Mankind's Ecosystem

We established that without considering humanity's future, our personal meaning would disappear, i.e.

$$max\left(E\left[\sum_{person l_i=0} p_i \cdot w_i\right]\right) \to 0.$$

In our formula, we need to account for the contribution of all our actions to humanity's future. The aggregate of all our actions affects the future environment and will contribute to a decrease or increase in the population. We can create a new term to evaluate and summarize this contribution.

It is tempting to add this new term to the formula and expect it to contribute negatively to the overall value. However, when the population drops drastically, personal contributions will grow dramatically. This is because the total number of people who could be potentially affected by our actions becomes smaller, making it easier to affect a smaller number of people. In the formula, this is represented by the denominator growing smaller while the numerator stays more or less the same: $p_i = \dfrac{n_i}{N}$, with N decreasing, p_i increases. The contribution of such a decrease will be geometric and cannot be countered by a simple linear term, even with a significant negative contribution.

In other words, an ecological term needs to be multiplied by, not added to, the equation. This also follows from another consideration: each of our actions can have both positive and negative effects. At any given moment, we can have both positive and unexpected negative effects. We can address this by combining both effects into one: $w_j = w^{pos}_j + w_j^{neg}$. This works if the effects are instantaneous and do not last beyond the next cycle. If the effects are lasting and their relative positive and negative values change, we need to carry over their values into the next cycle. It is much more convenient to count the ecological effect as a multiplication factor: $w_j = w_j \cdot w^{eco}_j$.

The new ecological power term w_j is estimated differently. It is the ratio of the total number of people in the next cycle over the total number of people now: $w^{eco}_j = \dfrac{N(t+1)}{N(t)}$. If the total number of people increases as a result of our action, the reach is positive, and vice versa if the number decreases. It is still a relative power of our actions, but it is not only a function of our own actions but also a function of other people's actions. To aggregate all of the actions, we can no longer add all the terms, as this will break the normalization of the formula. We have to create a product of all our actions. In essence, this becomes a geometric mean:

$$W = w_i^{action} \cdot w_1^{eco} \cdot w_2^{eco} \cdot w_3^{eco} \ldots = w_i^{action} \prod_i w_k^{eco} \text{, where}$$

$w_i^{eco} = \prod_i w_k^{eco}$, is a product of all consequences for one action. It is a product because each action or perma-impact has multiple effects that need to be multiplied to aggregate all of their impact.

In our latest iteration the formula now looks like this:

$$U = (E\left[\sum_{i=0}^{N_{person}} p_i \cdot w_i^{person} \cdot \prod_i w_k^{eco}\right] + E\left[\sum_{j=0}^{N_{common}} p_j \cdot w_j^{common} \cdot \prod_j w_k^{eco}\right])$$

It consists of three parts: the part that is specific to a person, common to humanity and the ecological part.

Let us consider a special case of the entirety of humanity and see if we can gain a new insight from this new formulation.

In the context of the entirety of humanity, we will combine personal and common power terms into a single term:

$$\left[\sum_{i=0}^{N_{person}} p_i \cdot w_i^{person} \right] + E\left[\sum_{j=0}^{N_{common}} p_j \cdot w_j^{common} \right] = \left[\sum_{i=0}^{N} p_i \cdot w_i^{human} \right]$$

, where $w_i^{human} = w_i^{person} + w_i^{common}$.

We are left with two terms, common and ecological:

$$U_{humanity} = E[\sum_{j=0} p_j \cdot w_j^{human}] \cdot \prod_j E[w_l^{eco}]$$, where w_j^{common} is power

of one of the common to humanity traits and w^{eco}_j is an impact of any given common human trait on ecology.

The first common part is a sum over the entire population and the result

of a summation is an average humanity power: $E\left[\sum_{j=0} p_j \cdot w_j^{human} \right] = \bar{W}$,

where $\bar{W}$ is an average humankind power.

The ecological part may have several contributing factors, but there is one known factor that attributes to a share of resources an average human consumes over the course of his or her life. We can separate out other factors away from this capacity term: $w^{eco}_j = w_j^{capacity} \cdot w^{other}_j$:

$$U_{eco} = \prod_k E[(\sum_{l=0} p_l \cdot w_i \cdot w_l^{eco})] = \prod_k E[(\sum_{l=0} p_l \cdot w_l^{other})] \cdot E[(\sum_{l=0} p_l \cdot w_l^{capacity})]$$

, where $w_j^{capacity}$ is the effect that spare resources available in the environment have on the growth of the population within that environment. This effect is attributed to each member of the population and not to an action. We will estimate its value as the ratio of currently available resources to the total maximum resource value:

$$w_j^{capacity} = \frac{S_{available}}{S_{max}} = \frac{S_{max} - S_{used}}{S_{mas}}$$, where S_{max} are total resources

available to a person within conditions of the current civilization and S_{used} are resources that are already being consumed by the individual.

The amount of resources should be proportional to the population size, as each individual takes approximately the same amount of resources within a given societal and technological regime. Technological revolutions can change maximum resource capacity, S_{max}, but in between they remain constant. That means that maximum and taken capacity can be considered constant and will not change under expectation operator:

$$E[\frac{S_{max} - S_{used}}{S_{mas}}] = \frac{S_{max} - S_{used}}{S_{mas}} = 1 - \frac{S_{used}}{S_{max}}.$$

Then we have the following terms:

$$U_{humanity} = E\left[\sum_{j=0} p_j \cdot w_j{}^{human} \cdot \prod_k E[w_l{}^{other}] \cdot E[w_l{}^{capacity}] \right] =$$

$$\bar{W} \cdot (\prod_k E[(\sum_{l=0} p_l \cdot w_l{}^{other}) \cdot \sum_{l=0} p_l(1 - \frac{S_{used}}{S_{max}}) = \bar{W} \cdot \bar{F} \cdot N(1 - \frac{S_{used}}{S_{max}}),$$

where $\bar{W}$ is an average humankind power, $\bar{F} = (\prod_k E[(\sum_{l=0} p_l \cdot w_l{}^{other})$ is an average environmental scale factor.

The average power is the rate of humanity's growth, multiplied by a scale factor, $\bar{F}$, it will amount to a scaled rate of humanity's growth, r'.

The resource factors, S_{used} and S_{max} are linearly dependent on the number of consumers of those resources. The bigger the population, the bigger amount of resources is used:

$$S_{used} = \beta \cdot N, S_{max} = \beta \cdot N_{max} \text{ and } (1 - \frac{S_{used}}{S_{max}}) = 1 - \frac{N}{N_{max}}.$$

This leads to

$$U_{humanity} = r' \cdot N \cdot (1 - \frac{N}{N_{max}}),$$

which is a logistic population growth equation.

The Price equation has not previously resulted in the derivation of heuristic formulas. The fact that we have achieved this with our equation, using a minimal number of assumptions, only strengthens our confidence in its validity.

The implications of the logistic growth equation reveal that the maximum population size is constrained by a carrying capacity. As humanity approaches this maximum, its growth rate slows down.

Recipe to Survive Extinction Events

Genes serve as records of successful solutions that organisms have discovered through trial and error in response to extinction events and processes in the past. Any environmental change could potentially lead to extinction. Considering the successful history of evolution, one might wonder why there isn't a single organism that encompasses all the best solutions. After all, Homo sapiens is the one species that has made it this far. Why isn't there a similar phenomenon in nature where only apex organisms outcompete the rest? Similarly, what is the ideal social system? Should we have one political and economic system that incorporates the best practices and lessons learned from human history, or should we have many diverse political systems, including autocratic and tyrannical governments?

These questions relate to a broader inquiry we've been asking for centuries: How much bio- or socio-diversity should exist in nature and society, and what are the driving factors behind it? To optimize decision-making for all of humanity, what is the right balance of authority and freedom of choice? What should the appropriate level of taxation be: a large uniform tax typical of socialist societies or low taxes characteristic of capitalist systems? Should insects congregate in swarms or be solitary? Should there be multicellular organisms or single-celled ones? Despite years of exploration, we have yet to arrive at a single solution.

To address these questions, let's examine the approach of biological and societal structures and information processing systems with the goal of avoiding extinction. For simplicity, let's assume that extinction events come in two types:

1. Environmental changes that cause all organisms without a specific trait to go extinct
2. Environmental changes that cause all organisms with a specific trait to go extinct

In this context, I'll use the term "trait" interchangeably with gene and impact.

A single trait can have both positive and negative effects, providing an advantage in one environment while causing a significant disadvantage in another. For example, an organism's physical size may provide an advantage in competing for resources and fending off predators, but it was a major disadvantage during the Chicxulub impact event that led to the extinction of large land-based dinosaurs and other large animals about 66 million years ago. Only smaller dinosaurs (e.g., chickens) and smaller animals that could find shelter or burrow underground survived. The question, then, is what the optimal distribution of genes responsible for various traits within species should be and what the ideal number of species should be to maximize survival rates for both types of extinction events.

Type 2 events occur less frequently throughout the history of living organisms but are very abrupt. Examples include mega-volcano eruptions, asteroid impacts, and explosions in the number of species that change the environment. In the past 500 million years, there have been about five major extinction events that resulted in more than 50% of life disappearing, meaning type 2 events happen roughly every 100 million years. The last such event, the Chicxulub impact, occurred less than 100 million years ago, so we are overdue for the next extinction.

Type 1 events occur more frequently but are gradual in nature and have a smaller magnitude, allowing living organisms to adapt through mutation and natural selection. Natural selection is the process of entire species dying because of type 1 environmental changes. Surviving species continue to mutate until they find a solution that halts extinction, and this solution is coded into DNA as a gene that makes the species fit for the environment.

The optimal decision for centralization versus agency is to maximize the utility value according to the formula, which maximizes the number of contributing impacts. In this context, we use our formula as the probability of survival of an expanded definition of life, where the survival of a single trait constitutes the survival of "life." Traits are divided into two parts: common and specific. Common traits are traits that are grouped together and shared with other species, forming larger groups of "genus" and "family"[122] (Taxonomy (Biology), n.d.) and specific traits are the ones that are not shared with any other species. Those could be new mutations or unique traits for the particular species. Each trait, represented by index i or j, can be a potential solution to the future extinction events:

$$U_{species} = (E\left[\sum_{i=0}^{N_{specific}} p_i \cdot w_i{}^{specific}\right] + E\left[\sum_{j=0}^{N_{common}} p_j \cdot w_j{}^{common}\right]) \cdot \prod_k E[(\sum_{l=0}^{} p_l \cdot w_l{}^{eco})$$

or more simply:

$$U_{species} = (U_{specific} + U_{common}) \cdot P_2{}^{cataclysm} \cdot P_1$$

With the type 1 and 2 extinction events the ecological part of equation, $w_l{}^{eco}$, has values:

1. $w_l{}^{eco} = 0$, for all groups and species with certain gene missing from the common part, or when $l \notin \{j \mid common\ set\}$, which corresponds to slow environmental change

2. $w_l{}^{eco} = 0$, for all groups and species with certain gene belongs to the common part, or when $l \subset \{j \mid common\ set\}$, which corresponds to abrupt environment change, i.e. extinction event

Let us consider what happens after cataclysm, or the order of occurrence is type 2 followed by type 1 events. This is what would happen immediately after a cataclysmic event, where a few species that survived the extinction will still need to survive through regular environmental changes right after.

Let us assume that there is a limited set of all the possible genes that correspond to all the possible traits, where M is the total number of different genes in the set. Let us also assume that in that set there is at least one trait that solves each and every type 1 environment changes.

---

[122] https://en.wikipedia.org/wiki/Taxonomy_(biology)

Consider two extreme configurations:
   A) In one, we will have one mega-successful species that collected all of the successful traits to survive type 1 environmental changes.
   B) In another, we will have billions of the simplest organisms each containing just one trait.

Let us consider what would happen to those configurations after a type 2 cataclysmic event happens followed by a series of type 1 events. The survival probability for that scenario can be written as:

$$U_{species} \cdot P_2^{\,cataclysm} \cdot \prod P_1.$$

Right after the type 2 event, the, A) species will not survive type 2, as type 2 will target a random trait i, and species A will have all the traits, as a result type 2 will target species A) everywhere, P_2 will be zero and the species A) will perish as a result. The whole life will also cease to exist because in that scenario life only comprised A) species. This is why there is such biodiversity on Earth, in the early days of evolution the extinction events of massive magnitude were happening more frequently due to the formation of the Earth and life was not as diverse or as numerous, so the magnitude did not have to be large to wipe out species.

On the opposite extreme, right after a type 2 event, only one species with an unfortunate trait will perish and the rest will survive. However, right after that event, most of the species will not survive the next, and more, gradual environmental change, as they have a very short portfolio of traits. Type 1 events will wipe out all but one species and the next type 1 event will wipe out the remaining species. This is why we do not see super simple organisms that frequently, with the exception of viruses. Even viruses survive only because other, more complex organisms exist and at the cost of having very high mutation rates and losing some of their cellular structure.

Intuitively a solution should be somewhere in the middle between A) and B), but after a more careful consideration, we could always find a suboptimal configuration between A and B that would lead to total extinction. For instance, if a common part is missing a lot of genes, the subsequent type 1 events could target traits that were missing from the common part, leading to all the species being wiped out.

The best solution is to have complex organisms with the common part that contains all the genes but one that will be specific to that species:

$$\sum_{j\neq k} p_j \cdot w_j^{common} + p_k \cdot w_k \,.$$ In this configuration there will be as many species as there are different genes. Let us ignore for the moment capacity considerations, i.e., whether the planet can support so many different species.

Let's consider how the occurrence of type 2 events followed by a series of type 1 events will affect this new configuration. Type 2 will wipe out all the species but the one that is missing the targeted trait. This surviving species will survive subsequent type 1 events with the probability $\dfrac{M-1}{M}$, where M is the total number of genes. The higher the number of genes the more the probability approaches 1. This is the best we can do.

This could explain the biodiversity that exists on Earth. A diverse range of species helps to ensure that ecosystems can withstand disturbances such as climate change, invasive species, and natural disasters. It allows for greater adaptability to changing environmental conditions. But most importantly it assures the survival of all of life on Earth.

In societal structures, there are also type 2 and type 1 changes in the ecological and geopolitical environments. Overpopulation, world wars and natural cataclysms happen rarely and abruptly, and political, economic changes and regional wars happen steadily throughout human history.

Societal diversity provides the same benefits to protect against massive political or economical upheavals.

Our solution to type 2 and type 1 brings out an unexpected conclusion to social structures: the most stable systems are not having one successful world government, but having as many governments as there are political structures. Having democracy as a world system may not be beneficial for human society stability and survival. The fact that the number of different kinds of governments currently can be counted on the fingers of both hands is concerning. The good news is that the types of government have increased from mostly feudal monarchies to several different types: monarchy, theocracy, dictatorships, socialism, capitalism-democracy and crony capitalism.

Diverse social structures are the key to mankind's wellbeing, but those structures need to be carefully balanced in order to maximize the odds of our civilization's survival.

Thoughts on the Origins of Evolution in a Fine-Tuned Universe

Evolution is a compelling mechanism that enables living organisms to adapt to changes in their environment. The concept of evolution is so powerful that it is tempting to explore its potential applications outside of the realm of living organisms. The process of evolution involves countless iterations resulting in gradual improvements in fitness, leading to adaptations that fit the environment almost perfectly. Examples of this can be seen in the remarkable ability of some animals and insects to camouflage themselves with their surroundings, the design of animal eyes, bird wings that enable flight, and even the elongated neck of the giraffe that allows it to reach vegetation other animals cannot.

Despite their appearance of intelligent design, these adaptations have evolved through a series of small, incremental steps, each providing an advantage over the previous generation. For instance, the gradual evolution and improvement of eye design can be observed from light-sensitive proteins in single-celled organisms to the complex eye structures of species such as the Nautilus.

Evolution not only enables species to adapt to their environment but also to each other's presence, leading to the development of symbiotic relationships between different species. These relationships evolve over time as species adapt to their environment and each other, resulting in mutually beneficial outcomes that promote equilibrium. The continued evolution of each species in response to the other leads to increasingly specialized and intertwined relationships. If one organism is removed from the relationship, it can create deleterious effects on the other. Examples of symbiotic relationships include lichen, which is a mutualistic relationship between a fungus and a photosynthetic partner, usually algae or cyanobacteria.

The delicate balance between biotic and abiotic factors in ecosystems highlights the importance of maintaining equilibrium to ensure the health and resilience of ecosystems and the species that inhabit them. Even minor disturbances can lead to significant alterations in the system's overall stability, underscoring the fragility of equilibrium in nature. Ecosystems on this planet are precisely balanced to allow for the existence of complex living organisms.

Our universe is another system that is precisely balanced to permit the existence of complex structures. The concept of a fine-tuned universe[123] (Fine-Tuned Universe, n.d.) suggests that the fundamental constants and laws of physics are perfectly "tuned" to allow for the emergence of galaxies, stars, planets, and life itself. If any of the certain free parameters in contemporary physical theories had varied even slightly from those observed, the evolution of the universe would have proceeded very differently, and life as we know it may not have been possible. This fine-tuning is often viewed as an argument for the existence of intelligent design, similar to the arguments used against evolution. Another explanation is the possibility of a multiverse, where our universe is just one of many with different physical properties.

However, the idea that the mechanisms that explain the sensitive equilibrium on Earth may also explain the equilibrium in the universe seems more appealing to me. While the mechanisms of biological evolution do not apply directly to the laws of physics, the concept of "cosmological evolution" or evolving laws of physics is a separate idea in the realm of theoretical physics and cosmology. The idea of evolving laws of physics suggests that the fundamental constants and laws we observe in our universe might have emerged through some form of selection process. In this context, it is

---

[123] en.wikipedia.org/wiki/Fine-tuned_universe

possible that the laws of physics and the fine-tuned universe are the result of a cosmic evolutionary process. Some theories propose that our universe is part of a vast multiverse, where different regions have different physical properties. In this scenario, our universe could be one of many that have a specific set of constants and laws that allow for the emergence of complex structures and eventually life.

Personally, I find the proposition that the laws of physics went through multiple iterations of gradual improvements much more attractive. Cosmologists do not know what happened at the moment of the Big Bang[124] (Big Bang - Simple English Wikipedia, the Free Encyclopedia, n.d.), which marked the beginning of space and time as we know them. The earliest known period of the universe is called the Planck epoch[125] (Planck Epoch - Simple English Wikipedia, the Free Encyclopedia, n.d.), which lasted from the moment of the Big Bang approximately 13.8 billion years ago until about 10^{-43} seconds (also known as the Planck time) after the event. During the Planck epoch, the universe was incredibly hot and dense, with temperatures and energy levels so extreme that the laws of physics we currently understand (including general relativity and quantum field theory) did not apply. At these energy scales, all four fundamental forces of nature – gravity, electromagnetism, and the strong and weak nuclear forces – were believed to be unified into a single force.

During the Planck epoch, there could have been an enormous number of iterations and cycles where the laws of physics were shaping up and interacting with each other, similar to how living organisms interacted with each other during the formation of life on Earth. These interactions eventually created a precisely balanced equilibrium that allows for the existence of stable and complex structures. Even small changes to the values of certain constants or the laws of physics could result in a radically different and even unstable universe. As Stephen Hawking noted, "The laws of science, as we know them at present, contain many fundamental numbers, like the size of the electric charge of the electron and the ratio of the masses of the proton and the electron...The remarkable fact is that the values of these numbers seem to have been very finely adjusted to make possible the development of life"[126] (Hawking, 1988).

Fundamental constants such as the gravitational constant, nuclear force, and cosmological constant play crucial roles in shaping the universe as we know it. The strength of gravity is essential for the formation of stars and galaxies, and the strong nuclear force is responsible for holding atomic nuclei together. Finally, the cosmological constant represents the energy density of

---

[124] simple.wikipedia.org/wiki/Big_Bang

[125] simple.wikipedia.org/wiki/Planck_epoch

[126] en.wikipedia.org/wiki/A_Brief_History_of_Time

the vacuum or empty space and is associated with the acceleration of the universe's expansion.

It is suspected that the instability in the balance of the fundamental forces and their strength showed up much earlier in the universe, and the most unstable combinations fell apart, giving space to a more stable force that eventually gave rise to the universe we observe now. Although there is no experimental evidence of such evolution, we know that the fundamental laws of nature looked very different in the first moment of the Big Bang, and there were a lot of interactions between those fields due to the energy density and because the universe was expanding, the structures were cooling rapidly and undergoing rapid phase transitions. This process could also explain why the laws of physics are now invariant or exhibit the same properties irrespective of location or orientation. The most stable fundamental forces replicated across the universe via interaction, and the rest decayed, leading to the formation of a stable and balanced universe.

This exciting possibility would make evolution a fundamental force of nature, rather than an exceptional phenomenon on one planet. It would imply that the process of gradual improvement through small incremental steps leading to stability and balance is not just limited to living organisms on Earth but extends to the entire universe. The instability in the balance of the fundamental forces and their strength that showed up much earlier in the universe could have led to the decay of the most unstable combinations, giving space to a more stable force that eventually gave rise to the universe we observe now.

Although there is no experimental evidence of such evolution, it is known that the fundamental laws of nature looked very different in the first moment of the Big Bang. The universe was in a state of extreme energy density, and the laws of physics as we currently understand them did not apply. Due to the rapid expansion of the universe, the structures were cooling rapidly and undergoing rapid phase transitions, leading to the emergence of new stable forces.

This process of rapid phase transitions and the emergence of new stable forces in combination with cosmological inflation[127] (Liddle, n.d.) could explain why the laws of physics are now invariant or exhibit the same properties irrespective of location or orientation. The most stable fundamental forces replicated across the universe via interaction, and the rest decayed. This process followed by the inflation of the space filled with stabilized forces lead to the formation of a stable and balanced universe.

If evolution is a fundamental force of nature, it would suggest that the process of gradual improvement leading to stability and balance is an inherent property of the universe itself. This would have profound implications for our understanding of the universe and our place within it, and it would highlight the interconnectedness and interdependence of all things in the

---

[127] en.wikipedia.org/wiki/Inflation_(cosmology)

universe. It would make evolution not just a biological phenomenon on one planet but a fundamental aspect of the universe itself, shaping the evolution of galaxies, stars, and planets, and ultimately leading to the emergence of complex structures and life.

Guided Meditation Poem

As a result of visiting various places of worship, I developed a deep appreciation for rituals, habits, and particularly meditation practices. On one occasion, a friend invited me to a Buddhist temple, which inspired me to create my own meditation. My intention was to practice it every night, examining my actions and decisions throughout the day, assessing their harmony with my objectives, and focusing my thoughts on accomplishing those objectives and pondering humanity's future. Through numerous repetitions and refinements, this meditation transformed into a poem that I would like to present below.

Find a quiet space, free from distraction,
Sit or lie down, embrace relaxation,
Close your eyes, back straight and at ease,
Arms and legs poised, feeling the peace.
 (1 minute of focused breathing)
Breathe in deeply, hold it awhile,
Exhale slowly, releasing your doubts,
Focus your mind on each breath you take,
Feeling the air, embracing the break.
 (1 minute of focused breathing)
Stay with your breath, let it ground you in place,
No other thoughts, just this moment and space,
If your mind wanders, bring it back, be kind,
To the sensation of breath, letting the mind unwind.
 (1 minute of focused breathing)
Breathing lightly, scan your body with care,
Relaxing the tension, releasing despair,
As peace enters your mind, focus on tranquility,
With each breath you take, embrace serenity.
 (2 minutes of focused breathing)
Now delve deeper, into your core,
Finding wisdom, an inner rapport,
Connected to life, an unbroken chain,
Realize your purpose, humanity's gain.
 (1 minute of focused breathing)
Envision your core expanding its reach,
Connecting with loved ones, like a celestial bridge,

Sharing actions, ideas, knowledge, and grace,
A profound difference, the world to embrace.
  (1 minute of focused breathing)
With each breath, feel your circle grow,
A vast network of people, a luminous glow,
As you inhale, draw in their dreams,
Exhale your support, as the energy streams.
  (1 minute of focused breathing)
Let your impact expand, encompassing all,
Communities, cities, humanity's call,
Breathe in their aspirations, exhale your intent,
Positive energy shared, a world of content.
  (1 minute of focused breathing)
Imagine yourself guarding the human circle,
Responsible and caring, the world to nurture,
Consider the actions needed to protect and serve,
A peaceful, formidable future, for all to observe.
  (1 minute of focused breathing)
Lastly, in stillness, let silence unfold,
Remember the thoughts, the feelings you hold,
And when you are ready, open your eyes,
Embrace your next step, towards human ties.

References and resources

References:

О, если ты спокоен... (2011, December 22). YouTube. Retrieved March 25, 2023, from https://www.youtube.com/watch?v=WQS2QK8-vBU

Abt, H. A. (1996). What Fraction of Papers in Astronomy and Physics Are Not Cited in 40 Years? *Publications of the Astronomical Society of the Pacific, 139*, 989. 10.1088/1538-3873/aac692

Annaud, J.-J. (Director). (2001). *Enemy At The Gates* [Film]. imdb. https://www.imdb.com/title/tt0215750/

Asimov, I. (1991). *I, Robot*. Random House Worlds. https://en.wikipedia.org/wiki/Laws_of_robotics

Barchas-Lichtenstein, J. (2020, October 28). Finding relevance in the news: The scale of self-reference. *National Center for Biotechnology Information, 49*(61), 171. 10.1016/j.pragma.2020.10.001 and *Journal of Pragmatics, 171*, 49-61. https://www.ncbi.nlm.nih.gov/pmc/articles/PMC7665069/

Barro, R. J. (1996). Determinants of Economic Growth: A Cross-Country Empirical Study. *NATIONAL BUREAU OF ECONOMIC RESEARCH, 5698*. 10.3386/w5698

Baumeister, R. F., & Leary, M. R. (1995). The need to belong: Desire for interpersonal attachments as a fundamental human motivation. *American Psychological Association, 117*(3), 497–529. 10.1037/0033-2909.117.3.497

Benoit, K. (n.d.). *On Causality*. Ken Benoit. Retrieved March 25, 2023, from https://kenbenoit.net/on-causality/

Big Bang - Simple English Wikipedia, the free encyclopedia. (n.d.). Simple Wikipedia. Retrieved April 10, 2023, from https://simple.wikipedia.org/wiki/Big_Bang

Bird, K., Sherwin, M. J., Groueff, S., & Bradbury, N. (n.d.). *J. Robert Oppenheimer*. Wikipedia. Retrieved March 25, 2023, from https://en.wikipedia.org/wiki/J._Robert_Oppenheimer

Bugel, L. (2000). *NuTeV Experiment Tour*. Rochester University. https://www.pas.rochester.edu/~ksmcf/NuTeV/bugel/tour.html

Burns, E., & Brush, K. (n.d.). *What is Deep Learning and How Does It Work?* TechTarget. Retrieved March 25, 2023, from https://www.techtarget.com/searchenterpriseai/definition/deep-learning-deep-neural-network

Buterin, V. (n.d.). *A NEXT GENERATION SMART CONTRACT & DECENTRALIZED APPLICATION PLATFORM*. Blockchain Lab. Retrieved April 9, 2023, from https://www.the-blockchain.com/docs/Ethereum_white_paper-a_next_generation_smart_contract_and_decentralized_application_platform-vitalik-buterin.pdf

Carter, J. (2019, April 11). In Photos: This Is What We Will Look Like In 5.5 Billion Years When The Sun Is Dying. *In Photos: This Is What We Will Look Like In 5.5 Billion Years When The Sun Is Dying*. https://www.forbes.com/sites/jamiecartereurope/2021/01/22/in-photos-this-is-what-we-will-look-like-in-55-billion-years-when-the-sun-is-dying/?sh=3780c94863c3

Castaneda, C. (1968). *The teachings of Don Juan; a Yaqui way of knowledge*. Washington Square Press. https://en.wikipedia.org/wiki/The_Teachings_of_Don_Juan

Catholic Church and same-sex marriage. (n.d.). Wikipedia. Retrieved March 25, 2023, from https://en.wikipedia.org/wiki/ Catholic_Church_and_same-sex_marriage

CHINA AND ROME: HOW DO THEY COMPARE? (n.d.). Houston ISD. Retrieved April 9, 2023, from https://www.houstonisd.org/cms/lib2/ TX01001591/Centricity/Domain/20935/ Comparison%20of%20Rome%20and%20Han.pdf

Collapse of Silicon Valley Bank. (n.d.). Wikipedia. Retrieved March 25, 2023, from https://en.wikipedia.org/wiki/ Collapse_of_Silicon_Valley_Bank

Collective decision-making in honey bees: how colonies choose among nectar sources. (n.d.). University of Sussex. Retrieved April 9, 2023, from http://users.sussex.ac.uk/~ezequiel/iam/Seeley_91.pdf

Cross section, Flux, Luminosity, Scattering Rates. (2013, September 9). UF Physics. Retrieved April 2, 2023, from http://www.phys.ufl.edu/ ~avery/course/4390/f2015/lectures/cross_section_flux.pdf

Dawkins, R., DAWKINS, R. A., Dawkins, C. S. P. o. t. P. U. o. S. R., & Dawkins, D. (1989). *The selfish gene*. Oxford University Press. https://en.wikipedia.org/wiki/The_Selfish_Gene and https:// www.amazon.com/Selfish-Gene-Popular-Science/dp/0192860925

Decentralized Court : r/ethereum. (2016, April 26). Reddit. Retrieved March 25, 2023, from https://www.reddit.com/r/ethereum/comments/ 4gigyd/decentralized_court/

Determinism. (n.d.). Wikipedia. Retrieved March 28, 2023, from https:// en.wikipedia.org/wiki/Determinism

Dunbar's number. (n.d.). Wikipedia. Retrieved March 25, 2023, from https://en.wikipedia.org/wiki/Dunbar%27s_number

Dürer, A. (n.d.). *Faith*. New World Encyclopedia. Retrieved March 25,
2023, from https://www.newworldencyclopedia.org/entry/Faith

Einstein, A. (n.d.). *Quote by Albert Einstein: "The world will not be
destroyed by those who do..."* Goodreads. Retrieved March 25, 2023,
from https://www.goodreads.com/quotes/8144295-the-world-will-not-
be-destroyed-by-those-who-do

Ellwood, A. (2012, August 22). The Dream Team: Hipster, Hacker, and
Hustler. *Forbes*. https://www.forbes.com/sites/andyellwood/
2012/08/22/the-dream-team-hipster-hacker-and-hustler/?
sh=435dea892c85

Expected value. (n.d.). Wikipedia. Retrieved March 25, 2023, from https://
en.wikipedia.org/wiki/Expected_value

Extance, A. (2020, June 22). The First Gene on Earth May Have Been a
Hybrid. *Scientific American*. Retrieved March 25, 2023, from https://
www.scientificamerican.com/article/the-first-gene-on-earth-may-have-
been-a-hybrid/

Fine-tuned universe. (n.d.). Wikipedia. Retrieved April 10, 2023, from
https://en.wikipedia.org/wiki/Fine-tuned_universe

Fridbergas, I. (Director). (1987). *Dorogoy Edison* [Film]. Ekran. Retrieved
March 25, 2023, from https://www.imdb.com/title/tt0090957/

Fritz Haber. (n.d.). Wikipedia. Retrieved March 25, 2023, from https://
en.wikipedia.org/wiki/Fritz_Haber

The Functionalist Perspective on Religion | Boundless Sociology |. (n.d.).
Course Hero. Retrieved March 25, 2023, from https://
courses.lumenlearning.com/boundless-sociology/chapter/the-
functionalist-perspective-on-religion/

Gervais, R. (2013, June 11). *Ricky Gervais on Twitter: "You did not exist for about 14 billion years. You exist now & when you die you will not exist again. Forever. Enjoy your existing years :)"*. Twitter. Retrieved March 25, 2023, from https://twitter.com/rickygervais/status/344426405897072640?lang=en

Gladwell, M. (2011). *Outliers: The Story of Success*. Little, Brown and Co. 10.1080/15210960903028818

Gödel's incompleteness theorems. (n.d.). Wikipedia. Retrieved March 25, 2023, from https://en.m.wikipedia.org/wiki/G%C3%B6del%27s_incompleteness_theorems

God is dead quote Friedrich Nietzsche Parable of the Madman. (n.d.). Age of the Sage. Retrieved March 25, 2023, from https://www.age-of-the-sage.org/philosophy/friedrich_nietzsche_quotes.html

Gowaty, P. A. (n.d.). *Sexual reproduction*. Wikipedia. Retrieved March 25, 2023, from https://en.wikipedia.org/wiki/Sexual_reproduction

Greene, B. (2010). *The Elegant Universe: Superstrings, Hidden Dimensions, and the Quest for the Ultimate Theory*. W. W. Norton. https://en.wikipedia.org/wiki/The_Elegant_Universe

Hanushek, E. A. (2013). Economic growth in developing countries: The role of human capital. *Economic growth in developing countries: The role of human capital.*, 37, 204-212. 10.1016

Harari, Y. N. (2015). *Sapiens: A Brief History of Humankind* (Y. N. Harari, J. Purcell, & H. Watzman, Trans.). HarperCollins. https://en.wikipedia.org/wiki/Sapiens:_A_Brief_History_of_Humankind

Harari, Y. N. (2017). *Homo Deus: A Brief History of Tomorrow* (Y. N. Harari, Trans.). HarperCollins. https://en.wikipedia.org/wiki/Homo_Deus:_A_Brief_History_of_Tomorrow

Harris, S. (n.d.). *New Atheism*. Wikipedia. Retrieved March 25, 2023, from https://en.wikipedia.org/wiki/New_Atheism

Hawking, S. (1988). *A brief history of time : from the big bang to black holes*. Bantam Books. doi.org/10.1007/BF01074212

Hawkins, J. (2019, January 16). *The Thousand Brains Theory of Intelligence*. Numenta. Retrieved March 25, 2023, from https://numenta.com/blog/2019/01/16/the-thousand-brains-theory-of-intelligence/

Health, J. R. (n.d.). The Role of Meaning in Life Within the Relations of Religious Coping and Psychological Well-Being. *The Role of Meaning in Life Within the Relations of Religious Coping and Psychological Well-Being*. https://www.ncbi.nlm.nih.gov/pmc/articles/PMC4580713

Hesse, H. (December 6, 2002). *Magister Ludi : the glass bead game*. Picador. https://en.wikipedia.org/wiki/The_Glass_Bead_Game

History of penicillin. (n.d.). Wikipedia. Retrieved March 25, 2023, from https://en.wikipedia.org/wiki/History_of_penicillin#The_breakthrough_discovery

Holodomor. (n.d.). Wikipedia. Retrieved June 15, 2023, from https://en.wikipedia.org/wiki/Holodomor

How Popular Is Chess? (2020, March 9). Chess.com. Retrieved March 25, 2023, from https://www.chess.com/news/view/how-popular-is-chess-8306

Howson, C. (2003). *Hume's Problem: Induction and the Justification of Belief*. Clarendon Press. https://en.wikipedia.org/wiki/Problem_of_induction#:~:text=First%20formulated%20by%20David%20Hume,things%20based%20on%20previous%20observations

Hutchinson, B. (n.d.). *Meet the Walking Shark*. Oceanic Society.
Retrieved March 25, 2023, from https://www.oceanicsociety.org/
resources/ocean-facts/the-shark-that-can-walk-on-land/

Kaplan, H. S., & Robson, A. J. (2002). The emergence of humans: The
coevolution of intelligence and longevity with intergenerational
transfers. *The Proceedings of the National Academy of Sciences*,
99(15), 10221-10226. 10.1073/pnas.15250289

Kaufmann, W. (n.d.). *Nihilism*. Wikipedia. Retrieved March 25, 2023, from
https://en.wikipedia.org/wiki/Nihilism

Kipling, R. (1910). *Rewards and Fairies/If—*. Wikisource. https://
en.wikisource.org/wiki/Rewards_and_Fairies/If%E2%80%94

Kramer, K. L. (2005). Children's Help and the Pace of Reproduction:
Cooperative Breeding in Humans. *Evolutionary Antropology*, *14*(6),
224-237. 10.1002/evan.20082

Kroker, M. B. (2014). The "Great Divergence" Redefined: the Rise and
Fall of the West and the Recovery of China. *Inquiries Journal*, *6*(9),
3/3. Retrieved April 9, 2023, from http://www.inquiriesjournal.com/
articles/917/3/the-great-divergence-redefined-the-rise-and-fall-of-the-
west-and-the-recovery-of-china

Lagrangian mechanics. (n.d.). Wikipedia. Retrieved March 27, 2023, from
https://en.wikipedia.org/wiki/Lagrangian_mechanics

Lanting, F. (2022, May 19). *Biodiversity*. National Geographic Society.
Retrieved March 25, 2023, from https://
education.nationalgeographic.org/resource/biodiversity

Laws of robotics. (n.d.). Wikipedia. Retrieved March 25, 2023, from
https://en.wikipedia.org/wiki/Laws_of_robotics

Liddle, A. (n.d.). *Inflation (cosmology)*. Wikipedia. Retrieved March 25,

2023, from https://en.wikipedia.org/wiki/Inflation_(cosmology)

Life Definition & Meaning. (2023, March 8). Merriam-Webster. Retrieved

March 26, 2023, from https://www.merriam-webster.com/dictionary/

life

LIGO Hanford Observatory. (2016, February 11). *News | Gravitational

Waves Detected 100 Years After Einstein's Prediction | LIGO Lab |

Caltech*. LIGO Caltech. Retrieved March 25, 2023, from https://

www.ligo.caltech.edu/news/ligo20160211

Lipman, M. (2013, March 26). *Boris Berezovsky: An Oligarch Dies*. The

New Yorker. Retrieved April 1, 2023, from https://

www.newyorker.com/news/news-desk/boris-berezovsky-an-oligarch-

dies

List of religions and spiritual traditions. (n.d.). Wikipedia. Retrieved March

25, 2023, from https://en.wikipedia.org/wiki/

List_of_religions_and_spiritual_traditions

Martínez, A. A. (2018, March 19). *Was Giordano Bruno Burned at the

Stake for Believing in Exoplanets?* Scientific American Blogs.

Retrieved March 25, 2023, from https://blogs.scientificamerican.com/

observations/was-giordano-bruno-burned-at-the-stake-for-believing-

in-exoplanets/

Martorano, J. (2019, April 30). Nietzsche and the Meaning of Life |

Yorktown, NY News TAPinto. *TAPinto*. https://www.tapinto.net/towns/

yorktown/articles/nietzsche-and-the-meaning-of-life

McDONALD, J., & WU, H. (2021, April 10). Top Chinese official admits

vaccines have low effectiveness. *AP News*. https://apnews.com/

article/china-gao-fu-vaccines-offer-low-protection-coronavirus-675bcb6b5710c7329823148ffbff6ef9

Meme. (n.d.). Wikipedia. Retrieved March 25, 2023, from https://en.wikipedia.org/wiki/Meme

Michelson–Morley experiment. (n.d.). Wikipedia. Retrieved April 5, 2023, from https://en.wikipedia.org/wiki/Michelson%E2%80%93Morley_experiment

Miller, G. (2017, November 20). Why Ancient Mapmakers Were Terrified of Blank Spaces. National Geographic. Retrieved March 25, 2023, from https://www.nationalgeographic.com/history/article/maps-history-horror-vacui-art-cartography-blank-spaces

Monte Carlo method. (n.d.). Wikipedia. Retrieved March 25, 2023, from https://en.wikipedia.org/wiki/Monte_Carlo_method

Mountcastle, V. (1978). An Organizing Principle for Cerebral Function The Unit Model and the Distributed System. Cambridge, MA — MIT Press, 7-50. http://nicorg.pbworks.com/w/file/fetch/49365852/Mountcastle%20Organizing%20Principle.pdf

Murphy, S. C., von Hippel, W., & Barlow, F. K. (n.d.). https://journals.sagepub.com/doi/abs/10.1177/0146167215588754

Musk, E. (n.d.). Neuralink. Wikipedia. Retrieved March 25, 2023, from https://en.wikipedia.org/wiki/Neuralink

Mutation as a Stress Response and the Regulation of Evolvability. (n.d.). NCBI. Retrieved March 25, 2023, from https://www.ncbi.nlm.nih.gov/pmc/articles/PMC3319127/

Nadler, S., & Mignini, F. (n.d.). Baruch Spinoza. Wikipedia. Retrieved March 25, 2023, from https://en.wikipedia.org/wiki/Baruch_Spinoza

Newton's law of universal gravitation. (n.d.). Wikipedia. Retrieved March 25, 2023, from https://en.wikipedia.org/wiki/ Newton%27s_law_of_universal_gravitation

Nietzsche, F. (n.d.). *Quote by Friedrich Nietzsche: "I cannot believe in a God who wants to be prais..."* Goodreads. Retrieved March 25, 2023, from https://www.goodreads.com/quotes/34567-i-cannot-believe-in-a-god-who-wants-to-be

Nietzsche, F. (2021). *God Is Dead. God Remains Dead. And We Have Killed Him.* (M. A. Scarpitti & R. K. Hill, Trans.). Penguin Publishing Group. https://en.wikipedia.org/wiki/God_is_dead

On Causality. (n.d.). Ken Benoit. Retrieved March 28, 2023, from https:// kenbenoit.net/on-causality/

Page, A. E., & French, J. C. (2020). Reconstructing prehistoric demography: What role for extant hunter-gatherers? *Evolutionary Anthropology*, 22(6), 1-10. 10.1002/evan.21869

Peale, N. V. (2019, April 11). *Think outside the box*. Think outside the box. Retrieved March 25, 2023, from https://newspaperarchive.com/ chicago-tribune-oct-25-1969-p-13-335162371-fullpage.jpg/

Perov, V. (n.d.). *Meaning of life*. New World Encyclopedia. Retrieved March 25, 2023, from https://www.newworldencyclopedia.org/entry/ meaning_of_life

Pierce, J. (2018, August 24). *Do Animals Experience Grief? | Science.* Smithsonian Magazine. Retrieved March 25, 2023, from https:// www.smithsonianmag.com/science-nature/do-animals-experience-grief-180970124/

Planck epoch - Simple English Wikipedia, the free encyclopedia. (n.d.).
Simple Wikipedia. Retrieved April 10, 2023, from https://
simple.wikipedia.org/wiki/Planck_epoch

Podd, R. (2020). Reconsidering maternal mortality in medieval England:
aristocratic Englishwomen, c. 1236–1503. *Cambridge University
Press*, 32(2), 115-137. https://www.cambridge.org/core/journals/
continuity-and-change/article/abs/reconsidering-maternal-mortality-in-
medieval-england-aristocratic-englishwomen-
c-12361503/60D88E212AE18AD1B755C7906C5EC668

Popova, M. (2018, March 16). *John Updike's Playful and Profound Ode to
the Neutrino, Read by "Humans of New York" Creator Brandon
Stanton*. The Marginalian. Retrieved March 25, 2023, from https://
www.themarginalian.org/2018/03/16/john-updike-cosmic-gall-
brandon-stanton/

Population bottleneck. (n.d.). Wikipedia. Retrieved March 25, 2023, from
https://en.wikipedia.org/wiki/Population_bottleneck#Humans

Prasad, M. (n.d.). *Technological singularity*. Wikipedia. Retrieved March
25, 2023, from https://en.wikipedia.org/wiki/Technological_singularity

Price equation. (n.d.). Wikipedia. Retrieved April 2, 2023, from https://
en.wikipedia.org/wiki/Price_equation

Printing press. (n.d.). Wikipedia. Retrieved March 25, 2023, from https://
en.wikipedia.org/wiki/Printing_press

Psacharopoulos, G. (1994). Returns to investment in education: A global
update. World Development. *Returns to investment in education: A
global update. World Development*, 22(9), 1325-1343. https://
www.sciencedirect.com/science/article/abs/pii/0305750X94900078

Radiocarbon dating. (n.d.). Wikipedia. Retrieved March 25, 2023, from
https://en.wikipedia.org/wiki/Radiocarbon_dating

Religion in the European Union. (n.d.). Wikipedia. Retrieved March 25,
2023, from https://en.wikipedia.org/wiki/
Religion_in_the_European_Union

Rice, S. H. (2008, September 25). A stochastic version of the Price
equation reveals the interplay of deterministic and stochastic
processes in evolution - BMC Ecology and Evolution. *BMC
Evolutionary Biology, 8*(262). 0.1186/1471-2148-8-262

Romans. (2017). In G. W. Barker, R. P. Martin, D. A. Hubbard, J. W.
Watts, L. A. Losie, C. P. E. o. N. T. L. a. L. B. M. Metzger, J. D. W.
Watts, & B. M. Metzger (Eds.), *Romans (2-Volume Set---38A And
38B)*. Zondervan. https://www.bible.com/bible/111/ROM.2.6-8.NIV

Roser, M., Ritchie, H., Ortiz, E., & Rodés, L. (n.d.). *World Population
Growth*. Our World in Data. Retrieved March 25, 2023, from https://
ourworldindata.org/world-population-growth

Sand mandala. (n.d.). Wikipedia. Retrieved March 25, 2023, from https://
en.wikipedia.org/wiki/Sand_mandala

SC2 Player Count. (2021, February 13). TL.net. Retrieved April 3, 2023,
from https://tl.net/forum/starcraft-2/569204-sc2-player-count

Schippers, M. C., & Ziegler, N. (n.d.). Life Crafting as a Way to Find
Purpose and Meaning in Life. *Life Crafting as a Way to Find Purpose
and Meaning in Life*. https://www.ncbi.nlm.nih.gov/pmc/articles/
PMC6923189/.

Scorpions - Wind Of Change (Official Music Video). (2009, November 1).
YouTube. Retrieved March 25, 2023, from https://www.youtube.com/
watch?v=n4RjJKxsamQ

Seluanov, A., Gladyshev, V., & Vijg, J. (2018, November 16). Mechanisms of cancer resistance in long-lived mammals. *Nature Reviews Cancer*, *18*(433), 441. 10.1038/s41568-018-0004-9

Shearmur, J., & Turner, P. N. (n.d.). *Karl Popper*. Wikipedia. Retrieved April 22, 2023, from https://en.wikipedia.org/wiki/Karl_Popper

Simone, N. (2014, November 9). *I Wish I Knew How It Would Feel to Be Free*. YouTube. Retrieved March 25, 2023, from https://music.youtube.com/watch?v=gKXtM-dgZzg&feature=share

68–95–99.7 rule. (n.d.). Wikipedia. Retrieved March 26, 2023, from https://en.wikipedia.org/wiki/68%E2%80%9395%E2%80%9399.7_rule

Slater, A., & Bremner, G. (n.d.). *Nature versus nurture*. Wikipedia. Retrieved March 25, 2023, from https://en.wikipedia.org/wiki/Nature_versus_nurture

Smith, G. A. (2021, December 14). About Three-in-Ten U.S. Adults Are Now Religiously Unaffiliated. *Pew Research*. Retrieved March 25, 2023, from https://www.pewresearch.org/religion/2021/12/14/about-three-in-ten-u-s-adults-are-now-religiously-unaffiliated/

Smith, J. M., & Price, G. R. (n.d.). *Evolutionarily stable strategy*. Wikipedia. https://en.wikipedia.org/wiki/Evolutionarily_stable_strategy

Spencer, I., Schaff, P., & Clark, T. (n.d.). *Seven deadly sins*. Wikipedia. Retrieved March 25, 2023, from https://en.wikipedia.org/wiki/Seven_deadly_sins

SS Arctic disaster. (n.d.). Wikipedia. Retrieved March 25, 2023, from https://en.wikipedia.org/wiki/SS_Arctic_disaster#Confusion_and_panic

Standard Model. (n.d.). Wikipedia. Retrieved March 26, 2023, from
   https://en.wikipedia.org/wiki/Standard_Model

A stochastic version of the Price equation reveals the interplay of
   deterministic and stochastic processes in evolution. (2008). *BMC
   Evolutionary Biology, 8*(262). https://bmcecolevol.biomedcentral.com/
   articles/10.1186/1471-2148-8-262

Super-Kamiokande. (n.d.). Wikipedia. Retrieved March 25, 2023, from
   https://en.wikipedia.org/wiki/Super-Kamiokande

Taxonomy (biology). (n.d.). Wikipedia. https://en.wikipedia.org/wiki/
   Taxonomy_(biology)

Taylor, P. (2022, September 8). *Total data volume worldwide 2010-2025*.
   Statista. Retrieved March 25, 2023, from https://www.statista.com/
   statistics/871513/worldwide-data-created/

Thornberry, T. L. (2022, May 16). *Explosive Calderas (U.S.* National Park
   Service. Retrieved March 25, 2023, from https://www.nps.gov/
   articles/000/explosive-calderas.htm

Tung, H.-T., & Davoyan, A. R. (2022, March). Low-Power Laser Sailing
   for Fast-Transit Space Flight. *ACS Publications, 22*(3), 1108-1114.
   https://doi.org/10.1021/acs.nanolett.1c04188

Updike, J. (1960, December 9). Cosmic Gall. *The New Yorker*, 36.

Uppsala Conflict Data Program. (n.d.). Uppsala Conflict Data Program:
   UCDP. Retrieved April 8, 2023, from https://ucdp.uu.se/

UR-100N. (n.d.). Wikipedia. Retrieved March 28, 2023, from https://
   en.wikipedia.org/wiki/UR-100N

Vaitaitis, A. (n.d.). Search for Neutral Heavy Leptons in a High-Energy
   Neutrino Beam. *Search for Neutral Heavy Leptons in a High-Energy*

Neutrino Beam. https://journals.aps.org/prl/abstract/10.1103/
 PhysRevLett.83.4943

Vaitaitis, A. (n.d.). *Sterile neutrino*. Wikipedia. https://en.wikipedia.org/
 wiki/Sterile_neutrino

Walker, P. L., Johnson, J. R., & Lambert, P. M. (1988). Age and sex
 biases in the preservation of human skeletal remains. *American
 Journal of Physical Anthropology, 76*(2), 183-8. 10.1002/
 ajpa.1330760206

Wall, M. (2021, December 13). *Dinosaur-killing asteroid: What we know
 about the famous space rock*. Space.com. Retrieved March 25, 2023,
 from https://www.space.com/dinosaur-impactor-origin

Wave–particle duality. (n.d.). Wikipedia. Retrieved March 25, 2023, from
 https://en.wikipedia.org/wiki/Wave%E2%80%93particle_duality

What were the punishments for theft? (n.d.). Historical locks. Retrieved
 March 25, 2023, from https://www.historicallocks.com/en/site/h/locks-
 and-magic/taboos-and-magical-knots/punishments-for-theft/

Winnings. (2022, October 19). Liquipedia. Retrieved March 25, 2023,
 from https://liquipedia.net/starcraft2/Winnings

Zhang, F., & Church, G. (n.d.). *CRISPR*. Wikipedia. Retrieved March 25,
 2023, from en.wikipedia.org/wiki/CRISPR

Printed in Great Britain
by Amazon

40006138R00175